A Peoples Education Lab Manual for
AP*/Honors

Physics C Exam

By James Mooney
Taft School
Watertown, CT

Peoples Education
Your partner in student success™

Publisher: Tom Maksym

Executive Editor: Steven Jay Griffel

Vice President of Production: Doreen Smith

Pre-Press and Production Manager: Jason Grasso

Project Manager: Matthew Hjembo

Senior Book Coordinator: Paul Zakrzewski

Production Assistants: Chip Cliffe, Joseph Lisa, Richard Lehmbeck

Designer: Carol Deckert

Copy Editor: Michael O'Neill

Art Director: Amy Rosen

Photo Researcher/Permissions Manager: Kristine Liebman

Technical Art: Chip Cliffe, Matthew Hjembo, Richard Lehmbeck, James Mooney, Paul Zakrzewski

Cover Design: Cristina Castro Pelka, Michele Sakow

Marketing Manager: Kathy Wanamaker

Peoples Education™
Your partner in student success™

Copyright © 2005
Peoples Education, Inc.
299 Market Street
Saddle Brook, New Jersey 07663

ISBN 978-1-4138-0492-8
ISBN 1-4138-0492-6

All rights reserved. No part of this book may be kept in an information storage or retrieval system, transmitted or reproduced in any form or by any means without prior written permission of the Publisher.

*AP is a registered trademark of the College Board, which was not involved in the production of, and does not endorse, this book.

Printed in the United States of America.

10 9 8 7 6 5 4 3

To Erin, Jenn, Eileen, and Molly

Whenever I thought I was overwhelmed, I just had to think of you.

Table of Contents

Chapter 2 Vectors and Motion in Two Dimensions

Chapter 3 Newton's Laws

Chapter 4 Work and Energy

Chapter 5 Impulse and Momentum

Chapter 6 Rotational Motion and Angular Momentum

Chapter 7 Gravitation

Chapter 8 Oscillations

Chapter 9 Electric Force and Electric Field

Chapter 10 Electric Potential and Electric Potential Energy

Chapter 11 Electric Circuits

Chapter 12 Magnetostatics

Chapter 13 Electromagnetic Induction

Chapter 14 AP Physics and the Laboratory

Chapter 15 Physics C and Calculus

Appendix

Practice Test

Answers and Explanations

Glossary

The Advanced Placement Program and AP Exams

The Advanced Placement (AP) Program was created by the College Board in cooperation with secondary schools around the country. Using course outlines developed by university and high school teachers, secondary schools offer college level courses in a wide range of disciplines. Standardized tests written by a committee consisting of college and high school faculty are administered in each subject area in early May. If you do well on a given test, then you can receive credit at the college you eventually attend. The tests are read and graded, and your scores are reported to your chosen colleges. The scoring scale and interpretation are

5—extremely well qualified
4—well qualified
3—qualified
2—possibly qualified
1—no recommendation

Colleges and the AP Exams

Most colleges require that you take the SAT. In addition, they usually strongly recommend that you take several SAT II tests as well. AP exams are not a requirement. However, it is fair to say that a high school program that includes one or more AP courses will enhance your chances for acceptance at the college you want to attend. Consider the following points.

- The AP curricula are all demanding and rigorous. Just your enrollment in an AP course sends a signal that you are looking for academic challenge.
- A good grade on the AP exam will provide a standardized measure of your work over the year that will be easy for a college admissions committee to interpret.

Perhaps the prime motivation for the AP program is the college credit that can be earned by high school students. The level of credit earned by a given score on the AP exam is not standardized; it varies from college to college and is usually determined within the particular department that would be granting the credit. For example, the physics department at Hadron University may give credit for AP Physics C scores of 4 or higher, while the same department at Lepton College may give credit for scores of 3 or better. Even if your score is not high enough to get credit (a few schools require a 5), a solid showing on the test can get you placed into a higher level introductory course.

Which AP Exams to Take

It is difficult to do well in a course that does not interest you, particularly if the course is as rigorous as an AP course. You shouldn't sign up for any AP unless the subject matter really turns you on. However, if you're interested in several disciplines, there's no limit to the number of APs you can take in a given year. Over the first couple of weeks in May, two tests are given each day, one in the morning and one in the afternoon. Obviously, a course load of five APs would be demanding over the year, and the tests could all fall within a narrow time frame depending on which tests you were taking. This is an important consideration, and you can find the test dates for each year at the AP Web site, http://apcentral.collegeboard.com. If two of the tests you want to take are scheduled for the same time slot, you can arrange to take one of them at a later date. The test will be different from the one given in the usual time slot, but of course it will cover all the same material.

Below are listed the mean scores in some commonly taken AP exams.

TEST	MEAN GRADE (in 2001)
Physics C Mech	3.3
Physics C, E, & M	3.3
Physics B	2.8
Calculus AB/BC	3.0/3.6
Chemistry	2.8
English Literature	3.0
European History	2.9
French	2.8
Latin	2.9
U.S. Government & Politics	2.8
Spanish Language	3.6

Where to Take an AP Exam

AP exams are given at schools that teach the associated AP courses. If you're taking AP Physics C, chances are the test will be held at your school as well. Check with your teacher, guidance counselor, or AP coordinator. If your school doesn't offer AP courses or tests, you can contact AP Services to find a school nearby that will let you take the tests there.

AP Services
P.O. Box 6671
Princeton, NJ 08541-6671
(609) 771-7300 or toll-free (888) CALL-4-AP (888-225-5427)
Fax: (609) 530-0482
TTY: (609) 882-4118
E-mail: apexams@info.collegeboard.org

Registering for AP Exams

To register for an AP exam, you'll need to fill out several forms and pay a registration fee ($78 in 2004) for each AP test you want to take. While the fee is considerable, if your AP score gets you placement or credit with the college you attend, you'll probably wind up saving some serious tuition money.

You should register for the AP exam with your AP Coordinator. If your school doesn't have an AP program, you can contact a nearby school that does have an AP Coordinator for all the information.

Receiving and Reporting Your AP Scores

The reading and grading for the exams takes the entire month of June. Scores are mailed out over the first half of July. The colleges that you designated will also receive the scores then. If you can't wait the extra week or two, you can pay a fee and find out your score over the phone after July 1.

Withholding and Canceling AP Grades

Suppose you are certain that you did so poorly on the test that you are afraid it will hurt your chances at a particular school. By submitting a signed request to the AP program by June 15, you can prevent a score from being reported to a particular college. You can even have the score permanently canceled so that it will not appear on any record, even the record you receive from the AP program with your other scores. Unfortunately, to withhold or cancel a score, you must do so before you actually know what the score is. Be sure to think it over well before you proceed in withholding or canceling. You will see in the next two chapters that an acceptable grade on an AP exam doesn't always correspond to a high percentage of correct answers.

Content and Format of the AP Physics C Exam

Many excellent textbooks cover the material essential to the C exam. But publishers usually try to appeal to a larger audience than just AP students, so these books contain quite a bit more material than the AP syllabus warrants. If you've been using one of these books in your school, you may find that even all of the essential material for the test isn't covered in class simply because there's not enough time. This chapter outlines the AP C syllabus, highlighting the specific topics that you need to cover. Then we'll look at the actual format of the test so that you'll be familiar with how the material appears on the exam.

Content

The C-level course focuses on two main subject areas: Newtonian mechanics and electricity and magnetism. The student is assumed to have a working knowledge of both differential and integral calculus, and it is recommended that a student taking Physics C be enrolled concurrently in a math course taught at least at the level of the Math AB exam. At the college level, Physics C is equivalent to an introductory physics course for students who are entering the physical sciences. There is some overlap with the Physics B syllabus, but Physics C covers these areas in much greater detail and at a higher mathematical level.

The first column in the following table lists the various topics and subtopics that comprise the C-level syllabus. The second column indicates what percentage of the total test is drawn from that topic.

	Percentage Goals for Exams
	Physics C
I. Newtonian Mechanics	**50%**

A. Kinematics (vectors, vector algebra, vector components, coordinate systems, displacement, velocity, and acceleration)
  1. Motion in one dimension
  2. Motion in two dimensions, including projectile motion
	9%

B. Newton's laws of motion, including friction and centripetal force
    1. Static equilibrium
    2. Dynamics of a single particle
    3. Systems of two or more bodies

10%

C. Work, energy, and power
    1. Work and work-energy theorem
    2. Conservative forces and potential energy
    3. Conservation of energy
    4. Power

7%

D. Systems of particles and linear momentum
    1. Center of mass
    2. Impulse and momentum
    3. Conservation of linear momentum and collisions

6%

E. Circular motion and rotation
    1. Uniform circular motion
    2. Angular momentum and its conservation
        a. Point particles
        b. Extended bodies, including rotational inertia
    3. Torque and rotational statics
    4. Rotational kinematics and dynamics

9%

F. Oscillations and gravitation
    1. Simple harmonic motion (dynamics and energy relationships)
    2. Mass on a spring
    3. Pendulum and other oscillations
    4. Newton's law of gravity
    5. Orbits of planets and satellites
        a. Circular
        b. General

9%

II. Electricity and Magnetism

50%

A. Electrostatics
    1. Charge, field, and potential
    2. Coulomb's law, and field and potential of point charges
    3. Fields and potentials of other charge distributions
        a. Planar
        b. Spherical symmetry
        c. Cylindrical symmetry
    4. Gauss's law

15%

B. Conductors, capacitors, and dielectrics
   1. Electrostatics with conductors
   2. Capacitors
     a. Parallel plate
     b. Spherical and cylindrical
   3. Dielectrics
	7%

C. Electric circuits
   1. Current, resistance, and power
   2. Steady-state direct current circuits with batteries and resistors only
   3. Capacitors in circuits
     a. Steady state
     b. Transients in RC circuits
	10%

D. Magnetostatics
   1. Forces on moving charges in magnetic fields
   2. Forces on current-carrying wires in magnetic fields
   3. Fields of long current-carrying wires
   4. Biot-Savart and Ampere's law
	10%

E. Electromagnetism
   1. Electromagnetic induction, including Faraday's law and Lenz's law
   2. Inductance, including LR and LC circuits
   3. Maxwell's equations
	8%

At the end of each chapter in this book, you'll find practice exercises for both multiple-choice and free-response questions. Some of these practice questions expand on concepts developed in the chapter and are necessary for you to completely understand the material. The free-response questions focus on each chapter's topics, so they aren't always as wide-ranging as those on the AP exam, but they're written at the level of questions on the AP exam.

Format

The AP C Physics test is actually administered as two separate tests: one for mechanics and one for electricity and magnetism. You'll get a separate grade for each test if you take both of them. It is also possible to take just the mechanics test or just the E & M test. Each individual test is divided into two sections: Section I is multiple choice, and Section II is free response. Section I consists of 35 questions, and it will account for 50 percent of your grade. You have 45 minutes to complete this section. Section II consists of problems or free-response questions for which you will also be allowed 45 minutes. There have always been 3 problems on the free-response section of the C level test, but the College Board has stated that this could change in the future. If you take both the mechanics and the E & M tests, you have a total of three hours to complete them.

Section I

This section consists of individual questions with five choices. While most questions are self contained, two or three questions at a time may be linked by a common figure or written description. The questions fall into four basic categories: conceptual, numerical calculation, algebraic calculation, and graphical.

Conceptual Questions

As the name implies, these questions test your understanding of basic concepts without asking you to perform any calculations using the concepts. Here's a sample question:

Two teams engage in a tug-of-war with a rope held horizontal. Which is true of the winning team?

(A) They were stronger.
(B) They had more mass.
(C) They exerted a greater tension force through the rope.
(D) They exerted a greater force on the ground parallel to the surface.
(E) They exerted a greater force on the ground perpendicular to the surface.

To answer correctly with D, you would need to understand that both tension and friction forces will act in the horizontal direction on each team and that the tension forces acting on each team will always be equal but opposite by Newton's third law. No calculation is needed, however, to arrive at the correct answer.

Numerical Calculation Questions

On Section I of the test, you will *not* be allowed to use a calculator, so it follows that the questions with numerical calculations will involve "nice" numbers. Some questions will even involve using trigonometric functions, but the angles will be 0°, 30°, 37°, 45°, 53°, 60°, and 90°. The sines, cosines, and tangents of these angles, as well as the values of physical constants and some other conventions, will be provided on a Table of Information sheet at the beginning of both Section I and Section II. This information is also included in the appendix at the back of this book. You don't need to commit this information to memory, but you should be familiar with what is there and what is not. Of course, calculations involve using the laws of physics in mathematical form, so you'll need to know the many equations that relate the various physical quantities. You will *not* have an equation sheet provided on Section I. Here's an example of a numerical calculation question:

A 5-kg mass is sliding across a horizontal surface at a constant speed while being pulled by a rope with tension 30 N held at 30° above the horizontal. The force of friction is most nearly

(A) $25\sqrt{3}$ N   (B) $15\sqrt{3}$ N   (C) 25 N   (D) 15 N   (E) 20 N

Because there is no acceleration, the friction force will equal the horizontal component of the tension, 30 cos30. The correct answer, B, includes the square root factor provided in the Table of Information. Since calculators are not allowed for this section, you would not be expected to express the square root as a decimal.

Algebraic Calculation Questions
In this type of question, certain quantities are given symbolically, and you must use them to determine an answer that you express symbolically as well. Here's an example:

A mass m is accelerated from rest across a smooth horizontal surface by a rope held parallel to the surface. The tension T in the rope is constant. After a time t, the instantaneous power delivered to the mass by the rope is

(A) $\dfrac{T}{m}t$ (B) $\dfrac{T^2}{m}t$ (C) $\dfrac{T}{m}t^2$ (D) $\dfrac{T^2}{m}t^2$ (E) $\dfrac{T^2}{m}$

Here the tension, mass, and time are given, expressed symbolically as T, m, and t, respectively. To determine the correct answer, B, you can apply Newton's second law, one-dimensional kinematics, and the formula relating power, force, and velocity.

$$P = Tv = T(at) = T\left(\frac{T}{m}t\right) = \frac{T^2}{m}t$$

You won't have to do any complex manipulations, but you'll need to be comfortable working with algebraic expressions when you're answering these questions.

Graphical Questions
This type of question comes in two varieties. In the first, you may be asked to identify the behavior of a specific property while one of the parameters that describes it is allowed to vary. You might, for example, need to identify the graph that best depicts the magnetic field due to a long wire as a function of R, the distance from the center of the wire. In the second variety of question, you may work with graphs depicting the time dependence of physical quantities. You could be given a choice of five graphs, for example, and then be asked which best depicts the kinetic energy as a function of time for a projectile fired horizontally from a given height. Here's a specific example:

A wire of constant length is moved through a uniform magnetic field at a constant velocity, with the velocity vector perpendicular to the field. A graph of the induced voltage V_{in} between the ends of the wire as a function of time would look like:

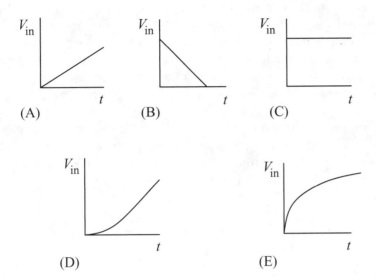

The induced voltage will be a constant with magnitude BLv as long as the field and speed are constant, so C is the correct answer.

A variation of this type of question begins by displaying five graphs. Two or three questions then require that answers be chosen from the five graphs.

SECTION II

On the free-response section of the test, you *will* be allowed to use a calculator. Both scientific calculators and more complex graphing calculators are permitted. Calculators with a typewriter QWERTY keyboard aren't allowed, under the assumption that these are closer to computers than calculators. You won't have to clear the memory of your calculator, but since you *will* be provided with a complete equation sheet, there is little need to cram your calculator memory with other information. The equation sheets for each test are included in the appedix at the back of this book. Be sure to look over the information on these sheets carefully. Not every equation is there, but the fundamental ones are, and quite a few others as well.

Two types of free-response questions can appear in Section II: physical situation problems and lab questions.

Physical Situation Problems

This is a variation of end-of-chapter problems that you're probably quite familiar with. A physical situation is described, often with an accompanying diagram, and you're asked a series of questions about the situation and its development. These problems can be completely numerical, so that you're calculating a numerical answer at the end of each section, or completely algebraic, so that your answers are all expressed in terms of symbols. Unlike the typical end-of-chapter problem, the AP free-response problem doesn't usually deal with just one topic. It would be rare, for example, to encounter a problem that covers just one-dimensional kinematics. You're more likely to have to solve a problem that begins with questions about kinematics but then brings in concepts like force, energy, or momentum. While each problem usually has a particular focus area, questions within the problem sometimes touch on topics that might be considered well outside the focus area. A question on induction, for example, might bring in concepts from mechanics, and a question on electrostatics might require the use of Newton's second law.

Sometimes you'll be asked to explain something about one of your answers in a section of a larger problem. In a problem with an object rolling down an incline, for example, you might be asked to explain the effect of changing the coefficient of friction. These short descriptive questions can usually be answered without detailed mathematical analysis although using specific equations to support your answer is a good idea.

Lab Questions

Since 1996, the AP Physics Committee has included questions that specifically test a student's lab experience. The question may be self contained, or it may be part of a larger question. Chapter 14 looks at these questions in detail. To do well on these questions, you should have performed the basic labs usually included with an introductory physics course. In addition to being familiar with measuring apparatus and the measuring process, you should be able to

1. devise an experiment to measure a basic property
2. explain in words and equations how an experiment achieves the desired result
3. analyze an experiment for sources of error

You may be asked to report data to an appropriate level of precision, so you may need knowledge of significant digit arithmetic. It's only on this type of question, though, that you'll ever have to worry about significant digits.

Weighted and Composite Scores

Section I and Section II of each test are weighted equally when your AP grade is calculated. The 3 problems of Section II count for 15 points each, totaling 45 points for that section. Within a given problem, different parts will carry different weight. There are 35 multiple-choice questions in Section I. To find your weighted score for Section I, AP counts the number of points you earned using the criteria:

- 1 point awarded for each correct answer

- $\frac{1}{4}$ point subtracted for each incorrect answer

- 0 points awarded for each question left blank

The total number of points earned is then multiplied by $\frac{45}{35} = 1.286$. This is your weighted score for Section I. The last step is needed to make the total number of points in Section I the same as the 45 points of Section II.

The weighted score for the free-response section is just the number of points you earned. No points are subtracted for wrong answers.

Finally, your composite score is the sum of the weighted scores for the two sections.

Calculating Your AP Grade

Your composite score on the test is then converted to an AP grade. The cutoff points for the different AP grades are determined by a statistical analysis of the composite scores. There is some variation in these cutoff points from year to year, but not a lot. The following table shows the distribution for the AP Physics C Exam given in 1998, results that are typical of other years as well.

Composite Scores and AP Grades, C Mechanics

Composite Score	AP Grade	Qualification
55–90	5	Extremely Well Qualified
43–54	4	Well Qualified
32–42	3	Qualified
21–31	2	Possibly Qualified
0–20	1	No Recommendation

Composite Scores and AP Grades, C, E, & M

Composite Score	AP Grade	Qualification
49–90	5	Extremely Well Qualified
35–48	4	Well Qualified
26–34	3	Qualified
15–25	2	Possibly Qualified
0–14	1	No Recommendation

What should grab your attention in this table is the range of composite scores that receive a qualified of better AP grade. While a student who gets 90 percent of the total points available gets a 5, a student who only got 61 percent correct will also get a 5. Indeed, a student scoring just 36 percent will get a 3.

It is essential that you have a strategy for maximizing your score on the test. You want to be sure that you get to all the questions that you can answer correctly. You need to know how much time should be invested in a given question. You need to know about intelligent guessing. We'll talk about these strategies in the next chapter.

Strategies for Taking the AP Physics Exam

The best way to succeed on the AP exam is to put in the time learning the material. Using this book with its practice exercises and tests will help you sharpen your focus, but even the best of students will encounter questions on the test that they're not sure about. In this chapter, we'll look at strategies for dealing with test situations where you're either uncertain or simply don't know how to proceed. It's important to recognize ahead of time that you'll face these situations on the test, so you'll need to have an organized approach for handling them that doesn't take too much of your allotted time. Remember that you don't have to get everything correct to get a good AP grade—far from it. As you saw in the last chapter, a composite score of about 60 percent of the total points will get you a 5, and a composite score that's less than 50 percent can still get you a 4.

Multiple-Choice Strategies

The scantron will read your multiple-choice answer sheet and tabulate all the correct, incorrect, and unanswered questions. It doesn't question how you arrived at your answers. If you actually understood the material in a question but got the wrong answer because you didn't read the question carefully, you won't get partial credit. On the other hand, if you made an intelligent guess to arrive at the correct answer, you'll get full credit even though you didn't know the answer exactly. Let's look at some of the specific ways you can get this machine to record the highest possible score for you.

GRID YOUR ANSWERS CAREFULLY

If you make mistakes while entering your answers into the grid, it can cost you dearly. This is most likely to happen after you skip a question. If you left question 20 blank and then mistakenly put the answer to question 21 in the space for question 20, a chain of incorrect answers could follow. Don't do it.

Perhaps the best way to avoid this is to recite a complete sentence to yourself as you fill in the oval: "Question 21: answer is A." As you recite this, look at the number of the question and verify that it is the correct one.

MAKE THE MOST OF THE TIME YOU HAVE INVESTED

As you work through the multiple-choice section, you'll want to choose the answer that you think is correct. Obvious. But what do you do if you can't decide between two or more of the choices? There are two things to keep in mind:

1. An incorrect answer carries with it a $\frac{1}{4}$ point penalty, as described in the last chapter. If you answered 5 questions randomly, chances are you'd get 1 correct since there are 5 possible answers to each question. This 1 point gained would be exactly canceled by the $4\frac{1}{4} = 1$ point lost as a result of the other 4 incorrect answers. Random guessing neither helps you nor hurts you if there are enough questions that statistics can be applied in the analysis. But if you can eliminate some of the answers, it greatly increases your odds for guessing the correct answer, and the $\frac{1}{4}$ point penalty will not even the score. If you could eliminate 3 of the 5 answers in each of 5 questions, statistically you would expect to get 2 or 3 of the 5 correct. With the penalty taken into account, your score on these 5 questions would be $2 - 3(\frac{1}{4}) = 1.75$ or $3 - 2(\frac{1}{4}) = 2.5$. Both results are obviously much better than the 0 points you'd get for not answering at all. It's always to your advantage to guess if you can eliminate at least one answer.

2. You have to read and answer questions at the rate of about one every ninety seconds to be sure you'll get a chance to attempt every question. You'll find questions where you won't be able to eliminate all the answers, even though you may be sure that with just a little more time you'll figure it out. You'll feel the urge to put the question aside so that you can come back to it later. *This is a flawed strategy.* By reading the question and eliminating some of the answers, you have invested a certain amount of time in the question, and you have improved your odds at getting it correct. If you don't answer it now, you can't count on having the time later to return to it, and if you don't answer it at all, then you'll have lost your investment. Any question that you can understand well enough to eliminate at least one answer should be answered right then. If you *do* have time at the end, you can come back and erase your answer if you change your mind, but time is at a premium. Your goal is to achieve the highest possible score from the machine, not to answer every question that you might be able to figure out eventually.

All this being said, if a question looks totally unfamiliar, skip it. Don't waste precious time trying to eliminate answers when you're not even sure what the question is all about.

ELIMINATING ANSWERS

Certain types of questions lend themselves to a systematic testing procedure that will help you determine if an answer could possibly be correct.

Dimensional Analysis

Applying dimensional analysis will be useful on questions involving algebraic calculations. You'll be asked to determine a certain quantity from some givens, and if you know the dimensions of the quantity you're trying to determine, you can check the possible answers to see if they have the correct dimensions. If the dimensions aren't right, the answer can't be correct. Let's reconsider the question used as an example in the last chapter:

A mass m is accelerated from rest across a smooth horizontal surface by a rope held parallel to the surface. The tension T in the rope is constant. After a time t, the instantaneous power delivered to the mass by the rope is

(A) $\dfrac{T}{m}t$ (B) $\dfrac{T^2}{m}t$ (C) $\dfrac{T}{m}t^2$ (D) $\dfrac{T^2}{m}t^2$ (E) $\dfrac{T^2}{m}$

Since power has the units of (force) • (velocity), you could analyze the dimensions of the possible answers to see if any have the wrong dimensions. (A) could not be correct since $\dfrac{T}{m}$ has the dimensions of acceleration, and (acceleration) • (time) has the dimensions of velocity. Using this tactic, you could eliminate all the answers except B.

Order of Magnitude

It helps to be aware of the order of magnitude of various phenomena. If you're answering a question that asks for a speed and one of your choices is 4×10^9 m/s, you can eliminate it immediately since it is faster than the speed of light. If you're asked to determine the gravitational force between two objects, the size of $G \cong 10^{-11}$ should pop into your mind. If the masses aren't too big, the force will be small, and you can eliminate large answers. Remember that physical constants are available to you on the Table of Information sheet, and on this type of question these values will be useful to you. If you see a question that has a choice of answers that vary over several orders of magnitude, thinking in terms of orders of magnitude may get you to the answer quickly. Consider the following question:

A current of 3.2 A flows in a segment of copper wire. The number of electrons crossing the cross-sectional area of the wire every second is most nearly

(A) 3.2 (B) 2×10^{19} (C) 2×10^{-19} (D) 3.2×10^{19} (E) 3.2×10^{-19}

If you have a basic understanding of how many electrons are involved when even a modest current is established in a wire, you could eliminate all the answers except B and D. Of course, to distinguish between these two, you'd have to use more than order of magnitude thinking, but if you were stuck at this point, you'd have a 50 percent chance of getting the correct answer.

Limiting Behavior

Graphical questions lend themselves to analysis using limiting behavior. In this approach, you need to have some knowledge about what happens when one of the variables takes on limiting values. For example, the magnetic field outside a long wire decreases as $1/R$, so if you had a choice of graphs supposedly describing this field, you would look for this behavior. Electric field and electric potential become infinite at the position of a point charge, so you can easily eliminate graphs inconsistent with this situation. Here's an example of this type of question:

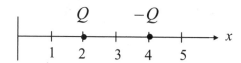

Two equal and opposite charges lie along the x-axis as shown in the figure. The graph of the electric potential as a function of x is closest to which of the following?

(A)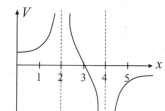

(B)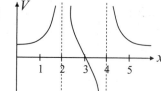

(C)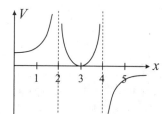

(D)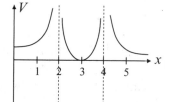

(E)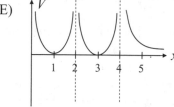

The potential approaches $+\infty$ near the positive charge and $-\infty$ near the negative charge, so only A could be correct.

Free-Response Strategies

Unlike Section I, which is read and graded by a machine, Section II is read by a real person, either an AP teacher or a college professor involved in the AP Program. To do your best on this section of the test, you should know something about how the test is written and graded. A well-written test question must be able to differentiate among the various levels of students. A question in which 90 percent of the students received 12 or more out of 15 points would not adequately differentiate between the student who had weaknesses on related material and the student who really knew her stuff. Similarly, a question in which 90 percent of the students received 7 or fewer out of 15 points would not be well designed. The best questions have a spread in the point distribution centered on 7 out of 15 points, achieved through a process that can be called "front loading" a problem. Easier parts of the question are put up front in Parts A, B, and C. Usually a student with even a little knowledge about what the question asks can get points here. Most questions go on to ask Parts D, E, and beyond, and these get progressively more difficult. It's important to remember that the last part to a question, which may totally stump you, is probably worth no more than two or three points.

Most questions begin with a diagram and these may be intimidating when you first look at them if the subject area of the diagram was not one of your strengths. Resist the urge to skip the question. Remember, front loading means there should be some easy stuff at the beginning. Most questions start out by asking for the most basic answers, so don't let a diagram scare you off. You'll maximize your score by getting most of the points on the questions you're really comfortable with, and getting as many points as you can on the questions that you know you're not going to be able to complete. Getting those extra points at the beginning of the tough problems can make all the difference in your AP grade.

You should also be familiar with how the free response section is graded. The AP Physics reading takes place in early June. A significant force of AP teachers, college professors, and aides work together for about six days to read through the exams and assign scores to the tests. Before the reading begins, a set of standards is developed for each free-response question. The standards identify the points to be awarded on each section of a problem. They also identify how partial credit is to be awarded if your answer is incorrect.

Let's see how this works in practice. A reader will typically handle just one problem over the course of the reading. Because each reader must grade literally thousands of exams, as he looks at a given problem, he is scanning for correct answers. A well-designed problem will not allow a correct answer to be reached by an incorrect method, so if the reader sees the correct answer, you get the points for that section. (There are rare exceptions to this in problems that specifically ask you to derive something, showing your assumptions and intermediate steps. In these cases, more than just a correct answer will be needed for full credit.)

So what happens if your answer is not correct? Each reader keeps her copy of the standards right next to her, showing the solution to the problem worked out and the points to be awarded for various steps done correctly. If your answer to a given section was incorrect, the reader looks through the section to see how many of the steps you did correctly. If certain things appear on your paper, you get a certain amount of partial credit. The idea is to make the grading process as objective as possible, so that two readers reviewing the same test would assign the same partial credit.

How can this knowledge help you maximize your grade? First, show your work clearly, including all intermediate steps. Make it simple for the reader to see the logic of your work. It's very easy to make a math or algebra error so that your answer to a given section is wrong, but this will cost you only one point, the so-called answer point, if all the other steps are there and correct. If they're not present, a wrong answer means you lose all points for that section, a harsh but ultimately fair penalty. What's more, if you use your incorrect answer in subsequent sections of the problem, you won't be further penalized as long as these steps are done correctly. This means a single calculation error will cost you a total of only one point if you show the steps leading to it.

As you prepare for the AP exam, practice your free-response writing. When in doubt, write down a step. Try to avoid leaps that go from initial equation to final answer with nothing in between.

What if you're stumped on a given section? If you know nothing about what is asked, don't waste time. Move on. But what if you have some ideas? Perhaps you know what equations are involved, or perhaps you can get a little way toward the answer. Put it all down. Even when the reader sees that you don't have the correct answer, he's still looking for very specific things, and if they're present, you will get some points. You can almost think of the reader with his standards as being an approximation of a scantron: If equation A is present, 1 point is awarded; if number X is substituted correctly, 1 point is awarded, and so on.

When a free-response question involves numerical calculations, 1 point may be awarded if all your answers have the correct units, even if the answers themselves are wrong. These problems will assign a total of 14 points to the various answers to each section. The "units point" is awarded for the problem as a whole if all answers have correct units. You can get the units point even if you don't answer all sections, as long as the sections that you do answer have the correct units.

RECAP

Let's look at the composite score/AP grade chart again.

Composite Scores and AP Grades, C Mechanics

Composite Score	AP Grade	Qualification
55–90	5	Extremely Well Qualified
43–54	4	Well Qualified
32–42	3	Qualified
21–31	2	Possibly Qualified
0–20	1	No Recommendation

Composite Scores and AP Grades, C, E & M

Composite Score	AP Grade	Qualification
49–90	5	Extremely Well Qualified
35–48	4	Well Qualified
26–34	3	Qualified
15–25	2	Possibly Qualified
0–14	1	No Recommendation

You will have done quite a bit of preparation for the exam by the time you're ready to take the test. You may have enjoyed studying physics and have come to appreciate its power and precision, but as you enter the test, you have to take on a different mindset. Your goal is to maximize your composite score, to get the highest point total possible. This means thinking of test taking as a skill with specific strategies to be followed—and followed rigorously. Get through the three hours of the test with your goal and strategy never far from your thoughts, and try not to get flustered. Being flustered is not part of the strategy. If you feel as if you're ready to crack, think of the table above. You can be far from perfection and still get a respectable AP grade.

Cross-Reference with Popular C-Level Textbooks

The Study Guide for AP Physics C is targeted specifically to the topics of the C-level syllabus. There are several excellent textbooks that are appropriate for use in a C-level course, but none of them is designed *just* for a C-level course. As such they cover more material than required for the AP test and sometimes the coverage of a given topic is more general than would be required. Still, the problems, diagrams, and extended conceptual descriptions of these textbooks are an excellent resource that complements this Study Guide. The table below lists the subject chapters of this Study Guide and the corresponding sections of several excellent C-level texts. In some cases a section listed will contain some material that is not part of the AP syllabus as well as some that is part of the syllabus. When in doubt, compare the content of the textbook section to the material in the Study Guide.

Title	Author	Edition	Publisher
Fundamentals of Physics	Halliday, Resnick and Walker	7th	Wiley
Physics for Scientists and Engineers	Serway and Jewett	6th	Brooks Cole
University Physics	Young and Freedman	11th	Addison Wesley
Physics for Scientists and Engineers	Tipler and Mosca	5th	W.H. Freeman

Study Guide for AP Physics C	Halliday	Serway	Young	Tipler
Ch 1 Motion in One Dimension	2.1–2.10	2.1–2.7	2.1–2.6	2.1–2.4
Ch 2 Vectors and Motion in Two Dimensions	3.1–3.8; 4.1–4.7	3.1–3.4; 4.1–4.5; 7.3; 11.1	1.7–1.10; 3.1–3.4	3.1–3.5; 6.2; 10.1
Ch 3 Newton's Laws	5.1–5.9; 6.1–6.5	5.1–5.8; 6.1–6.2	4.1–4.6; 5.1–5.4	4.1–4.7; 5.1–5.3
Ch 4 Work and Energy	7.1–7.9; 8.1–8.8	7.1–7.8; 8.1–8.6	6.1–6.4; 7.1–7.5	6.1–6.4; 7.1–7.2
Ch 5 Impulse and Momentum	9.1–9.11	9.1–9.6	8.1–8.5	8.1, 8.3–8.6
Ch 6 Rotation Motion and Angular Momentum	10.1–10.10 11.1–11.11 12.1–12.5	10.1–10.9; 11.1–11.4; 21.1–12.3	9.1–9.5; 10.1–10.6; 11.1–11.3	9.1–9.6; 10.1–10.3; 12.1–12.4
Ch 7 Gravitation	13.1–13.8	13.1–13.4, 13.6–13.7	12.1–12.5	11.1–11.3
Ch 8 Oscillations	14.1–14.7	15.1–15.5	13.1–13.6	14.1–14.3
Ch 9 Electric Force and Electric Field	21.1–21.6 22.1–22.9 23.1–23.9	23.1–23.7; 24.1–24.4	21.1–21.7; 22.1–22.5	21.1–21.6; 22.1–22.5
Ch 10 Electric Potential and Electric Potential Energy	24.1–2.12 25.1–25.8	25.1–25.6; 26.1–26.5, 26.7	23.1–23.5; 24.1–24.6	23.1–23.5; 24.1–24.6
Ch 11 Electric Circuits	26.1–26.7 27.1–27.9	27.1–27.2, 27.6; 28.1–28.4	25.1–25.5; 26.1–26.2, 26.4	25.1–25.6
Ch 12 Magnetostatics	28.1–28.4, 28.6, 28.8–28.9; 29.1–29.5	29.1–29.2; 29.4–29.5; 30.1–30.4	27.1–27.6; 28.1–28.7	26.1–26.2; 27.1–27.2, 27.4
Ch 13 Electromagnetic Induction	30.1–30.11 31.1–31.3; 32.1–32.5	30.5; 31.1–31.4, 31.6–31.7; 30.6; 32.1–32.3, 32.5	29.1–29.7; 30.2–30.5	28.1–28.8; 29.5; 27.3; 30.1–30.2
Ch 15 Physics C and Calculus		6.4	9.6	8.2

CHAPTER 1

Motion in One Dimension

Motion is all around us, so it's easy to understand why the earliest physical thinkers focused on describing motion and determining its causes. In this chapter and the next, you'll learn how to describe motion without considering what is actually causing the motion. This study is called **kinematics**. You'll need to understand the nature of the quantities used to precisely describe motion and the relationships these quantities have with each other. With his long inclines and water clocks, Galileo Galilei was the first to study kinematics experimentally. Just as he did, you'll begin with objects constrained to move along a straight line, or one-dimensional motion.

Position and Displacement

To describe where an object is, you must introduce a coordinate system, pick an origin, and choose the positive direction for each axis. In one dimension you need only one axis, frequently labeled the x-axis for horizontal motion or the y-axis for vertical motion. The **position** of an object is its value of x. As the object moves, its position changes. The change in position is called the **displacement** of the object, written as Δx. The delta symbol, Δ, stands for the change in a quantity, with the change always determined using "final−initial." For displacement, the equation is

$$\Delta x = x_f - x_i$$

where x_f is the final position of the body and x_i is the initial position. As an object moves, its position depends on time, and this functional dependence is often written as $x = x(t)$. Position and displacement are both directed quantities, which means they carry a sign that determines their direction relative to the coordinate system. (When you generalize later to more than one dimension, you'll see that such directed quantities are called vectors.) If an object moving in one dimension never changes direction, the magnitude of its displacement will equal the distance traveled. But if the object does change direction, you'll have to break up its path carefully into segments to determine the total distance traveled. When you throw a ball straight up in the air to a height of 7 m, its displacement is 0 when you catch it, but it has traveled a distance of 14 m.

Velocity

Velocity is the rate at which the position of an object changes. The **average velocity** over a time interval is the displacement during the interval divided by the duration of the interval:

$$v_{av} = \frac{\Delta x}{\Delta t}$$

Let's look at the x vs. t graph for the motion (figure 1).

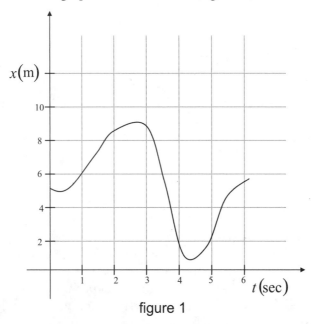

figure 1

From the graph you can see that at $t = 1$ s, the object is at about $x = 6$ m, and at $t = 4$ s, it is at about $x = 2$ m. During this 3 second interval:

$$v_{av} = \frac{\Delta x}{\Delta t} = \frac{2 - 6}{4 - 1} = -1.33 \; \frac{m}{s}$$

If the function $x = x(t)$ changes considerably, then the average velocity is very sensitive to the interval over which it is averaged. For example, if you had chosen the time interval from 1 to 3 s, then x would have changed from about 6 to about 9 m, for an average velocity of

$$v_{av} = \frac{\Delta x}{\Delta t} = \frac{9 - 6}{3 - 1} = +1.5 \; \frac{m}{s}$$

You'll notice that the average velocity involves a change on the vertical axis divided by a change on the horizontal axis. This is a slope formula, and the average velocity is the slope of the line connecting the two points defining the interval.

Average velocity isn't the most precise way to describe motion because it depends on the particular interval you've chosen to average over. For more precision, you'll need to use instantaneous velocity. You can probably surmise that as an object moves, it has a well defined velocity at every instant. The problem with defining such a quantity is that at each instant it is frozen like a photograph, so how do you determine the displacement and the time interval? You can use the fact that if the interval is small enough, the function will not change much. **Instantaneous velocity** at a given time is the average velocity over a tiny interval (imagine it infinitely small) centered at that time:

$$v = \left(\frac{\Delta x}{\Delta t}\right)_{small} = \lim_{\Delta t \to 0} \frac{\Delta x}{\Delta t} = \frac{dx}{dt}$$

Because the average velocity is the slope of the line connecting the two endpoints of the interval, the instantaneous velocity will be the slope of the tangent line drawn to the graph at the given time. Of course, from your work in calculus, you should recognize that the derivative of a function gives the slope of the tangent line.

EXAMPLE

By drawing a tangent line to the curve at $x = 2$ (figure 2), you can see from the slope that the instantaneous velocity is approximately 1.2 m/s.

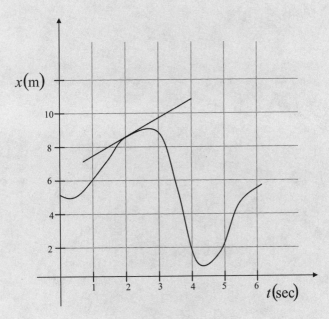

figure 2

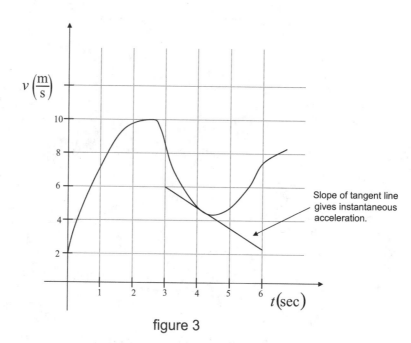
EXERCISE

An object is moving in one dimension according to the formula $x(t) = 2t^3 + t^2 - 4$. Find its velocity at $t = 2$ s

$$v(t) = \frac{dx}{dt} = 6t^2 + 2t$$

$$v(2) = 28 \ \frac{m}{s}$$

Acceleration

Acceleration is the rate at which velocity changes. Just as you did for velocity, you can define **average acceleration** over an interval or **instantaneous acceleration** at a given time.

$$a_{av} = \frac{\Delta v}{\Delta t} \qquad a = \left(\frac{\Delta v}{\Delta t}\right)_{small} = \lim_{\Delta t \to 0} \frac{\Delta v}{\Delta t} = \frac{dv}{dt} = \frac{d^2 x}{dt^2}$$

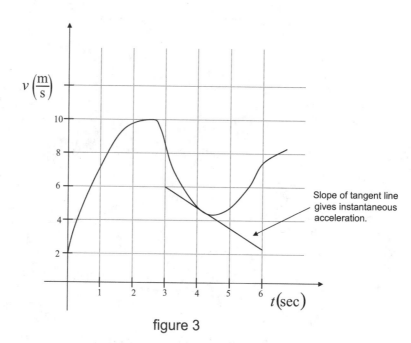

Slope of tangent line gives instantaneous acceleration.

figure 3

If you look at a graph of v vs. t (figure 3), the average acceleration over an interval is just the slope of the line connecting the two ends of the interval, and the instantaneous acceleration is the slope of the tangent line drawn to the graph at the given time.

There is one other useful piece of information you can get from the v vs. t graph. Given the functional form $v = v(t)$, you can integrate as follows:

$$v(t) = \frac{dx}{dt} \Rightarrow dx = vdt$$

$$\int_{x_0}^{x} dx = \int_{0}^{t} vdt$$

$$x - x_0 = \int_{0}^{t} vdt$$

The left-hand side of the last equation is the displacement over the interval, and the right-hand side is the area under the v vs. t graph. Thus by calculating the area under such a graph, we can determine the displacement. This is particularly simple if the graph is a sequence of connected lines.

EXAMPLE

Find the displacement over the interval from 0 to 6 s in the two graphs below.

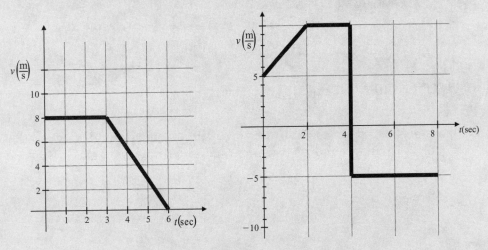

figure 4

The left graph can be thought of as a rectangle and a triangle, giving an area of

$$area = 8 \cdot 3 + \frac{1}{2}(3 \cdot 8) = 36 \text{ m}$$

In the right graph, you can count the boxes to determine the area. Each box has a value $5 \cdot 2 = 10$ m. From 0 to 4 s, you have 3.5 boxes. From 4 to 6 s, you have 1 box, but the area is negative since it lies below the t-axis and corresponds to decreasing x-values. Thus you have a total of 2.5 boxes or 25 m for the displacement.

Given the functional form of the acceleration, you can integrate to find the velocity.

$$a(t) = \frac{dv}{dt} \Rightarrow dv = adt$$

$$\int_{v_0}^{v} dv = \int_0^t adt$$

$$v - v_0 = \int_0^t adt$$

EXERCISE

Find the position and velocity of an object for arbitrary times if it has an acceleration of $a(t) = 2t - 4$, an initial velocity of $+4$ m/s, and an initial position $x = 0$ at time $t = 0$.

From the preceding equations you can write:

$$v - 4 = \int_0^t (2t - 4)dt \qquad\qquad x - 0 = \int_0^t (t^2 - 4t + 4)dt$$

$$v(t) = t^2 - 4t + 4 \qquad\qquad x(t) = \frac{1}{3}t^3 - 2t^2 + 4t$$

Constant Acceleration Equations

When acceleration is constant, you can use some simple equations that relate the various kinematic variables. To understand their content, consider the v vs. t graph (figure 5).

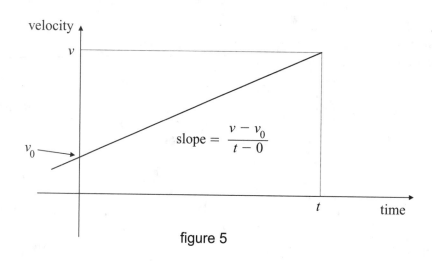

figure 5

Since the acceleration is the slope of the v vs. t graph, constant acceleration means a straight line. If the interval begins at $t = 0$ and extends to some arbitrary time t, the slope is $a = \frac{\Delta v}{\Delta t} = \frac{v - v_0}{t - 0}$, or you can write

$$v = v_0 + at$$

Since the graph is a straight line, the average velocity over the interval is the median of the velocities at the endpoints: $v_{av} = \frac{1}{2}(v + v_0)$. Since by definition $v_{av} = \frac{\Delta x}{\Delta t}$, you can write

$$\Delta x = \frac{1}{2}(v + v_0)t$$

You can combine these two equations algebraically to eliminate certain variables and obtain other equations. The end result is a set of four equations:

1. $v = v_0 + at$ 3. $\Delta x = v_0 t + \frac{1}{2}at^2$

2. $\Delta x = \frac{1}{2}(v + v_0)t$ 4. $v^2 = v_0^2 + 2a\Delta x$

Rather than thinking in terms of the graphs, you can derive these equations from direct integration beginning with the definition of a and using the fact that it is constant. For example:

$$a = \frac{dv}{dt} \Rightarrow dv = adt$$

$$\int_{v_0}^{v} dv = \int_{0}^{t} adt$$

$$v - v_0 = at \Rightarrow v = v_0 + at$$

You can apply these equations to the motion of an object over an interval where the acceleration a is constant. During this interval, the velocity changes from v_0 to v while a displacement Δx occurs. In a typical problem, you'll be given three of the five quantities v, v_0, a, Δx, and t; you can determine the remaining two by using the four equations. You can usually use several different ways to solve such problems, depending on which equations you decide to use and which quantities you decide to solve for first.

EXERCISE

An automobile moving along a straight road passes an observer who records a speed of 20 m/s. A second observer 100 m from the first records a speed of 30 m/s. Find the value of the acceleration, assuming it is constant, and the time it took to travel the 100 m.

For this interval you have:
$$v_0 = 20 \, \frac{m}{s}$$

$$v = 30 \, \frac{m}{s}$$

$$\Delta x = 100 \text{ m}$$

$$t = \, ?$$

$$a = \, ?$$

You can use the fourth equation to find the acceleration since it does not involve t:
$$v^2 = v_0^2 + 2a\Delta x$$

$$30^2 = 20^2 + 200a$$

$$a = 2.5 \, \frac{m^2}{s}$$

You can then use the first equation to find t:

$$v = v_0 + at$$

$$30 = 20 + 2.5t$$

$$t = 4s$$

One of the most important situations where you can apply one-dimensional constant acceleration is the case of an object moving vertically under only the influence of gravity. Gravity causes all masses near the Earth's surface to experience an acceleration of $g = 9.8$ m/s^2 directed downward. On the AP test, you will always be permitted to replace 9.8 m/s^2 with 10 m/s^2 when you're solving numerical problems.

EXAMPLE

A boy on a balcony 25 m above the ground throws a ball straight up with a speed of 20 m/s. The ball misses the balcony on the way down. Neglecting air resistance, determine the maximum height, the total time in the air, and the speed of the ball just before impact with the ground.

First, let's choose the balcony as the origin and make "up" the positive y-direction. To determine the maximum height, select an interval defined by the start of the motion as the ball leaves the boy's hand and the top of the motion where the velocity is instantaneously 0. Over this interval you'll have:

$$v_0 = 20 \, \frac{m}{s}$$

$$\Delta y = \, ?$$

$$v = 0$$

$$t = \, ?$$

$$a = -10 \, \frac{m}{s^2}$$

You know two of the five quantities, so you can solve for the others. Choosing the first equation, you can find t:

$$v = v_0 + at$$

$$0 = 20 - 10t$$

$$t = 2 \text{ s}$$

You could then use the second equation to find Δy:

$$\Delta y = \frac{1}{2}(v_0 + v)t$$

$$\Delta y = \frac{1}{2}(0 + 20)(2) = 20 \text{ m}$$

The highest point will be 45 m above the ground.
To find the total time in the air, you could choose an interval beginning with the start of the motion and ending just before the ball hits. For this interval you have:

$$v_0 = 20 \, \frac{m}{s}$$

$$\Delta y = -25 \text{ m}$$

$$v = \, ?$$

$$t = \, ?$$

$$a = -10 \, \frac{m}{s^2}$$

You can use the third equation to get t and the first equation to get v:

$$\Delta y = v_0 t + \frac{1}{2}at^2 \qquad\qquad v = v_0 + at$$

$$-25 = 20t - 5t^2 \qquad\qquad v = 20 - 10(5)$$

$$(t - 5)(t + 1) = 0 \qquad\qquad v = -30\ \frac{\text{m}}{\text{s}}$$

$$t = 5\text{s}$$

This is just one possible path to the solutions. Depending on the intervals you choose to analyze and the variables you solve for first, you could use different equations to end up with the same results.

KEY FORMULAS

Average Velocity $\qquad\qquad v_{\text{av}} = \dfrac{\Delta x}{\Delta t}$

Instantaneous Velocity $\qquad\qquad v = \lim\limits_{\Delta t \to 0} \dfrac{\Delta x}{\Delta t} \qquad v = \dfrac{dx}{dt}$

Average Acceleration $\qquad\qquad a_{\text{av}} = \dfrac{\Delta v}{\Delta t}$

Instantaneous Acceleration $\qquad\qquad a = \lim\limits_{\Delta t \to 0} \dfrac{\Delta v}{\Delta t} \qquad a = \dfrac{dv}{dt}$

General Velocity from Acceleration $\qquad v - v_0 = \displaystyle\int_0^t a\,dt$

General Position from Velocity $\qquad x - x_0 = \displaystyle\int_0^t v\,dt$

Constant Acceleration Equations $\qquad$ 1. $v = v_0 + at$

$\qquad\qquad\qquad\qquad\qquad\qquad\qquad$ 2. $\Delta x = \dfrac{1}{2}(v + v_0)t$

$\qquad\qquad\qquad\qquad\qquad\qquad\qquad$ 3. $\Delta x = v_0 t + \dfrac{1}{2}at^2$

$\qquad\qquad\qquad\qquad\qquad\qquad\qquad$ 4. $v^2 = v_0^2 + 2a\Delta x$

CHAPTER 1 PRACTICE EXERCISES

SECTION I MULTIPLE CHOICE

1. A ball is thrown straight up in the air. When air resistance is ignored, which of the following is true at the ball's highest point?
   I. The velocity is 0.
   II. The acceleration is 0.
   III. The acceleration is directed downward.

   (A) I only (B) II only (C) III only (D) I and II only (E) I and III only

Questions 2 and 3

Objects R and S start at the same origin, and their velocity vs. time graphs are shown on the same set of axes.

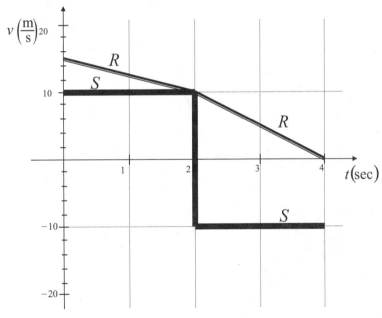

figure 6

2. After 2 s, the two objects are

   (A) 25 m apart
   (B) at the same position
   (C) 5 m apart
   (D) 20 m apart
   (E) moving at constant speed

3. After 4 s,

   (A) R has traveled 35 m
   (B) R is instantaneously at rest
   (C) S has returned to its original position
   (D) A and B only
   (E) A, B, and C

Questions 4 and 5

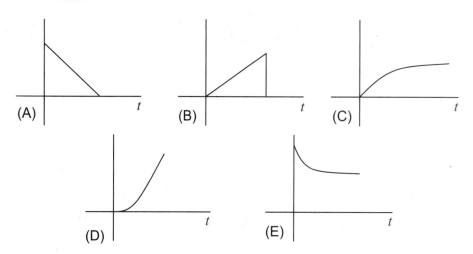

figure 7

A car with an initial positive velocity slows to a stop with a constant acceleration.

4. Which graph best represents its position vs. time graph?

   (A) A (B) B (C) C (D) D (E) E

5. Which graph best represents the velocity vs. time graph?

   (A) A (B) B (C) C (D) D (E) E

6. A ball is thrown straight up near the edge of a 25 m cliff with a speed of 20 m/s. If it misses the cliff edge on the way down, it will hit the ground in a time closest to

   (A) 2 s (B) 3 s (C) 4 s (D) 5 s (E) 7 s

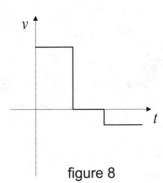

figure 8

7. An object moves with a velocity vs. time graph as shown. The position vs. time graph for the same time period would be

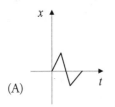

(A)

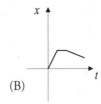

(B)

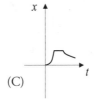

(C)

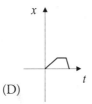

(D)

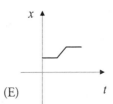

(E)

figure 9

8. An object moves vertically according to $y(t) = 12 - 4t + 2t^3$. At $t = 3$ s, its acceleration is

(A) 4 m/s^2 (B) 50 m/s^2 (C) 54 m/s^2 (D) 36 m/s^2 (E) 12 m/s^2

9. A car currently moving at 10 m/s accelerates nonuniformly according to $a(t) = 3t^2$. After 2 s, its velocity is

(A) 22 m/s   (B) 18 m/s   (C) 3 m/s   (D) 8 m/s   (E) 12 m/s

10. An object moves in one dimension such that $x(t)$ is proportional to $t^{\frac{5}{2}}$. This means v^2 will be proportional to

(A) $t^{\frac{3}{2}}$ (B) $t^{\frac{7}{2}}$ (C) t^3 (D) t^7 (E) t

PRACTICE EXERCISES

SECTION II FREE RESPONSE

1. A two stage rocket leaves its launch pad moving vertically with an average acceleration of 4 m/s². At 10 s after launch, the first stage of the rocket (now without fuel) is released. The second stage now has an acceleration of 6 m/s².
   (a) How high is the rocket when the first stage separates?
   (b) How fast is the rocket moving upon first stage separation?
   (c) What will be the maximum height attained by the first stage after separation?
   (d) What will be the distance between the first and second stages 2 s after separation?

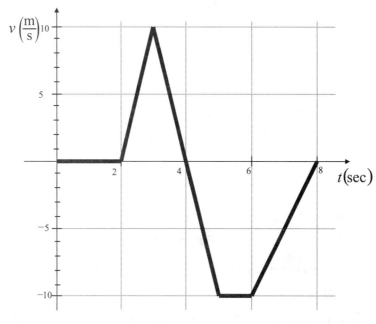

figure 10

2. A vehicle moves in one dimension with the velocity vs. time graph shown.
   (a) Over what time intervals is the velocity increasing?
   (b) Over what time intervals is the velocity decreasing?
   (c) Determine the displacement during the interval from $t = 2$ to $t = 5$ s.
   (d) On the axes below, sketch the acceleration vs. time graph of the vehicle over the entire time.

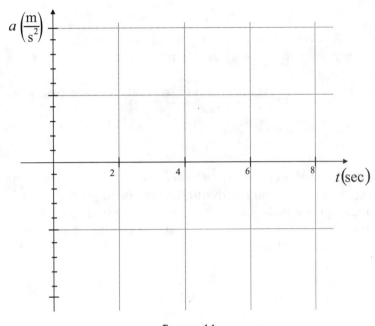

figure 11

3. For times greater than 0, an object beginning at the origin moves in one dimension according to $v(t) = \dfrac{12}{6 + 7t}$.
   (a) Determine the distance traveled by the object over the first 10 s.
   (b) Determine the acceleration of the object after 2 s.

Answers and Explanations

MULTIPLE CHOICE

1. The answer is E. The acceleration of an object moving only under only the influence of gravity near the Earth's surface is 9.8 m/s^2 directed downward. This is true at the highest point where the velocity is 0.

2. The answer is C. The area under the graphs will be the displacements of each. For S, you have a rectangle and area 20 m, while for R you have a rectangle and triangle with area 25 m. Since they begin at the same position, they will be 5 m apart.

3. The answer is E. After 4 s, the area under R is 35 m, and its velocity is instantaneously 0. S has 0 displacement because the areas above and below the t-axis are equal.

4. The answer is C. The graph must approach a constant x-value. Both C and E do this, but the tangents to E have negative slope, indicating negative velocity before stopping.

5. The answer is A. Constant acceleration means a straight line v vs. t graph. B does not approach 0 velocity continuously as described in the problem.

6. The answer is D. Use equation 1 to quickly find the time to the highest point:

$$v = v_0 + at$$
$$0 = 20 - 10t \Rightarrow t = 2s$$

Symmetry of the motion then says it takes 4 s to return to the same level where it is now moving down at 20 m/s with another 25 m to go. Even with no acceleration, this would take only a little more than 1 s more, so with acceleration, you can expect D. Of course, you could use motion equations entirely, but estimations like this are useful on the multiple-choice section.

7. The answer is B. Since velocity is the slope of the x vs. t graph, you need a large positive slope followed by a 0 slope, followed by a smaller negative slope. C is not consistent with constant velocities within the three intervals.

8. The answer is D. Two derivatives give $a = 12t$, so $a(3) = 36\ \dfrac{m}{s^2}$.

9. The answer is B. You must integrate once to get

$$v - 10 = \int_0^2 3t^2 dt \Rightarrow v = 18\ \frac{m}{s}$$

10. The answer is C. $v = \dfrac{dx}{dt} \approx t^{\frac{3}{2}}$. Then v^2 goes as t^3.

FREE RESPONSE

1. (a) Use equation 3 with $v_0 = 0$.

$$\Delta y = v_0 t + \frac{1}{2}at^2$$
$$\Delta y = 0 + \frac{1}{2}(4)(10)^2 = 200m$$

(b) Use equation 1.

$$v = v_0 + at$$
$$v = 0 + (4)(10) = 40\ \frac{m}{s}$$

(c) The first stage now moves under only the influence of gravity, with the initial position and velocity given in A and B. At the maximum height, the velocity is 0, so use equation 4.

$$v^2 = v_0^2 + 2a\Delta y$$

$$0 = 40^2 + 2(-10)(y - 200)$$

$$y = 280 \text{ m}$$

(d) You need to find the position of each object 2 s after separation and subtract. You can use equation 3 in each case.

First Stage

$$\Delta y = v_0 t + \frac{1}{2}at^2$$

$$y - 200 = 40(2) + \frac{1}{2}(-10)(2)^2$$

$$y = 260 \text{ m}$$

Second Stage

$$\Delta y = v_0 t + \frac{1}{2}at^2$$

$$y - 200 = 40(2) + \frac{1}{2}(6)(2)^2$$

$$y = 292 \text{ m}$$

The two stages are 32 m apart.

2. The slope of the v vs. t graph is the acceleration, and if the acceleration is positive, the velocity is increasing. If the acceleration is negative, the velocity is decreasing.

(a) Velocity is increasing over the intervals 2–3 s and 6–8 s since the slope (acceleration) is positive over these intervals.

(b) Velocity is decreasing over the interval 3–5 s since the slope is negative.

(c) You can get the displacement from the area under the graph. From 2–4 s is a triangle with area $= \Delta x = \frac{1}{2}(2)(10) = 10$ m. From 4–5 s is another triangle with area $= \Delta x = \frac{1}{2}(1)(-8) = -4$ m. The total displacement is 6 m.

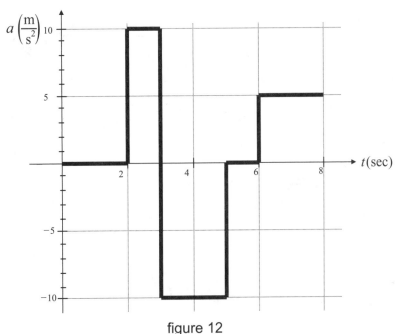

figure 12

You can find the slopes of the various segments on the v vs. t graph. The discontinuous jumps on this graph are not physical, because in a real world situation, the v vs. t graph wouldn't have sharp corners but would be rounded. This would make the corresponding a vs. t graph continuous.

3. (a) The displacement is determined by one integration of the velocity.

$$\Delta x = \int_0^t v(t')dt'$$

$$x - 0 = \int_0^t \frac{12dt'}{6 + 7t'}$$

$$x(t) = \frac{12}{7}\ln\left(\frac{6 + 7t}{7}\right) \Rightarrow x(10) = 4.1 \text{ m}$$

(b) You can find the acceleration by differentiating once.

$$a = \frac{dv}{dt} = (12)(-1)(6 + 7t)^{-2}(7)$$

$$a(t) = \frac{-84}{(6 + 7t)^2}$$

$$\Rightarrow a(2) = -0.21 \frac{\text{m}}{\text{s}^2}$$

CHAPTER 2

Vectors and Motion in Two Dimensions

In the previous chapter you learned how to describe motion in one dimension. In this chapter you'll find out how to extend this knowledge to two or more dimensions. By using vectors and their components, you'll discover that describing multidimensional motion can be reduced to combining several one-dimensional descriptions. You can easily adapt all the work from the past chapter to handle the more complicated motion.

Scalars and Vectors

The quantities you will study in AP Physics fall into two basic categories: scalars and vectors. A **scalar** needs only one number to completely quantify it. Examples of scalars are time, temperature, mass, and energy. Because it exists in two or three dimensions, a **vector** needs two or three numbers, respectively, to completely quantify it.

The big difference between vectors and scalars is that vectors have a direction associated with them. In two dimensions, two numbers that can describe a vector are its magnitude (how big it is) and its direction. You can specify direction most precisely with an angle, measured in degrees or radians in relation to one of the coordinate axes. Vectors are labeled by using boldface—**A**—or by putting an arrow on top of the label—$\vec{A}$. You can specify the magnitude of the same vector by using just the label A without the boldface or arrow. Vectors are depicted graphically with arrows; the length of the arrow indicates the relative size or magnitude of the vector, and the direction of the arrow indicates the direction of the vector (figure 1).

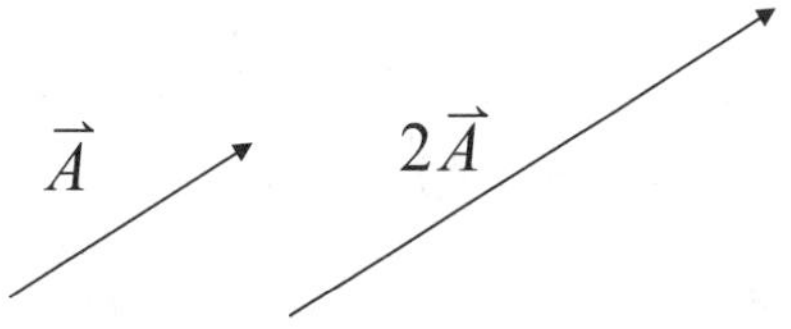

$$\vec{A} \qquad 2\vec{A}$$

figure 1

A vector can be multiplied by a scalar. This process will change the magnitude of the vector but not its direction. The vector $2\vec{A}$ is in the same direction as $\vec{A}$ but is twice as big. Examples of vectors are displacement, velocity, acceleration, and force. If you describe an object moving in two dimensions by saying it has a speed of 20 m/s, for example, you have given only the magnitude of the velocity. If you explain that the vector is directed at 30° above the + x-axis, then you have completely specified its velocity.

Vector Addition

Let's say you're traveling in a railroad car along a straight section of track at 10 m/s, and you throw a ball at 10 m/s relative to you in the same direction as the train is traveling. A person standing next to the tracks watching you and the train go by would say that the ball has a velocity of 20 m/s in the direction of the train motion. If you threw the ball out the window of the train at the same speed, however, what would the observer say about the speed and direction of the ball now? Such a question requires vector addition of the two velocities. You will see in later chapters that vector addition is common, so let's explore how to add and subtract vectors.

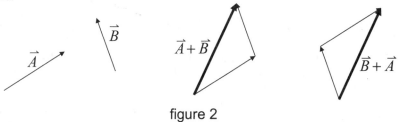

figure 2

Consider two arbitrary vectors, $\vec{A}$ and $\vec{B}$ (figure 2). To find the sum of the two vectors, move one of them, $\vec{B}$, so that its tail sits on the head of $\vec{A}$. The sum of the two vectors, called the **resultant**, is the vector that extends from the tail of $\vec{A}$ to the head of $\vec{B}$. You can easily see that this process doesn't depend on the order of the vectors, because $\vec{A} + \vec{B} = \vec{B} + \vec{A}$. If you need to add three or more vectors, just continue the process, making a "train" of vectors with the resultant extending from the tail of the first to the head of the last (figure 3).

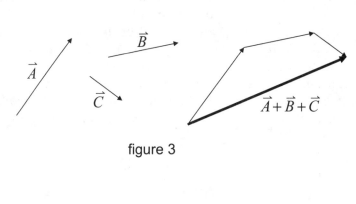

figure 3

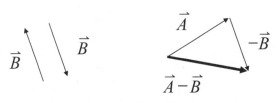

figure 4

The negative of a vector, $-\vec{B}$, is a vector with the same magnitude as $\vec{B}$ but pointing in the opposite direction (figure 4). This means that you can subtract two vectors by adding one vector to the negative of the other: $\vec{A} - \vec{B} = \vec{A} + (-\vec{B})$.

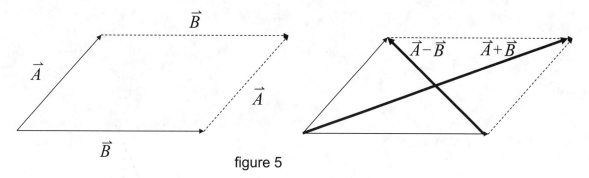

figure 5

If you draw the two vectors $\vec{A}$ and $\vec{B}$ so that they are tail to tail, you can imagine completing a parallelogram (figure 5). From the figure you can clearly see that the sum of the two vectors $\vec{A} + \vec{B}$ is directed along the diagonal that begins at the two tails and that it is equal in magnitude to the length of the diagonal. The difference of the two vectors is the other diagonal, with the direction depending on whether you want $\vec{A} - \vec{B}$ or $\vec{B} - \vec{A}$. This process is sometimes called the parallelogram method of vector addition and subtraction. Because the parallelogram is made of sides composed of the two vectors, this method is really just a different name for the original method.

Components of a Vector

These graphical methods can help you conceptualize the resultant of two vectors, but to be more precise you need an analytic method that doesn't depend on the imprecision of making scale drawings. Keep in mind that an arbitrary vector $\vec{A}$ can be written in a unique way as the sum of two special vectors: One is directed along the x-axis, and the other is directed along the y-axis (figure 6).

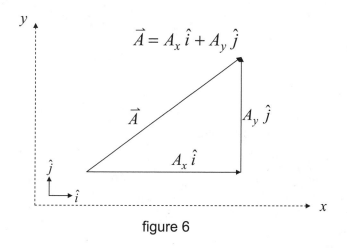

figure 6

Vectors of length one unit that point in either the x- or y-direction are called **unit vectors**. The unit vector pointing along the x-axis is labeled $\hat{\imath}$, and the unit vector pointing along the y-axis is labeled $\hat{\jmath}$, using a carat instead of an arrow. An arbitrary two-dimensional vector can be written like this:

$$\vec{A} = A_x\,\hat{\imath} + A_y\,\hat{\jmath}$$

Here A_x and A_y are called the x- and y-components of the vector $\vec{A}$. You can think of the vector as the sum of two vectors: The first is A_x units along the x-axis, and the second is A_y units along the y-axis. Using components to describe a vector makes it simpler to perform vector arithmetic. You can apply this concept to the magnitude-and-direction approach using basic right-triangle trigonometry. Consider the vector $\vec{B}$ with magnitude B, making an angle θ with respect to the $+$ x-axis (figure 7).

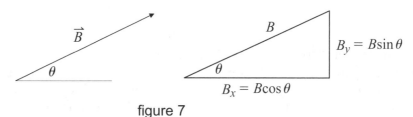

figure 7

From the definition of sine and cosine, you can write

$$B_x = B\cos\theta \qquad B_y = B\sin\theta$$

You can work in the other direction as well: Given the components B_x and B_y, you can find the magnitude and direction of the vector:

$$B = \sqrt{B_x^2 + B_y^2} \qquad \tan\theta = \frac{B_y}{B_x}$$

EXERCISE

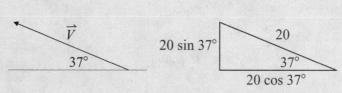

figure 8

Find the components of a velocity vector $\vec{V}$ with magnitude 20 m/s, making an angle of 37° with the negative x-axis (figure 8).

$$V_x = -20\cos37 = -16\,\frac{m}{s} \qquad\qquad V_y = 20\sin37 = 12\,\frac{m}{s}$$

EXERCISE

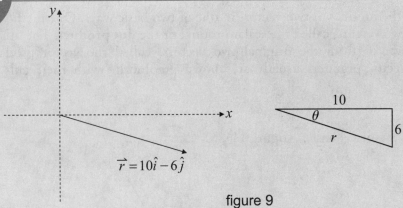

figure 9

Find the magnitude and direction of the position vector $\vec{r} = 10\,\hat{i} - 6\,\hat{j}$ shown in figure 9.

$$r = \sqrt{r_x^2 + r_y^2}$$

$$\tan\theta = -\frac{6}{10} \Rightarrow \theta = -31° \text{ (31° below + } x\text{-axis)}$$

$$r = \sqrt{10^2 + (-6)^2} = 11.7 \text{ m}$$

EXERCISE

Vector addition is particularly simple in the language of components. The components of vector $\vec{C} = \vec{A} + \vec{B}$ are just the sums of the two vectors being added (figure 10):

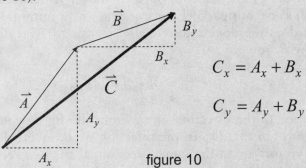

$$C_x = A_x + B_x$$

$$C_y = A_y + B_y$$

figure 10

Given the vectors $\vec{A} = -7\,\hat{i} + 4\,\hat{j}$ and $\vec{B} = 5\,\hat{i} + 9\,\hat{j}$, find the vector $\vec{C} = \vec{A} + \vec{B}$.

$$C_x = A_x + B_x \qquad\qquad C_y = A_y + B_y$$

$$C_x = -7 + 5 = -2 \qquad C_y = 4 + 9 = 13$$

$$\vec{C} = -2\,\hat{i} + 13\,\hat{j}$$

Vector Multiplication

You can calculate the product of two vectors in one of two basic ways. One method produces a scalar from the two vectors, called the scalar product or the **dot product**. The other method produces a new vector from the original two vectors, called the vector product or the **cross product**. Vector products usually are shown graphically with their tails touching, "tail to tail."

DOT PRODUCT

Consider the two vectors $\vec{A}$ and $\vec{B}$ (figure 11).

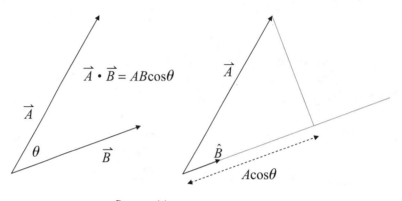

figure 11

The dot product of these two vectors is defined as:

$$\vec{A} \cdot \vec{B} = AB\cos\theta$$

The magnitude of the dot product is controlled by the angle between the two vectors. It's a maximum for parallel or antiparallel vectors and a minimum for vectors that are perpendicular. What does the dot product really tell you? If you divide both sides of the preceding equation by B, you get

$$\vec{A} \cdot \frac{\vec{B}}{B} = \vec{A} \cdot \hat{B} = A\cos\theta$$

where $\hat{B}$ is a unit vector in the direction of $\vec{B}$. From the figure you can see that $A\cos\theta$ is simply the component of $\vec{A}$ that lies in the direction of $\vec{B}$, so the dot product tells you to what extent the two vectors are in the same direction. If the two vectors are perpendicular, then $\theta = 90°$ and $\vec{A} \cdot \vec{B} = 0$; they have no component along each other. If the two vectors are the same, $\theta = 0$ and $\vec{A} \cdot \vec{A} = A^2$.

You can use the definition of the dot product and the properties of the unit vectors $\hat{i}$ and $\hat{j}$ to get a simple formula for the dot product in terms of the vector components. Let $\vec{A} = A_x\hat{i} + A_y\hat{j}$ and $\vec{B} = B_x\hat{i} + B_y\hat{j}$. Then

$$\vec{A} \cdot \vec{B} = (A_x\hat{i} + A_y\hat{j}) \cdot (B_x\hat{i} + B_y\hat{j}) = A_xB_x(\hat{i} \cdot \hat{i}) + A_yB_y(\hat{j} \cdot \hat{j}) + (A_xB_y + A_yB_x)(\hat{i} \cdot \hat{j})$$

Since $\hat{i}$ and $\hat{j}$ are perpendicular, $\hat{i} \cdot \hat{j} = 0$, and since they have length one unit, $\hat{i} \cdot \hat{i} = \hat{j} \cdot \hat{j} = 1$. The resulting equation is:

$$\vec{A} \cdot \vec{B} = A_xB_x + A_yB_y$$

EXERCISE

Find the angle between the two vectors $\vec{A} = -7\hat{i} + 4\hat{j}$ and $\vec{B} = -2\hat{i} + 9\hat{j}$ from the previous exercise.

Geometrically this would be a messy exercise, but analytically you can do it quite simply by using the dot product. First, remember that

$$\vec{A} \cdot \vec{A} = A^2 = 49 + 16 = 65 \qquad \vec{B} \cdot \vec{B} = B^2 = 4 + 81 = 85$$
$$A = \sqrt{65} \qquad\qquad\qquad B = \sqrt{85}$$

You can use the component form of the dot product to get

$$\vec{A} \cdot \vec{B} = (-7)(-2) + (4)(9) = 50$$

$$50 = AB\cos\theta = \sqrt{(65)(85)}\cos\theta \Rightarrow \theta = 47.7°$$

EXERCISE

Find the component of $\vec{A} = 5\hat{i} + 6\hat{j}$ that lies along the vector $\vec{B} = 4\hat{i} - 8\hat{j}$.

Based on the preceding discussion, you're looking for $\vec{A} \cdot \hat{B}$. As in the previous example, find the magnitude of B:

$$\vec{B} \cdot \vec{B} = B^2 = 16 + 64 \qquad \Rightarrow \hat{B} = \frac{\vec{B}}{B} = \frac{1}{\sqrt{80}}(4\hat{i} - 8\hat{j})$$
$$B = \sqrt{80}$$

Then, using the component form of the dot product, you have:

$$\vec{A} \cdot \hat{B} = \frac{1}{\sqrt{80}}(20 - 48) = -3.1$$

Keep in mind that the dot product is a scalar. In two dimensions the product takes the four components in the two vectors and puts them together to form a single number. It has no direction, although it can be positive or negative.

CROSS PRODUCT

As mentioned earlier, it's possible to multiply two vectors together in such a way that a third vector is formed. The cross product is $\vec{C}$ written as:

$$\vec{C} = \vec{A} \times \vec{B}$$

The magnitude of this vector is:

$$C = AB\sin\theta$$

The magnitude is the area made by the parallelogram formed by $\vec{A}$ and $\vec{B}$ (figure 12).

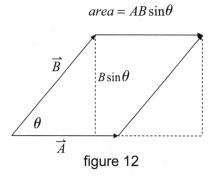

figure 12

The direction of $\vec{C}$ is defined as perpendicular to both $\vec{A}$ and $\vec{B}$. Since two vectors always define a plane, there are two directions, opposite to each other, that are perpendicular to both $\vec{A}$ and $\vec{B}$. These directions are called $\hat{n}$ and $-\hat{n}$ (figure 13).

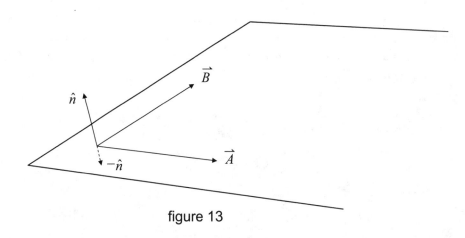

figure 13

To uniquely define the direction of the cross product, you must choose one of these two possibilities. You'll use the **right-hand rule** (figure 14) to make your choice:

Place the two vectors tail to tail. Align your right hand along the first vector in the product, $\vec{A}$, so that the base of your palm is at the tail of the vector and your fingertips are pointing toward the head. Then curl your fingers via the small angle toward the second vector, $\vec{B}$. If $\vec{B}$ is in a clockwise direction from $\vec{A}$, you'll have to flip your hand over to make this work. The direction in which your thumb is pointing is the direction of $\vec{C}$.

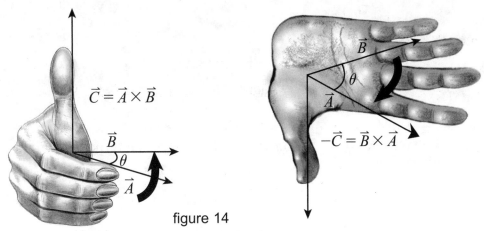

figure 14

According to this rule and the figure, $\hat{n}$ is the direction of the cross product, so

$$\vec{C} = AB \sin \theta \, \hat{n}$$

You'll notice that if you reverse the order of the cross product, the magnitude stays the same but the direction reverses.

$$\vec{A} \times \vec{B} = -\vec{B} \times \vec{A}$$

Two vectors that are parallel or antiparallel will have a cross product of 0, as you can see from calculating $\sin 0 = \sin 180° = 0$ or thinking in terms of a parallelogram with 0 area. While there is a formula for the components of $\vec{C}$ in terms of the components of $\vec{A}$ and $\vec{B}$, you won't need this level of analysis for the AP test.

Motion in Two Dimensions

To describe motion in two dimensions precisely, you'll need the **position vector**, $\vec{r}$. This vector always has its tail at the origin and its head at the current position of the object being described (figure 15).

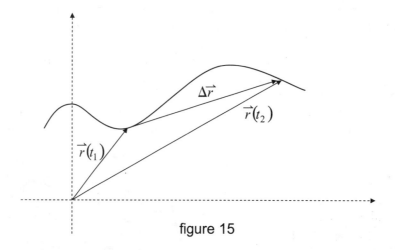

figure 15

Because the object changes position as time evolves, the position vector is a function of time: $\vec{r} = \vec{r}(t)$. The components of the position vector are just the x- and y-positions of the object, so in unit vector notation you can write:

$$\vec{r}(t) = x(t)\hat{i} + y(t)\hat{j}$$

The displacement vector is defined as the change in the position vector:

$$\Delta\vec{r} = \vec{r}(t_2) - \vec{r}(t_1)$$

Just as in the one-dimensional case, you can define the average velocity over the interval as the displacement divided by the time:

$$\vec{v}_{av} = \frac{\Delta\vec{r}}{\Delta t}$$

You can calculate the instantaneous velocity by taking the limit of an infinitesimal time interval:

$$\vec{v} = \lim_{\Delta t \to 0} \frac{\Delta\vec{r}}{\Delta t} = \frac{d\vec{r}}{dt}$$

Note that in the limit $\Delta t \to 0$, $\Delta\vec{r}$ is tangential to the trajectory, implying that the instantaneous velocity is always tangential to the trajectory. Since the $\hat{i}$ and $\hat{j}$ unit vectors don't depend on time, taking the derivative of $\vec{r}(t)$ is straightforward:

$$\vec{v} = \frac{d\vec{r}}{dt} = \frac{dx}{dt}\hat{i} + \frac{dy}{dt}\hat{j}$$

In the same way, you can define the instantaneous acceleration:

$$\vec{a} = \frac{d\vec{v}}{dt} = \frac{d^2\vec{r}}{dt^2}$$

EXERCISE

An object is described by the position vector

$$\vec{r}(t) = (3t^3 - 4t)\hat{i} + \left(1 - \frac{1}{2}t^2\right)\hat{j}$$

Find its velocity and acceleration for arbitrary times.

$$\vec{v} = \frac{d\vec{r}}{dt} = (9t^2 - 4)\hat{i} + (-t)\hat{j} \qquad \vec{a} = \frac{d\vec{v}}{dt} = 18t\,\hat{i} - \hat{j}$$

PROJECTILE MOTION

An important example of motion in two dimensions is projectile motion. An object moving near the surface of Earth under the influence of only gravity is called a **projectile**. When you're working with a projectile, your calculations start after it has been projected. For example, a baseball hit with a bat becomes a projectile after it leaves the bat, and a cannonball becomes a projectile after it leaves the barrel of the cannon. Objects remain projectiles until some other influence, such as the ground, acts upon them. If you ignore air resistance, the only acceleration experienced by the projectile is $g = 9.8$ m/s$^2 \cong 10$ m/s^2 directed straight down. Since the projectile doesn't accelerate horizontally, the x-component of the velocity doesn't change. While the projectile does accelerate in the y-direction, it is constant acceleration, and you have learned how to handle constant acceleration in the previous chapter.

Ultimately, you can think of projectile motion as two separate motions occurring simultaneously: constant velocity in the x-direction and uniformly accelerated motion in the y-direction. In describing a projectile, you can use all the equations from the last chapter, but be careful about the kind of notation you use. Because the displacement and velocity have two components, you'll need to label them with the appropriate subscripts. With the notation defined in figure 16, you can write the following equations:

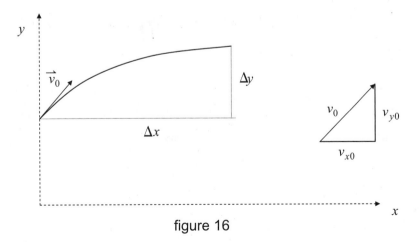

figure 16

Horizontal	Vertical
	$v_y = v_{y0} - gt$
$\Delta x = v_{x0}t$	$\Delta y = \frac{1}{2}(v_y + v_{y0})t$
$v_x = v_{x0}$	$\Delta y = v_{y0}t - \frac{1}{2}gt^2$
	$v_y^2 = v_{y0}^2 - 2g\Delta y$

For these equations, assume the positive directions are as shown in the figure, so that $a_y = -g$. Keep in mind that these equations are the basic constant acceleration equations of the last chapter; they look more complex because of the vector labeling, but that is required when you leave the world of one dimension.

EXAMPLE

A ball rolls off a table 1 m high with a speed of 4 m/s. How far from the base of the table does it land?

The object leaves the table moving horizontally, so $v_{y0} = 0$.
Since $v_{x0} = 4$ m/s, the horizontal equation gives you $\Delta x = 4t$. You can get t from the third vertical equation because you know $\Delta y = -1$m.

$$\Delta y = -1 = -\frac{1}{2}(10)t^2 \Rightarrow t = 0.45 \text{ s}$$

Substituting, you get $\Delta x = 4(0.45) = 1.79$ m.

Notice that the time the ball took to fall had nothing to do with the horizontal speed. If the object had been released from rest, it would have hit the floor in the same time. In general, the vertical motion of a horizontally projected object is identical to the motion of an object released from rest. Ignoring air resistance, a bullet fired horizontally and a bullet released from the same height from rest will hit the ground simultaneously, assuming the bullets travel over a flat surface.

EXAMPLE

An arrow is shot from a castle wall 10 m high. It leaves the bow with a speed of 40 m/s directed 37° above the horizontal.
    (a)   Find the initial velocity components.
    (b)   Find the maximum height of the arrow.
    (c)   Where does the arrow land?
    (d)   How fast is the arrow moving just before impact?

(a)

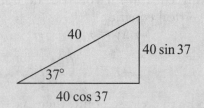

figure 17

$$v_{x0} = 40\cos37 = 32\ \tfrac{m}{s} \qquad\qquad v_{y0} = 40\sin37 = 24\ \tfrac{m}{s}$$

(The 37° right triangle is a 3-4-5 right triangle, and the AP test uses it frequently.)

(b) Use the fourth vertical equation. At the highest point, the y-component of velocity is 0.

$$v_y^2 = v_{y0}^2 - 2g\Delta y$$

$$0 = 24^2 - 20\Delta y$$

$$\Delta y = 28.8m$$

The maximum height is 38.8 m.

(c) Use the third vertical equation to find the time in the air. The vertical displacement for the entire motion is -10 m. Use the horizontal equation with this time value to get Δx.

$$y = v_{y0}t - \tfrac{1}{2}gt^2$$

$$-10 = 24t - 5t^2$$

$$t = 5.2s \text{ (use quadratic equation)}$$

$$\Delta x = 32t$$

$$\Delta x = 32(5.2) = 166\ m$$

(d) The x-component remains 32 m/s until the object hits. Use the first vertical equation and the time from (c) to get the y-component.

$$v_x = 32\ \tfrac{m}{s}$$

$$v = \sqrt{v_x^2 + v_y^2}$$

$$v = \sqrt{32^2 + (-28)^2} = 42.5\ \tfrac{m}{s}$$

$$v_y = v_{y0} - gt$$

$$v_y = 24 - (10)(5.2) = -28\ \tfrac{m}{s}$$

You can derive an interesting equation if you use the horizontal equation to eliminate the time variable in the third vertical equation:

$$\Delta x = v_{x0}t \qquad\qquad \Delta y = v_{y0}t - \frac{1}{2}gt^2$$

$$t = \frac{\Delta x}{v_{x0}} \qquad\qquad \Delta y = v_{y0}\left(\frac{\Delta x}{v_{x0}}\right) - \frac{1}{2}g\left(\frac{\Delta x}{v_{x0}}\right)^2$$

If you choose the origin to be the release point, then $\Delta x = x$ and $\Delta y = y$, and the preceding equation expresses y as a function of x in a quadratic form:

$$y = \left(\frac{v_{y0}}{v_{x0}}\right)x + \left(-\frac{g}{2v^2_{x0}}\right)x^2$$

This is the equation of a parabola, indicating that the trajectory of a projectile takes this shape if air resistance can be ignored.

UNIFORM CIRCULAR MOTION

Consider an object moving in a circle at a constant speed. Since the direction of the velocity vector is changing, the object is accelerating. Kinematics tells you a lot about the acceleration.

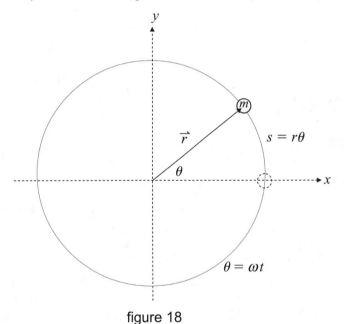

figure 18

With the origin at the center of the circle (figure 18), assume the object is moving counterclockwise crossing the positive x-axis at $t = 0$. In a time t it will move along an arc a distance $s = r\theta$, where θ, measured in radians, is the angle subtended by the arc. As time increases, both the angle and arc length increase. Taking the time derivative gives

$$\frac{ds}{dt} = r\frac{d\theta}{dt} \text{ or } v = r\omega$$

Here $v = \frac{ds}{dt}$ is the linear speed of the object along the arc, and $\omega = \frac{d\theta}{dt}$ is the rate at which the angle increases, the **angular velocity**. You are assuming that the linear speed is constant, so it follows that the angular velocity is constant as well. This means that after a time t the angle subtended is $\theta = \omega t$. Express the position vector in unit vector notation:

$$\vec{r}(t) = x(t)\hat{i} + y(t)\hat{j}$$

$$\vec{r}(t) = r\cos\theta\,\hat{i} + r\sin\theta\,\hat{j}$$

$$\vec{r}(t) = r\cos\omega t\,\hat{i} + r\sin\omega t\,\hat{j}$$

Taking the first and second derivative yields

$$\vec{v} = \frac{d\vec{r}}{dt} = \omega r\sin\omega t\,\hat{i} - \omega r\cos\omega t\,\hat{j}$$

$$\vec{a} = \frac{d\vec{v}}{dt} = -\omega^2 r\cos\omega t\,\hat{i} - \omega^2 r\sin\omega t\,\hat{j} = -\omega^2\vec{r}(t)$$

The last equation tells you that the acceleration is in the opposite direction of the position vector, that is, toward the center. It also tells you that the magnitude of the acceleration is

$$a = \omega^2 r = \frac{v^2}{r}$$

Because this acceleration is always directed toward the center, it is called the **centripetal acceleration**.

EXAMPLE

Riders at an amusement park move in a circle of radius 10 m, executing 8 revolutions every minute. Find the angular velocity and the centripetal acceleration.

Since there are 2π radians in every revolution, the angular velocity is

$$\omega = \frac{\Delta\theta}{\Delta t} = \frac{8(2\pi)}{60} = 0.84\ \frac{\text{rad}}{\text{s}}$$

Then the centripetal acceleration is

$$a = \omega^2 r = (0.84)^2(10) = 7.04\ \frac{\text{m}}{\text{s}^2}$$

KEY FORMULAS

Vector Components

$$A_x = A\cos\theta$$
$$A_y = A\sin\theta$$

Vector Addition $\vec{C} = \vec{A} + \vec{B}$

$$C_x = A_x + B_x$$
$$C_y = A_y + B_y$$

Dot Product

$$\vec{A} \cdot \vec{B} = AB\cos\theta$$
$$\vec{A} \cdot \vec{B} = A_x B_x + A_y B_y$$

Cross Product

$$\vec{C} = \vec{A} \times \vec{B}$$
$$C = AB\sin\theta$$

Vector Velocity

$$\vec{v} = \frac{d\vec{r}}{dt}$$

Vector Acceleration

$$\vec{a} = \frac{d\vec{v}}{dt} = \frac{d^2\vec{r}}{dt^2}$$

Projectile Motion

$$v_y = v_{y0} - gt$$

$$\Delta y = \frac{1}{2}(v_y + v_{y0})t$$

$$\Delta x = v_{x0}t \qquad \Delta y = v_{y0}t - \frac{1}{2}gt^2$$

$$v_x = v_{x0} \qquad v_y^2 = v_{y0}^2 - 2g\Delta y$$

Centripetal Acceleration

$$\vec{a} = -\omega^2\vec{r} \qquad a = \omega^2 r = \frac{v^2}{r}$$

CHAPTER 2 PRACTICE EXERCISES

SECTION I MULTIPLE CHOICE

Questions 1 and 2

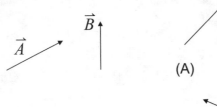

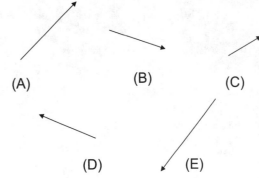

figure 19

1. The vector representing $\vec{A} - \vec{B}$ most closely is

   (A) A   (B) B   (C) C   (D) D   (E) E

2. The vector $\vec{X}$ that would satisfy the equation $\vec{A} + \vec{B} + \vec{X} = 0$ most closely is

   (A) A   (B) B   (C) C   (D) D   (E) E

3. The dot product of two vectors
   I.   is a scalar
   II. is 0 if the two vectors are perpendicular
   III. lies perpendicular to the plane defined by the two vectors

   (A) I only   (B) II only   (C) III only   (D) I and II only   (E) I, II, and III

4. The vectors $\vec{A}$ and $\vec{B}$ both have a magnitude of 5 units. The magnitude of the sum of these two vectors

   (A) has magnitude 10   (B) equals 0   (C) has magnitude 5
   (D) could be A or B, but not C (E) could be A, B, or C

5. Two vectors have their tails connected and their lengths fixed. If the angle between them is now varied, which of the following is true?
   I. The magnitude of the dot product is minimized when the vectors are perpendicular.
   II. The magnitude of the cross product is maximized when they are perpendicular.
   III. Each will always have a component lying along the other.

   (A) I only   (B) II only   (C) III only   (D) I and II only   (E) I, II, and III

6. Three balls are projected from the edge of a cliff. I is fired horizontally, II is fired at an angle of 30° above the horizontal with the same speed as I, and III is released from rest. Which of the following is true?

   (A) I and II hit at the same time, and III hits later.
   (B) I and II hit at the same time, and III hits earlier.
   (C) I and III hit at the same time, and II hits earlier.
   (D) I and III hit at the same time, and II hits later.
   (E) All hit at the same time.

7. At the highest point of its trajectory, a projectile fired at 30° above the horizontal from a starting height of 20 m

   (A) is instantaneously at rest
   (B) has traveled half the distance to its impact point
   (C) has 0 acceleration
   (D) has a horizontal velocity component equal to its initial value
   (E) has more than one of the above properties

8. An object moves in two dimensions described by the position vector

$$\vec{r}\,(t) = -2t\hat{i} + (\tfrac{1}{2}t^2 - 4t)\hat{j}$$

   The object reaches its minimum y-coordinate at $t =$

   (A) 0   (B) $\sqrt{8}$ s   (C) 4 s   (D) $\sqrt{2}$ s   (E) 2 s

9. Two objects, A and B, are executing uniform circular motion. Both have the same radius, but A experiences twice the acceleration that B experiences. The ratio of the angular velocity of A to that of B is

   (A) 4   (B) 2   (C) $\frac{1}{4}$ (D) $\sqrt{2}$ (E) $\frac{1}{2}$

PRACTICE EXERCISES

SECTION II FREE RESPONSE

1. A train is moving east at 30 m/s along a long, straight section of track. A person on the train has a dart gun that can shoot rubber-tipped darts at a speed of 10 m/s. If the person aims the gun at an angle of 30° north of east and pulls the trigger, what will be the magnitude and direction of the velocity of the dart as it leaves the gun, relative to a person on the ground watching the train pass by?

2. A projectile is fired from a balcony 20 m high at an angle of 30° above the horizontal. It strikes the ground 10.4 s later.
    (a) Find the initial speed.
    (b) Find the magnitude and direction of the velocity vector after 7 s.
    (c) With the balcony as the origin, find the x- and y-coordinates of the highest point of the motion.

3. An object moves in two dimensions with a position vector of

    $$\vec{r}(t) = \left(4 + 3t^2 - \frac{1}{3}t^3\right)\hat{i} + (t^2 - 5)\hat{j}$$

    (a) Find the magnitude and direction of the velocity at $t = 1$ s.
    (b) Find the position of the object when the x-component of the velocity is maximized.
    (c) Find the angle between the velocity vector and the acceleration vector at $t = 1$ s.

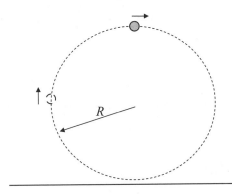

figure 20

4. A ball on a string moves in a vertical circle of radius R at a constant speed with a centripetal acceleration a. At its lowest point, the ball is a negligible height above the ground. After several revolutions, the string breaks at the highest point in the motion. In terms of R, a, and g, find the horizontal displacement of the ball from the time the string breaks.

Answers and Explanations ─────────────────────────●

MULTIPLE CHOICE

1. The answer is B. Put $-\vec{B}$ at the tip of $\vec{A}$, estimating the lengths. Connect from the tail of $\vec{A}$ to the head of $-\vec{B}$ to get the answer.

2. The answer is E. Put $\vec{B}$ at the tip of $\vec{A}$. The vector $\vec{C}$ must connect back to the tail of $\vec{A}$ so that the sum of all three is 0. This leads to E.

3. The answer is D. The dot product is a scalar and doesn't have a direction, so III isn't possible.

4. The answer is E. The magnitude of $\vec{A} + \vec{B}$ can be anywhere between 0 (opposite directions) and + 10 (parallel), depending on the angle they make with each other.

5. The answer is D. While the dot product can be negative, its magnitude is always greater than or equal to 0, so A is true. B is true according to the definition. When the two vectors are perpendicular, each has no component along the other, excluding III.

6. The answer is D. Horizontally fired projectiles will hit at the same time as those dropped from rest from the same height because the horizontal speed is not affected by gravity. Object II fired upward will reach some greater height where its speed is purely horizontal. This makes it a horizontal projectile from a greater height, which clearly will take longer to fall.

7. The answer is D. The object will never be at rest (until it hits) because the x-component of the velocity always stays the same. It is less than halfway to its impact point since it began 20 m off the ground, not at ground level. The acceleration is always 9.8 m/s² down, never 0.

8. The answer is C. The minimum y-coordinate occurs when $v_y = 0$.

    $$v_y = \frac{d}{dt}\left(\frac{1}{2}t^2 - 4t\right) = t - 4$$

    $$0 = t - 4 \Rightarrow t = 4\text{s}$$

9. The answer is D. $\dfrac{a_A}{a_B} = \dfrac{2}{1} = \dfrac{\omega_A^2 R}{\omega_B^2 R} = \dfrac{\omega_A^2}{\omega_B^2} \Rightarrow \sqrt{2} = \dfrac{\omega_A}{\omega_B}$

FREE RESPONSE

1. The velocity observed by a person at rest with the tracks will be the vector sum of the train velocity and the velocity of the dart with respect to the train. If you have difficulty seeing this, think of the limiting cases where the dart is fired in the same direction as the train velocity or in the opposite direction to the train velocity. In the first case, it should be clear that the final velocity is 40 m/s in the train direction, while in the second case it is 20 m/s in the train direction. These cases are both consistent with the vector addition of the two velocities. For the current situation, let east be the $+ x$ direction and north the $+ y$ direction.

$$v_x^{train} = 30$$

$$v_y^{train} = 0$$

Relative to the train, the dart velocity is

$$v_x^{dart/train} = 10\cos30 = 8.7 \ \frac{m}{s}$$

$$v_y^{dart/train} = 10\sin30 = 5 \ \frac{m}{s}$$

The velocity of the dart relative to the tracks is the sum of the two vectors, and you can find the components of the sum by adding the components of each vector.

$$v_x^{dart/track} = v_x^{train} + v_x^{dart/train} = 30 + 8.7 = 38.7 \ \frac{m}{s}$$

$$v_y^{dart/track} = v_y^{train} + v_y^{dart/train} = 0 + 5 = 5 \ \frac{m}{s}$$

To find the magnitude and direction, use the basic right-triangle trigonometry.

$$v^{dart/track} = \sqrt{38.7^2 + 5^2} = 39.0 \ \frac{m}{s}$$

$$\tan\theta = \frac{5}{38.7} = 0.13$$

$$\theta = 7.4°$$

2. (a) The final vertical displacement is $- 20$ m, so given the time and angle, you can use the third vertical equation to find the initial speed.

$$\Delta y = v_{y0}t - \frac{1}{2}gt^2$$

$$-20 = (v_0\sin30)(10.4) - 5(10.4)^2$$

$$v_0 = 100\frac{m}{s}$$

(b) The x-component of the velocity is $v_x = v_0\cos30 = 100(0.87) = 87$ m/s. This stays the same for the entire motion.

The initial y-component of the velocity is $v_{y0} = v_0 \sin 30 = 100(0.5) = 50$ m/s. Use the first vertical equation to find the value after 7 s:

$$v_y = v_{y0} - gt$$

$$v_y = 50 - 10(7)$$

$$v_y = -20 \; \frac{m}{s}$$

You can find the magnitude and direction of the velocity from basic trigonometry:

$$v = \sqrt{v_x^2 + v_y^2} = \sqrt{87^2 + (-20)^2} = 89.2 \; \frac{m}{s} \qquad \tan\theta = \frac{-20}{87}$$

$$\theta = -13°$$

(c) At the highest point, $v_y = 0$. If you find the time it takes to get here, you can then substitute to find the coordinates. Since the balcony is the origin, the coordinates and displacement are identical: $\Delta x = x \quad \Delta y = y$.

$$v_y = v_{y0} - gt \qquad\qquad x = v_{x0}t \qquad\qquad y = \frac{1}{2}(v_y + v_{y0})t$$

$$0 = 50 - 10t \qquad\qquad x = 87(5) \qquad\qquad y = \frac{1}{2}(0 + 50)(5)$$

$$t = 5s \qquad\qquad x = 435 \text{ m} \qquad\qquad y = 125 \text{ m}$$

3. For future reference, compute both $\vec{v}(t)$ and $\vec{a}(t)$:

$$\vec{v}(t) = \frac{d\vec{r}}{dt} = (6t - t^2)\hat{i} + 2t\hat{j} \qquad\qquad \vec{a}(t) = (6 - 2t)\hat{i} + 2\hat{j}$$

(a) $\vec{v}(1) = 5\hat{i} + 2\hat{j}$. From trigonometry, at this time you have:

$$v(1) = \sqrt{29} \; \frac{m}{s} \quad \tan\theta = \frac{2}{5} \Rightarrow \theta = 21.8°$$

(b) v_x is maximized when its derivative, a_x, is 0.

$$a_x = 6 - 2t = 0 \qquad\qquad \vec{r}(3) = 22\hat{i} + 4\hat{j}$$

$$t = 3s$$

(c) $\vec{a}(1) = 4\hat{i} + 2\hat{j}$. Then use the dot product to find the angle:

$$\vec{v} \cdot \vec{a} = (5\hat{i} + 2\hat{j}) \cdot (4\hat{i} + 2\hat{j}) = 24$$

$$24 = va\cos\theta = (\sqrt{29})(\sqrt{20})\cos\theta$$

$$\theta = 4.7°$$

4. Since $a = \frac{v^2}{R}$, you have $v = \sqrt{aR}$. This is the speed at the top when the string breaks. You now have a ball projected horizontally from a height $2R$ with initial speed v.

$$\Delta y = 2R = \frac{1}{2}gt^2 \Rightarrow t = 2\sqrt{\frac{R}{g}}$$

$$\Delta x = vt = \sqrt{aR}\left(2\sqrt{\frac{R}{g}}\right) = 2R\sqrt{\frac{a}{g}}$$

3

Newton's Laws

Mechanics is the branch of physics that deals with the description and causes of motion. Galileo was the first person to study motion scientifically, discovering what are now called kinematic relations among the quantities used to describe motion. You have seen these relations expressed in the basic equations used to describe one-dimensional, uniform accelerated motion, uniform circular motion and projectile motion. But while Galileo was the first to develop a quantitative description of motion, the remarkable Isaac Newton created an entire framework for linking the causes of motion to the motion itself. The foundation of this framework lies in what are called Newton's three laws of mechanics. Central to these laws is the concept of force. In fact, you can use the three laws to precisely define force and to directly relate it to the motion of objects.

Inertia and the First Law

You are probably familiar with what happens when an object in space, far away from any outside influence, is given an initial velocity: It continues undeflected at constant speed forever or until something interferes with it. A physicist would say that this behavior is a basic property inherent in all matter, a property called inertia. **Inertia** means that matter stays in a state of rest if it is currently at rest, and it stays in a state of constant speed in a straight line if it is moving. The measure of inertia is mass, with units of kilograms in the SI system. The more massive an object is, the more inertia it has. Newton's first law is sometimes called the law of inertia:

An object at rest will remain at rest, or if in uniform motion (constant speed in a straight line) will continue as such, unless acted upon by a net (unbalanced) force.

The concept of force first appears in the first law; a force must be present to cause an object to deviate from its state of either rest or uniform velocity. But you know from kinematics that such a deviation, a change in velocity, has to mean acceleration is present, so you can conclude that forces will be related to accelerations Inertia itself, however, is not a force, and no force is needed to keep an object moving. A nonzero net force is needed to change an object's velocity.

Types of Forces

When two systems interact, they exert forces on each other. In terms of Newton's first law, each system changes its velocity; it doesn't simply continue in a straight line at constant speed. Two systems must always be present for a force to occur: A ball hits a wall; your hand pushes on a desk; the Earth attracts the moon. Forces are categorized in terms of how the two systems interact. **Contact forces** involve two systems actually touching. **Noncontact forces** involve interactions between two systems that aren't actually touching.

CONTACT FORCES

When an object, such as a brick, rests upon another surface, such as a table, the table supports the brick with a force that is directed perpendicular to the surface of the table (figure 1).

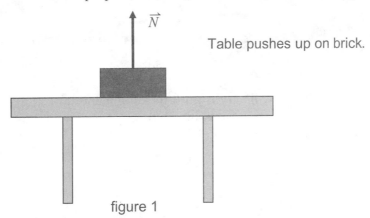

Table pushes up on brick.

figure 1

This is the **normal force**, $\vec{N}$, the force between two surfaces that acts perpendicular to the surface. The origin of this force lies in the electric forces that hold together the materials. When the brick is placed on the table, the table sags slightly as the molecules adjust their positions, much like the effect on a mattress when you lie down. If the brick slides across the table, a component of force exerted by the table will act parallel to the surface, in this case opposing the motion of the brick. This is a **friction force**, $\vec{f}$, the force exerted between two surfaces that acts parallel to the surface.

You can trace the origin of friction to electrical interactions between the materials. There are two types of friction: static friction, $\vec{f_s}$ when the two surfaces experience a sliding stress but don't actually move, and kinetic friction, $\vec{f_k}$, when the two surfaces do slide over each other. The amount of friction produced will depend on the degree to which the two surfaces are pushed into each other, or the normal force. Over a wide range of conditions, the magnitude of the kinetic friction force is directly proportional to the normal force:

$$f_k = \mu_k N$$

Here, μ_k is the coefficient of friction between the two surfaces, and it will depend on the nature of the interacting surfaces.

For static friction, the situation is different. A brick at rest on a level surface such as a table experiences no friction, but if you tilt the table (figure 2), it won't move until some maximum angle is reached.

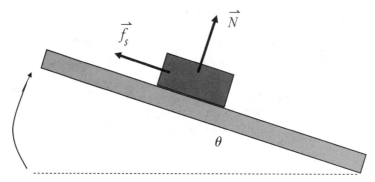

Static friction force can range between zero and a maximum value.

figure 2

The static friction force will vary from 0 to some maximum value, but this maximum value will depend on the nature of the interacting surfaces and how the surfaces are pushed together, or the normal force:

$$f_s \leq \mu_s N = f_s^{max}$$

Here μ_s is the coefficient of static friction between the two surfaces. Usually, $\mu_s > \mu_k$.

The force exerted by ropes or rods attached to objects is called **tension** $\vec{T}$. When you pull on one end of an ideal, massless rope, the rope transmits this force to the object, but it is the rope that is in direct contact with the object. You cannot push with a rope, but you can push something with a rigid rod, and this force is called compression. Once again, the origin of these forces lies in the electrical interactions of molecules.

NONCONTACT FORCES

Magnetic, electric, and gravitational forces do not require direct contact between the interacting systems. As you'll see later, such forces are transmitted by the fields created in the surrounding space, and each object interacts directly with the field of the other object. When you're using a force law relating two objects, you can apply Newton's laws, treating these types of forces no differently than tension, friction, or any other force.

For mechanics, the only force you need to consider from this category is gravitational attraction. The gravitational attraction between the Earth and an object near its surface is called the **weight**, W, of the object. You'll also look at the more general case of gravitational interaction in a separate chapter.

Freebody Diagrams

You'll find it much easier to apply Newton's laws if you can draw accurate freebody diagrams. A **freebody diagram** is a properly oriented representation of the system removed from its surroundings, but showing all interactions as force vectors, represented as arrows coming out of the body. You'll need to give the vectors appropriate descriptive labels, but you don't need to labor over your drawing. Usually a simple box or even a point will work just fine, unless you're dealing with rotation, which will be covered in a later chapter.

Let's look at a couple of examples.

A boy is using a rope to pull a sled up an incline, keeping the rope parallel to the incline surface. Draw a freebody diagram for the sled (figure 3).

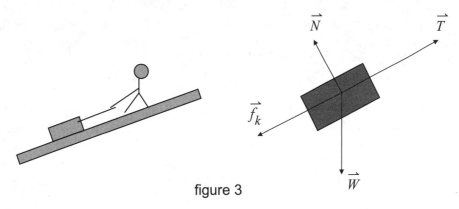

figure 3

Two weights connected by a rope are lifted by a second rope connected to the upper weight. Draw a freebody diagram for each weight (figure 4).

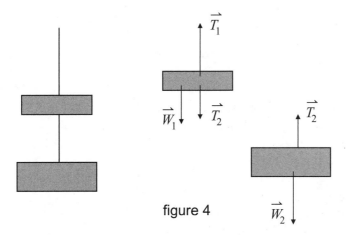

figure 4

Notice that the last example uses subscripts to differentiate between the different weights and the different tensions.

Action and Reaction and the Third Law

As you've learned, it takes two systems for an interaction to occur. Newton's third law addresses this interaction in a general way:

When an interaction takes place between two systems, each system exerts a force on the other, and these two forces are equal in magnitude and opposite in direction.

The two forces are sometimes called an action-reaction pair. When a bat hits a baseball, for example, the bat exerts a force on the ball, and the ball exerts an equal and opposite force on the bat. It doesn't matter which of these forces you call "action" and which you call "reaction," because neither is more fundamental than the other.

If you don't understand the third law completely, it's easy to become confused. In the example, for instance, you might argue that the two forces couldn't be equal because the ball obviously receives a much greater acceleration than the bat, but this argument ignores the difference in the inertia of the bat and ball. This point will become clearer when you read about the second law.

Another argument is that the forces couldn't be equal and opposite because then they would cancel each other out and nothing would accelerate. But each member of the action-reaction pair acts on a different object, so there's no question about the force on the ball or the bat canceling out with anything. Action-reaction pairs never act on the same object.

Finally, it's possible for two forces to be equal in magnitude and opposite in direction, and yet not be action-reaction pairs. The brick resting on a flat surface is a good example. Intuition probably tells you that the normal force acting up is just equal to the weight acting down. But this is not an action-reaction pair. The normal force results from an interaction between the brick and the table. Its reaction partner is a force exerted on the table (causing it to sag). The weight force is an interaction between the brick and the entire Earth. Its reaction partner is a force exerted on the entire Earth by the brick!

Newton's Second Law

Newton's second law is a quantitative statement that relates the vector sum of all forces acting on a system, the **net force**, to the acceleration of the system:

$$net\vec{F} = \vec{m}a$$

Keep in mind that for a fixed mass, the net force and acceleration are directly proportional: Doubling the force will double the acceleration. But the same force will produce different accelerations on systems with different masses. This equation sets the units of force in the SI system to be $\frac{kg \cdot m}{s^2}$, which is called a Newton (N). Because this is a vector equation, it is actually a separate equation for each component:

$$netF_x = ma_x \qquad netF_y = ma_y$$

Analyzing a physical system with this law is a four-step process:
Step 1. For each object, draw a freebody diagram with the forces properly labeled. If numerical values are given for the forces, include them. Otherwise, use symbolic notation such as T and W.

Step 2. For each object and each direction, determine the sum of all the force components using the symbols and numbers in Step 1. This will be $netF_x$ or $netF_y$ for each object.

Step 3. Equate your result from Step 2 to ma for each component: for example, $netF_x = ma_x$.

Step 4. Use these equations to determine any unknown factors.

Although you'll need to focus on these four steps when you're first learning, eventually they should become second nature. After you're familiar with the technique, you won't always need to state the obvious, but be careful. Faulty intuition often leads to errors that you could have avoided by considering the facts more carefully.

EXAMPLE

A mass m falls freely. Find the relation between the mass and the weight of the object. Because all motion is in y-direction, you can drop the x- and y-labels.
Step 1.

figure 5

Step 2. $netF = W$

Step 3. $W = ma$

Step 4. Because the mass falls freely, $a = g \Rightarrow W = mg$

This example leads to the important equation that relates mass and weight near the surface of Earth:

$$W = mg$$

EXAMPLE

A horizontal rope with tension 30 N pulls a 5 kg mass across a horizontal surface where the coefficient of kinetic friction is 0.4. Find the acceleration of the mass.

Step 1.

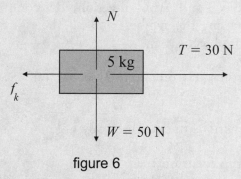

figure 6

Step 2. y-direction: $netF_y = N - W = N - 50$

x-direction: $netF_x = T - f_k = 30 - (0.4)$ N

Step 3. $N - 50 = 5a_y$

$30 - (0.4)N = 5a_x$

Step 4. There is no vertical acceleration, so $a_y = 0 \Rightarrow N = 50$ Newtons

$$30 - (0.4)(50) = 5a_x \Rightarrow a_x = 2 \, \frac{\text{m}}{\text{s}^2}$$

In numerical problems, be sure to include units in your answers. On the AP test, sometimes you can receive points for having correct units in all answers within a given problem.

EXAMPLE

A 200-kg beam is connected by a cable to a 300-kg beam below it. The two are raised with an acceleration of 0.5 m/s^2 by another cable attached to the 200-kg beam. Ignoring the masses of the cables, find the tension in each.

With all motions vertical, you can again drop the (x, y) subscripts.

Step 1.

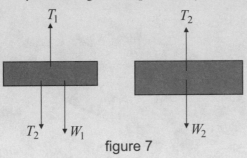

figure 7

Step 2.   on 200-kg mass: $netF_{top} = T_1 - T_2 - 2{,}000$

on 300-kg mass: $netF_{bot} = T_2 - 3{,}000$

Step 3. $T_1 - T_2 - 2{,}000 = 200(0.5)$

$T_2 - 3{,}000 = 300(0.5)$

Step 4. $T_2 - 3{,}150\ N \Rightarrow T_1 = 5{,}150\ N$

In Step 4 you had to solve simultaneously for the tensions in the two equations. But there's another approach you could have used in this problem that will be useful in other multiple-object problems where the objects all have the same acceleration. You can apply Newton's second law to the system as a whole:

Step 1.   same as above

Step 2. $netF_{sys} = T_1 - T_2 - 2{,}000 + T_2 - 3{,}000 = T_1 - 5000$

Step 3. $T_1 - 5{,}000 = 500(0.5)$

Step 4. $T_1 = 5{,}250\ N$

Note that in Step 2, the T_2 tension force canceled out. For the ideal, massless cables, the two T_2 forces were action-reaction pairs. Whenever you look at the entire system, the internal forces exerted by one part of the system on another part will always occur in pairs like this and will cancel out in the overall system equation. Notice also that this approach would not allow you to determine T_2, an internal force. You would have to apply the second law to one of the individual objects to find T_2.

Inclines

When an object is constrained to move on an incline (figure 8), its description is complicated by the fact that its acceleration has both vertical and horizontal components.

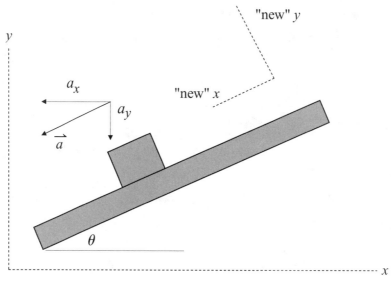

figure 8

But since you know that it has an acceleration component only along the incline, it makes sense to change the coordinate system so that the new x-axis lies parallel to the incline surface and the new y-axis is perpendicular to the surface. Doing this also simplifies the description of the surface forces. Friction will have only an x-component, and the normal force will have only a y-component. The downside is that the weight will have both x- and y-components. Given the angle of the incline, however, the decomposition of the weight force into its components is the same every time (figure 9).

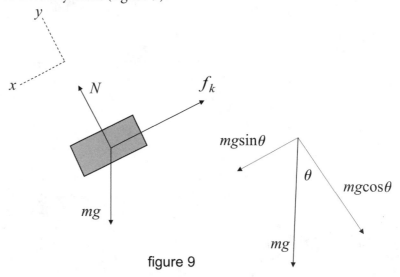

figure 9

With some practice, you should be able to analyze inclines easily.

EXAMPLE

A 5-kg mass is placed on a plank where the coefficients of friction are $\mu_s = 0.6$ and $\mu_k = 0.4$. The plank is raised slowly until the mass just starts to slide. Find the angle at which sliding occurs and the acceleration of the mass as it slides.

The angle where sliding just begins is called the angle of repose. As you approach this angle, you reach the maximum value of static friction that can be supplied by the surfaces: $f_s = \mu_s N$. The acceleration will be 0 until you reach this limiting angle.

    Step 1.

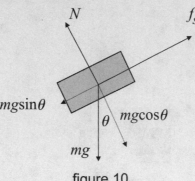

figure 10

Step 2. $netF_x = mg\sin\theta - f_s = mg\sin\theta - \mu_s N$ $netF_y = N - mg\cos\theta$

Step 3. $mg\sin\theta - \mu_s N = ma_x = 0$ $N - mg\cos\theta = ma_y = 0$

Step 4. $mg\sin\theta = \mu_s N = \mu_s mg\cos\theta \Rightarrow \mu_s = \tan\theta$ $N = mg\cos\theta$

           $\tan\theta = 0.6 \Rightarrow \theta = 31°$

To find the acceleration down the incline, change f_s to f_k, use the 31° result from the first part of the problem, and recognize that a_x is no longer 0.

Step 1.   same but with friction type changed

Step 2. $netF_x = mg\sin\theta - f_k = 50\sin 31 - (0.4)N$

         $netF_y = N - mg\cos\theta = N - 50\cos 31 = N - 43$

Step 3. $50\sin 31 - (0.4)N = 5a_x$ $N - 43 = 5a_y = 0 \Rightarrow N = 43N$

Step 4. $25.8 - 17.2 = 5a \Rightarrow a = 1.7 \frac{m}{s^2}$

Ideal Pulleys

Ideal pulleys are frictionless and add no inertia to the system. They serve as agents that redirect forces without otherwise affecting the dynamics. In a later chapter on rotation, you will learn how to account for the inertia introduced by a real pulley, but you should also be able to handle the simpler situation of an idealized pulley as well.

Consider two masses connected over an idealized pulley, the so-called Atwood's machine (figure 11).

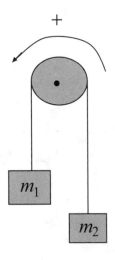

figure 11

Before you analyze the system, let's look at two important points:

1. A real pulley will not allow for the masses to accelerate if the tensions are equal on each side of the pulley. In the limit of the idealized pulley, however, these two tensions can be considered equal, so the tension is the same throughout the rope.

2. You'll need to adopt a sign convention to determine positive and negative quantities. One approach is to focus on the pulley rotation, arbitrarily calling counterclockwise rotation positive. Forces that tend to cause this type of rotation will be positive, while those that oppose it will be negative. Similarly, accelerations that increase the rate of counterclockwise rotation will be considered positive. In figure 11, the curved arrow indicates positive direction.

Now, on to the analysis:

Step 1.

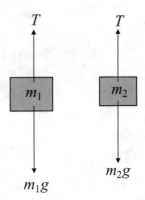

figure 12

Step 2. $netF_1 = m_1g - T$

$netF_2 = T - m_2g$

Step 3. $m_1g - T = m_1a$

$T - m_2g = m_2a$

Step 4. $a = \dfrac{m_1 - m_2}{m_1 + m_2}g \qquad T = \dfrac{2m_1m_2}{m_1 + m_2}g$

Since each mass has the same acceleration, you could have found the acceleration quickly by analyzing the system as a whole. Because the tensions are internal to the system, they cancel out.

Step 2. $netF_{sys} = m_1g - T + T - m_2g$

Step 3. $m_1g - m_2g = (m_1 + m_2)a$

Step 4. $a = \dfrac{m_1 - m_2}{m_1 + m_2}g$

Translational Equilibrium

A system is in **translational equilibrium** if the net force on the system is 0: $net\vec{F} = 0$. To analyze the system, just proceed as in any second law problem, but use the fact that the acceleration is 0.

EXAMPLE

A 5-kg traffic light is hung from two wires as shown in figure 13. Find the tension in the wires.

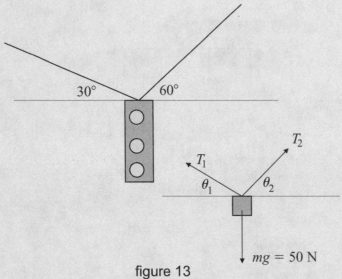

figure 13

Step 1.   See figure 13.

Step 2. $netF_x = T_{1x} + T_{2x}$ $netF_y = T_{1y} + T_{2y} - mg$

$= T_1\cos\theta_1 - T_2\cos\theta_2$ $= T_1\sin\theta_1 + T_2\sin\theta_2 - mg$

Step 3. $T_1\cos\theta_1 - T_2\cos\theta_2 = 0$ $T_1\sin\theta_1 + T_2\sin\theta_2 - mg = 0$

Step 4. $T_1(0.87) - T_2(0.80) = 0$ $T_1(0.50) + T_2(0.60) - 50 = 0$

$T_1 = 43.4$ N and $T_2 = 47.8$ N

Centripetal Force

In the chapter covering two-dimensional motion, you learned that an object moving in a circle of radius R with speed v experiences an acceleration directed toward the center having magnitude

$$a_{cp} = \frac{v^2}{R}$$

This is called the **centripetal acceleration**. Since there is acceleration, there must be a nonzero net force present as well. The force that produces the acceleration depends on the system in question. For a ball on a string moving in a horizontal circle, it will be tension, for example, and for Earth moving around the sun it will be gravity. But the generic name for the net force acting toward the center of an object moving in a circle is the **centripetal force**.

Keep in mind that the centripetal force is "supplied" by such real forces as tension and gravity. When you draw a freebody diagram for an object moving in a circle, you will still draw the usual forces present; never draw the centripetal force as a separate force. The only difference between analyzing a circular-motion problem and other second-law problems is that you know the direction of the acceleration immediately (toward the center), and you can express the acceleration in terms of v and R. Your first step in this analysis is to identify the center of the circle. The sum of all forces along the line connecting the object to the center will provide the centripetal force. The sum of all forces perpendicular to this direction often just adds up to 0, but if it doesn't, you can apply the second law in that direction to determine this component of the acceleration.

EXAMPLE

A 2-kg ball is rotated in a vertical circle by a light, rigid rod of length 3 m attached to a motor that keeps the ball moving at a constant speed of 12 m/s (figure 14). Find the tension in the rod at the highest and lowest points.

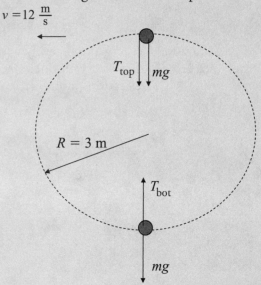

figure 14

Top	Bottom
Step 1. see figure	see figure

Step 2. $netF_{top} = T_{top} + mg$ $\qquad$ $netF_{bot} = T_{bot} - mg$

Step 3. $T_{top} + mg = ma_{cp} = m\dfrac{v^2}{R}$ $\qquad$ $T_{bot} - mg = ma_{cp} = m\dfrac{v^2}{R}$

Step 4. $T_{top} = m\dfrac{v^2}{R} - mg = 76$ N $\qquad$ $T_{bot} = m\dfrac{v^2}{R} + mg = 116$ N

Choose the direction toward the center as the positive direction, and pay careful attention to the signs.

EXAMPLE

A highway curve can be banked at just the right angle so that when a car moves through the curve at just the right speed, no friction is needed between the road and tires to turn the car while it maintains the same height on the bank. Find the relation between speed and banking angle (figure 15).

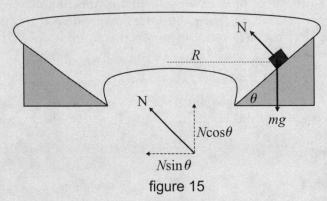

figure 15

Note that the center of the circle is above ground level, with the circle radius parallel to the ground. You'll need to find force components along this line and perpendicular to it, since you know the accelerations along these directions.

Step 1. See figure 15.

Step 2. $netF_x = N \sin \theta$ $\qquad\qquad$ $netF_y = N\cos\theta - mg$

Step 3. $N\sin\theta = ma_{cp} = m\dfrac{v^2}{R}$ $\qquad$ $N\cos\theta - mg = ma_y = 0$

Step 4. $\dfrac{N\sin\theta}{N\cos\theta} = \dfrac{\frac{mv^2}{R}}{mg}$

$\qquad$ $\tan\theta = \dfrac{v^2}{Rg}$

KEY FORMULAS

Newton's Second Law $\qquad$ $net\ \vec{F} = m\vec{a}$

Kinetic Friction $\qquad$ $f_k = \mu_k N$

Static Friction $\qquad$ $f_s \leq \mu_s N$

Weight $\qquad$ $W = mg$

Translational Equilibrium $\qquad$ $netF_x = netF_y = 0$

Centripetal Acceleration $\qquad$ $a_{cp} = \dfrac{v^2}{R}$

CHAPTER 3 PRACTICE EXERCISES

SECTION I MULTIPLE CHOICE

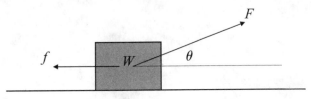

figure 16

1. A weight W is pulled by a rope at an angle θ across a horizontal surface where the coefficient of kinetic friction is μ. Which of the following is true for the friction force f acting on the mass?

(A) $f = \mu W$
(B) $f = \mu(W + F\cos\theta)$
(C) $f = \mu(W + F\sin\theta)$
(D) $f = \mu(W - F\sin\theta)$
(E) $f \leq \mu(W - F\cos\theta)$

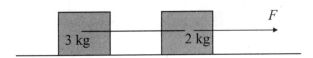

figure 17

2. A tension T exists in the rope connecting the two masses. The value of F is

(A) $\frac{3}{2}T$ (B) $\frac{3}{5}T$ (C) T (D) $\frac{5}{3}T$ (E) $\frac{5}{2}T$

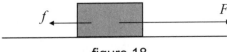

figure 18

3. When $F = 8$ N, the 4 kg mass accelerates to the right at 1 m/s^2. If F is doubled to 16 N, the acceleration will be

(A) $1\ \frac{m}{s^2}$ (B) $2\ \frac{m}{s^2}$ (C) $3\ \frac{m}{s^2}$ (D) $4\ \frac{m}{s^2}$ (E) $0.5\ \frac{m}{s^2}$

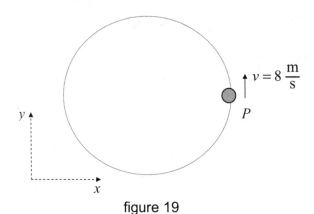

figure 19

4. A 3 kg mass is moving in a vertical circle of radius 4 m at a constant speed of 8 m/s. At point P, the magnitude and direction of the centripetal acceleration are given by

(A) $16 \frac{m}{s^2} + y$

(B) $48 \frac{m}{s^2} - x$

(C) $16 \frac{m}{s^2} - y$

(D) $16 \frac{m}{s^2} - x$

(E) $48 \frac{m}{s^2} + y$

5. Two teams engage in a tug-of-war with a rope held horizontal. Which is true of the winning team?

(A) They were stronger.
(B) They had more mass.
(C) They exerted a greater tension force through the rope.
(D) They exerted a greater force on the ground parallel to the surface.
(E) They exerted a greater force on the ground perpendicular to the surface.

6. A 3-kg mass moving at 6 m/s is brought to rest in 2 s. The magnitude of the net force acting on the mass is

(A) 18 N
(B) 9 N
(C) 6 N
(D) 12 N
(E) 36 N

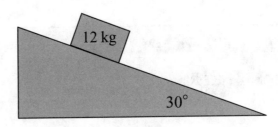

figure 20

7. A 12-kg mass is at rest on a 30° incline where the coefficient of static friction is 0.8. The friction force exerted on the mass is most nearly

(A) 120 N
(B) 104 N
(C) 83 N
(D) 60 N
(E) 96 N

8. A pendulum consists of a rope of length 2 m and a bob of mass 4 kg. It moves through its lowest point with a speed of 6 m/s. The tension in the rope is most nearly

(A) 40 N
(B) 72 N
(C) 32 N
(D) 112 N
(E) 48 N

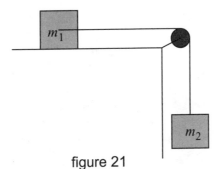

figure 21

9. Assuming no friction, to double the current value of the system acceleration, you can
   I. double the value of m_2
   II. halve the value of m_1
   III. halve the value of $(m_1 + m_2)$ by adjusting m_1 only

(A) I only
(B) II only
(C) III only
(D) I and II
(E) I and III

PRACTICE EXERCISES

SECTION II FREE RESPONSE

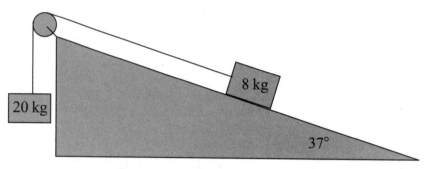

figure 22

1. In the diagram, the 8-kg mass moves up the incline, where the coefficient of kinetic friction is 0.4. Assume an ideal pulley.

    (a) Determine the friction force acting on the 8-kg mass.
    (b) Determine the acceleration of each mass.
    (c) Determine the tension in the connecting rope.

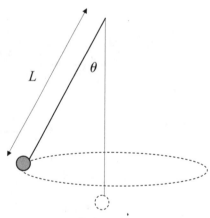

figure 23

2. A mass m is attached to a length L of string and hung straight down from a pivot. Small vibrations at the pivot set the mass into circular motion, with the string making an angle θ with the vertical.

    (a) Draw and label all forces acting on the object.
    (b) Obtain an expression for the speed v of the mass in terms of θ, L, and g.

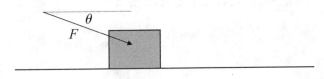

figure 24

3. A force is applied at an angle θ below the horizontal to a mass m resting on a horizontal surface where the coefficients of friction are μ_s and μ_k. The magnitude of F is slowly increased until the mass just starts to move. At this point its acceleration is a_0. Calculate the following in terms of μ_s, μ_k, θ, m, and g.

(a) Determine the value of F where movement just begins.

(b) Determine a_0.

Answers and Explanations

MULTIPLE CHOICE

1. The answer is D. The vertical component of F is $F\sin\theta$. In the y-direction, you then have $net\ F_y = 0 = N + F\sin\theta - W \Rightarrow N = W - F\sin\theta$.

2. The answer is D. $T = (3m)a \Rightarrow a = \frac{T}{3m}$. For the system you have $F = (5m)a \Rightarrow F = \frac{5}{3}T$.

3. The answer is C. Applying the second law, you have $netF = 8 - f = 4(1) \Rightarrow f = 4$ N. When F is doubled, the friction force doesn't change, so you have $netF = 16 - f = 12 = 4a \Rightarrow a = 3\ \frac{m}{s^2}$.

4. The answer is D. At P, the center is in the $-x$ direction and $a_{cp} = \frac{8^2}{4} = 16\ \frac{m}{s^2}$.

5. The answer is D. The tension force is the same for each team as a result of the third law, so only by pushing harder parallel to the ground can a team win. Strength and mass need not be a factor; imagine a football team on in-line skates.

6. The answer is B. Find the acceleration: $a = \frac{\Delta v}{\Delta t} = \frac{0-6}{2} = -3\ \frac{m}{s}$. Applying the second law, you have $netF = ma = 3(-3) = -9$ N.

7. The answer is D. The component of weight down the incline is $mg\sin\theta = 120(0.5) = 60$ N. For equilibrium, the static friction must just supply this value.

$$netF = T - mg = m\frac{v^2}{R}$$

8. The answer is D. At the lowest point you have:

$$T = 4\frac{6^2}{2} + 40 = 112\text{ N}$$

9. The answer is C. For the system as a whole, from the second law you have $netF = m_2g = (m_1 + m_2)a \Rightarrow a = \frac{m_2g}{(m_1 + m_2)}$. The answer follows from inspecting the formula.

FREE RESPONSE

1. Apply the solution steps to each object (figure 25).

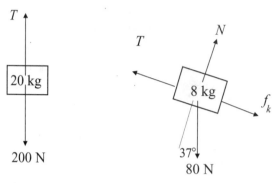

figure 25

	8 kg	20 kg
Step 1.	See figure 25.	See figure 25.

Step 2. $netF_y = N - 80\cos37$ $netF = 200 - T$

            $netF_x = T - 80\sin37 - 0.4\,N$

Step 3. $N - 64 = 0 \Rightarrow N = 64$ $200 - T = 20a$

           $T - 48 - 0.4(64) = 8a$

Note that the friction force is 25.6 N, the answer to A.

Step 4.   Add equations: $-48 - 25.6 + 200 = 28a \Rightarrow a = 4.5\,\frac{m}{s^2}$.

Substitute to find T: $200 - T = 10(4.5) \Rightarrow T = 110$ N.

2. (a) See figure 26.

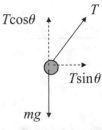

figure 26

(b) Only the tension has a component toward the center, so

$$netF_x = m\frac{v^2}{R} \qquad\qquad netF_y = T\cos\theta - mg = 0$$

$$T\sin\theta = m\frac{v^2}{L\sin\theta} \qquad\qquad T\cos\theta = mg$$

Dividing the two equations eliminates T, and you have $v = \sqrt{g\tan\theta(L\sin\theta)}$

3. (a) Apply the basic steps to the object, remembering that when the object is just about to slide, the static friction force is at its maximum value.
Step 1. See figure 27.

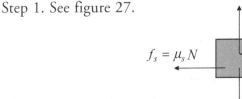

figure 27

Step 2. $netF_x = F\cos\theta - \mu_s N$ $\qquad\qquad netF_y = N - mg - F\sin\theta$

Step 3. $N - mg - F\sin\theta = 0$
$F\cos\theta - \mu_s N = 0$

Step 4. $N = mg + F\sin\theta$
$F\cos\theta - \mu_s(mg + F\sin\theta) = 0 \Rightarrow F = \dfrac{\mu_s mg}{\cos\theta - \mu_s\sin\theta}$

(b) As acceleration begins, this is the value of F, and now it is kinetic friction acting. The analysis in steps 1, 2, and 3 is the same except for the friction name change and the fact that there is a nonzero horizontal acceleration. You can then move to Step 4 to write:

$$N = mg + F\sin\theta$$

$$F\cos\theta - \mu_k(mg + F\sin\theta) = ma \Rightarrow a = \frac{F}{m}\cos\theta - \mu_k\left(g - \frac{F}{m}\sin\theta\right)$$

4

Work and Energy

While Newton's laws provide a complete description of mechanical systems, applying $F = ma$ directly isn't always the easiest way to approach a problem. In this chapter and the following two, you'll see that often you can determine the final properties of a system directly from the initial properties, without knowing all the details of the motion between the initial and final states. This approach involves using **conservation laws**, which tell you when certain physical properties remain constant throughout the motion. Knowing how and when to apply the conservation laws is essential to doing well on the AP test. In this chapter you'll learn about mechanical energy and the conditions for its conservation.

Work

When a force acts on an object while a displacement occurs, the force has done **work** on the object. Work is a scalar quantity that has no direction associated with it, but it can be positive or negative. The magnitude of the work done will depend on the magnitude of the force, how much of it is applied along the direction of the displacement, and the magnitude of the displacement. For a constant force, you'll use the definition (figure 1):

$$W_F = F\cos\theta\Delta x = \vec{F} \cdot \vec{\Delta x}$$

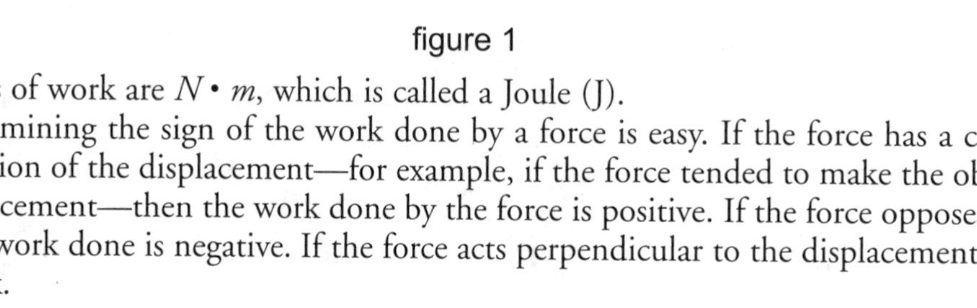

figure 1

The units of work are $N \cdot m$, which is called a Joule (J).

Determining the sign of the work done by a force is easy. If the force has a component in the direction of the displacement—for example, if the force tended to make the object undergo the displacement—then the work done by the force is positive. If the force opposes the motion, then the work done is negative. If the force acts perpendicular to the displacement, then it does zero work.

EXERCISE

Find the work done by all forces as a 4 kg mass slides 5 m down a 30° incline where the coefficient of kinetic friction is 0.3 (figure 2).

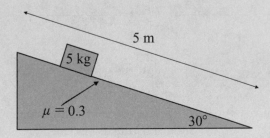

figure 2

$W_N = 0$ since it acts perpendicular to the motion

$W_{grav} = +(mg\sin\theta)\Delta x = (40)(0.5)(5) = 100$ J

$W_{fric} = -(\mu N)\Delta x = -(\mu mg\cos\theta)\Delta x = -(0.3)(40)(0.87)(5) = -52$ J

If you look at a graph (figure 3) of a one-dimensional constant force as a function of position, the work done has a simple interpretation: It is the area under the graph.

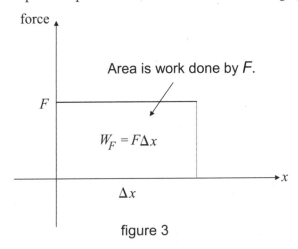

figure 3

When the force isn't constant but varies with the position, the work done will still be the area under the graph (figure 4). If the graph is a simple shape, you can use geometry to find the area.

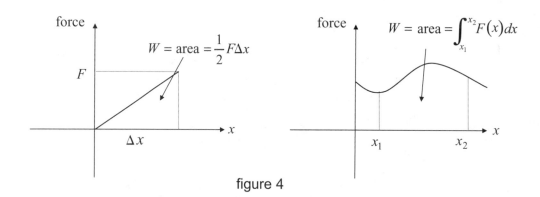

figure 4

For more complicated forces, you'll need to use calculus to find the area. In one dimension, you just integrate the force over the limits determined by the displacement.

$$W_F = \text{area} = \int_{x_1}^{x_2} F(x)\,dx$$

In more than one dimension, you must add up the little bits of work done by the force for each little displacement: $dW = \vec{F} \cdot \vec{dx}$

$$W = \int dW = \int_{\vec{x_1}}^{\vec{x_2}} \vec{F} \cdot \vec{dx}$$

This is called a line integral (figure 5), because the integration is done along a linear path.

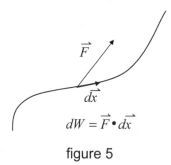

figure 5

Line integrals will also appear in the development of electricity and magnetism. You'll have to be able to evaluate them in some simple cases on the AP test, but for the most part, it's more important that you understand them conceptually as sums of many very small contributions.

An important example of a nonconstant force is the elastic force exerted by a spring either in tension or in compression. Hooke's law states that the force exerted by a spring displaced an amount x from its equilibrium position is calculated as $F = -kx$. Here k is called the **spring constant**, and it measures how stiff the spring is. Integrating the magnitude of the force from $x = 0$ to some arbitrary value will give you the magnitude of the work done by the spring as the mass is displaced from the equilibrium point to some point x.

$$W_{spring} = \int_0^x kx\,dx = \frac{1}{2}kx^2$$

Power

Power is the rate at which work is done. For a force doing an amount of work ΔW_F over a time interval Δt, the average power delivered is

$$P_{av} = \frac{\Delta W_F}{\Delta t} \qquad \text{The units of power are } \frac{J}{s} = \text{Watt}$$

To determine instantaneous power delivered, you'll need to average over a very small interval leading to a time derivative.

$$P = \frac{dW_F}{dt}$$

Referring to figure 5, you can see that the little bit of work done by a force $\vec{F}$ as a mass undergoes an infinitesimal displacement $d\vec{x}$ is

$$dW = \vec{F} \cdot d\vec{x}$$

Dividing by dt, the time interval over which the displacement occurs gives

$$\frac{dW}{dt} = P = \vec{F} \cdot \frac{d\vec{x}}{dt} = \vec{F} \cdot \vec{v}$$

EXAMPLE

Find the instantaneous power delivered by gravity to a 4 kg mass 2 s after it has fallen from rest.

The force and velocity are collinear, so $\cos\theta = 1$.

$$v = gt = 20 \text{ m/s} \qquad\qquad P = Fv = (mg)v = (40)20 = 800 \text{ W}$$

Notice that the instantaneous power delivered by gravity is not a constant even though the force is constant. Of course, this is because the velocity is changing.

Find the instantaneous power delivered by the net force at $t = 2$ s to a 0.5 kg mass moving in one dimension according to $x(t) = \frac{1}{3}t^3$.

$$v = \frac{dx}{dt} = t^2$$

$$netF = ma$$
$$netF = (0.5)(2t) = t$$

$$P = netFv = t^3$$
$$P(2) = 8 \text{ W}$$

$$a = \frac{dv}{dt} = 2t$$

Kinetic Energy

Up to this point, "work" has been just a new definition. If you look at the work done by the net force on the system, however, you can derive a relation that will be equivalent to Newton's second law but without the explicit appearance of acceleration. Let's consider a one-dimensional example (figure 6) in which a mass is accelerated through some displacement by the (constant) net force acting on it.

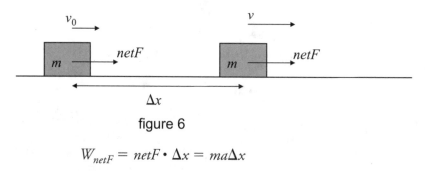

figure 6

$$W_{netF} = netF \cdot \Delta x = ma\Delta x$$

You can use a motion equation to obtain

$$W_{netF} = ma\left(\frac{v^2 - v_0^2}{2a}\right) = \frac{1}{2}mv^2 - \frac{1}{2}mv_0^2$$

(Note that the acceleration cancels out.)

With the **kinetic energy** of an object defined as $K = \frac{1}{2}mv^2$, this relation becomes

$$W_{netF} = \Delta K$$

This relation is called the **work-energy theorem**.

EXAMPLE

(Figure 7): A 10 kg mass is moving at 5 m/s over a rough surface. A 50 N horizontal tension force causes it to accelerate to 8 m/s while traveling 6 m. Find the coefficient of kinetic friction.

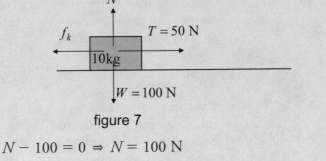

figure 7

$$N - 100 = 0 \Rightarrow N = 100 \text{ N}$$

$$W_{netF} = (50 - f_k)(6) = (50)(6) - (f_k)(6) = W_T + W_f$$

$$300 - \mu(100)6 = \Delta K = \frac{1}{2}(10)(8)^2 - \frac{1}{2}(10)(5)^2 = 195 \text{ J}$$

$$\mu = \frac{105}{600} = 0.18$$

In the second step, note that the work done by the net force equals the sum of the works done by each individual force acting:

$$W_{netF} = W_T + W_f = W_{total}$$

This will always be the case because the two sides of the equation differ only in the order in which math operations are performed. On the left side you add the force components first, then multiply by the displacement; on the right side you multiply each force component by the displacement, then add them up.

Conservative Forces

Suppose a mass is moved from ground level to a height H. You can calculate the work done by gravity for this process, assuming that the mass is raised directly to the final height (figure 8).

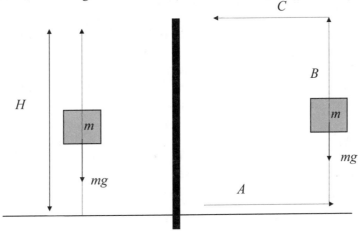

figure 8

Since the constant force of gravity acts opposite to the displacement, the result is $W_{grav} = -mgH$. Now suppose the mass doesn't move directly to the final height but follows the paths A → B → C. Since gravity does no work along paths A and C, and the work done along path B is the same as the direct path, then the work done in this process is the same. In fact, no matter what path you choose between two points, the work done by gravity will always be the same. Forces that meet this condition are called **conservative forces**, and gravity is an example of a conservative force. All one-dimensional forces that are functions only of position only are conservative, because the value of the definite integral of $F(x)$ depends only on the two endpoints:

$$W = \int_{x_1}^{x_2} F(x)dx = G(x_2) - G(x_1) \text{ where } F(x) = \frac{dG}{dx}$$

The elastic force $F = -kx$ associated with a spring is a simple example of a conservative force since it fits the above criteria. As a more complicated example, the force $F(x) = 5x^2 - 3x^5$ is conservative since it is one-dimensional and depends only on x. Outside of one dimension, a force that depends only on position won't be conservative unless certain conditions are met by the components of the force. At the C level, you won't need to know the specifics of these conditions. Because the work done by conservative forces is path-independent, the work can depend on only the endpoints of the path. This means that the work done by such forces is always 0 for a path that ends at the beginning point (closed path), since the work is obviously 0 if there is no displacement at all.

Forces also can be nonconservative, meaning that the work they do *does* depend on the path taken between the endpoints. Dissipative forces such as friction and air resistance are examples of nonconservative forces. For example, the work done by kinetic friction as a mass moves over a horizontal surface depends on the total length of the path: $W_f = -f(length)$. Obviously, an infinite number of possible paths of different lengths can connect two points on the surface. Similarly, the work done by the tension in a rope will in general depend on the path taken.

Potential Energy

It's possible to do work on an object and never change the kinetic energy. For example, you could very slowly lift a mass to some height above the ground. You'd have to perform work $W = mgH$ to get the mass there, because you'd apply a force just equal to mg to keep the mass moving up at a very slow but constant speed. Intuitively, you might expect that the work done could be "retrieved" by letting the mass fall and gain kinetic energy.

You can apply the same analysis to stretching a spring-mass system. If you very slowly pull the mass out an amount x from the equilibrium position, you must do work $W = \frac{1}{2}kx^2$. Once again, you might expect that this work could be "retrieved" by releasing the mass and letting the spring contract. In these cases, the work you put into the system is stored as **potential energy** (PE). Potential energy is energy associated with the position of the system.

Not all work that's put into slowly positioning a system, however, is "retrievable." If you slowly push a mass in a straight line across a rough horizontal surface, you do work $W = f_k \Delta x$. But when you release the mass, it just sits there; the work you put into positioning it does not reappear as kinetic energy (KE). Only with conservative forces can you get back in KE the work you put into positioning, so it is only for these forces that you can meaningfully define the potential energy.

For conservative forces, the change in PE, ΔU, is the amount of work it takes to slowly change the position of the system. Since slow change implies that the agent doing the positioning applies a force just opposite to the conservative force F, it follows that

$$\Delta U = -W_F$$

Only the change in the PE is defined because only changes in energy can be measured. You are free to choose the zero point of PE associated with a force at any convenient point. For example, if you're dropping objects to the floor, it makes sense to call the floor the zero point of gravitational PE. On the other hand, if you're dropping objects onto a desk, you might decide to call the desktop the zero point.

The definition of potential energy now leads to two important formulas for PE:

$U_{grav} = mgh$ where h is measured from the arbitrary zero point

$U_{spring} = \frac{1}{2}kx^2$ where x is measured from the equilibrium point

In general, for conservative forces in more than one dimension, the equation is

$$\Delta U = -W_F = \int_{\vec{x_1}}^{\vec{x_2}} \vec{F} \cdot d\vec{x}$$

For a one-dimensional example, consider $F(x) = 5x^2 - 3x^5$. If you call $x = 0$ the zero point of PE, you'll have:

$$U = -\int_0^x F(x')dx' = -\int_0^x (5x'^2 - 3x'^5)dx' = -\frac{5}{3}x^3 + \frac{1}{2}x^6$$

Conservation of Energy

Suppose a single conservative force F does work on a mass. The work-energy theorem is $W_F = \Delta K$. But because the force is conservative, you'll have $W_F = -\Delta U$. Combining them, you get

$$-\Delta U = \Delta K$$
$$0 = \Delta K + \Delta U = (K + U)$$

This means that the quantity $K + U$, the sum of the kinetic and potential energies, doesn't change. This quantity is called the **total mechanical energy** E.

$$E = K + U$$

If several conservative forces are acting, U is just the sum of each potential energy, and if only conservative forces are doing work on the system, you can apply the law of **conservation of mechanical energy**:

$$E_i = E_f$$

As the system moves under the influence of conservative forces, the individual amounts of kinetic and potential energies change, but the sum of all of them stays the same.

EXAMPLE

A 4-kg mass is fired from ground level with a speed of 50 m/s at an angle of 37° with the horizontal. A smooth horizontal platform is placed at the correct position so that the mass will land on it at the highest point of its motion. It then slides into a spring with $k = 1{,}600$ N/m.
    (a) Find the total energy of the mass.
    (b) Find the height of the platform.
    (c) Find the maximum spring compression.

(a) After the mass is fired, only gravity and elastic spring forces do work on the mass. The normal force exerted by the platform does no work as it acts perpendicular to the motion. At the initial projection, $E_1 = \frac{1}{2}(4)(50)^2 = 5{,}000$ J, and this will remain constant over the motion.

(b) At the highest point of the motion, only the x-component of the velocity is present, $v_x = 50\cos 37 = 40$ m/s. To find the height of the platform, you can use energy conservation:

$$E_1 = E_2$$

$$5{,}000 = \tfrac{1}{2}mv^2 + mgh = \tfrac{1}{2}(4)(40)^2 + (4)(10)h$$

$$h = 45 \text{ m}$$

(c) Upon full compression, the energy is all potential and you can apply energy conservation again.

$$E_1 = E_2$$

$$5{,}000 = mgh + \tfrac{1}{2}kx^2 = (4)(10)(45) + \tfrac{1}{2}(1{,}600)x^2$$

$$x = 2 \text{ m}$$

Force from Potential Energy

Consider a small displacement $\vec{dl}$ of an object as it moves along some path under the influence of a conservative force $\vec{F}$ (figure 9).

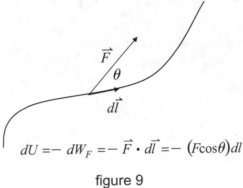

$$dU = -dW_F = -\vec{F} \cdot \vec{dl} = -(F\cos\theta)dl$$

figure 9

The change in the PE is

$$dU = -dW_F = -\vec{F} \cdot \vec{dl} = -(F\cos\theta)dl$$

The quantity $F\cos\theta = F_l$ is the component of $\vec{F}$ in the direction of the displacement $\vec{dl}$. You can write:

$$dU = -(F\cos\theta)dl = -F_l dl$$

$$F_l = -\frac{dU}{dl}$$

This equation tells you that if you know how the potential energy depends on a particular coordinate, you can find the component of the force in the direction of this coordinate by taking the appropriate derivative.

EXAMPLE

Consider the potential energy of two molecules given by

$$U = \frac{A}{r^{12}} - \frac{B}{r^6} \qquad r \text{ is the intermolecular separation}$$

You can find the force along the line joining the two molecules by taking the derivative with respect to r:

$$F = \frac{dU}{dr} = \frac{-12A}{r^{13}} + \frac{6B}{r^7}$$

Graphs of Potential Energy

Many systems in mechanics can be described by a potential energy function that depends on only one variable. With a graph of this potential energy, you can make some specific statements about the possible motions that the system can execute. Consider the graph of the spring PE: $U = \frac{1}{2}kx^2$ (figure 10).

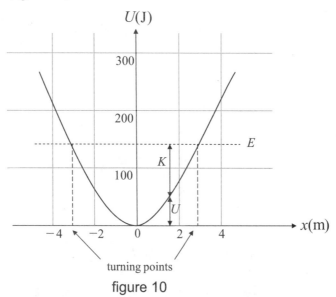

figure 10

The following statements apply to any such graph:

1. For a given total energy E, turning points of the motion will occur where the energy is all potential, such as where the graph intersects the horizontal total energy line. In this case, you have:

$$E = \frac{1}{2}kx^2 \Rightarrow x = \pm\sqrt{\frac{2E}{k}}$$

2. The vertical separation between the curve and the total energy line is the KE of the system at that point, based on $K = E - U$.

3. The force at a given point is the negative slope of the curve. For this graph, it is

$$F = \frac{dU}{dx} = -kx.$$

4. Where the graph reaches maxima or minima, the force will be 0, and stable equilibrium points will be located at the minima. For this graph, $x = 0$ is a point of stable equilibrium. Here a small displacement in either direction will result in a force that tends to restore the object to $x = 0$ again.

In describing the motion of an object moving under the influence of a potential, imagine a bead sliding along the curve. It would slow down and speed up in the same way the system would.

KEY FORMULAS

Work (constant force)

$$W_F = F\cos\theta\Delta x = \vec{F} \cdot \Delta \vec{x}$$

Work (nonconstant force)

$$W_F = \int_{x_1}^{x_2} F(x)\,dx \qquad W_F = \int_{\vec{x}_1}^{\vec{x}_2} \vec{F} \cdot d\vec{x}$$

Power

$$P_{av} = \frac{\Delta W_F}{\Delta t} \qquad P = \frac{dW_F}{dt} = \vec{F} \cdot \vec{v}$$

Kinetic Energy

$$K = \frac{1}{2}mv^2$$

Work-Energy Theorem

$$W_{total} = \Delta K$$

Potential Energy

$$\Delta U = -W_F \qquad \Delta U = -\int_{\vec{x}_1}^{\vec{x}_2} \vec{F} \cdot d\vec{x}$$

PE Gravity

$$U_{grav} = mgh$$

PE Spring

$$U_{spring} = \frac{1}{2}kx^2$$

Total Mechanical Energy

$$E = K + U$$

Conservation of Energy

$$E_i = E_f$$

Force from Potential Energy

$$F_l = -\frac{dU}{dl}$$

PRACTICE EXERCISES

SECTION I MULTIPLE CHOICE

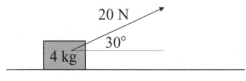

figure 11

1. A 4-kg mass accelerates 6 m across a frictionless surface under the influence of a 20 N force as shown in the figure. The work done over this interval is

    (A) $10\sqrt{3}\,$J   (B) $60\sqrt{3}\,$J   (C) $60\,\frac{\sqrt{3}}{2}\,$J   (D) 60 J   (E) 120 J

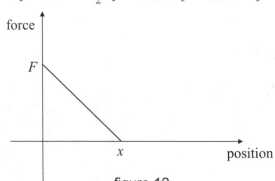

figure 12

2. Starting from the origin with speed v_0, a mass m moves in one dimension under the influence of the force shown in the figure. When the mass reaches x, its kinetic energy will be

    (A) $\frac{1}{2}Fx + \frac{1}{2}mv_0^2$

    (B) $\frac{1}{2}Fx$

    (C) $Fx + \frac{1}{2}mv_0^2$

    (D) Fx

    (E) $\frac{1}{2}Fx - \frac{1}{2}mv_0^2$

3. Starting from rest and a height of 10 m, a 2 kg mass slides down a 30° incline, reaching the bottom with a speed of 10 m/s. What is the approximate work done by friction?

    (A) 0   (B) $-10\sqrt{3}$ (C) -100 J   (D) -200 J
    (E) cannot be determined without the coefficient of friction

4. A mass is attached to an ideal spring on a smooth horizontal surface. It is displaced an amount Δx_0 and released. Which of the following is true?
    I.   The KE is largest when the mass passes through the equilibrium point.
    II. The PE is largest when the mass has a displacement of $\pm \Delta x_0$.
    III. The PE and KE will never be equal.

    (A) I only   (B) II only   (C) III only   (D) I and II only   (E) I and III only

5. A 2-kg mass is raised 6 m at a constant speed of 3 m/s by a vertical rope. The power supplied by the rope is most nearly

    (A) 120 W   (B) 360 W   (C) 6 W   (D) 36 W   (E) 60 W

6. When is total mechanical energy of a system conserved?
    I.   always
    II. when nonconservative forces are present but do no work
    III. when nonconservative forces are not present

    (A) I only   (B) II only   (C) III only   (D) I, II, and III   (E) II and III only

7. A mass moves under the influence of a potential energy given by $U(x) = 2x^3 - x$. At the point $x = 1$, the force on the mass will be

    (A) 5 N, + direction
    (B) 5 N, − direction
    (C) 1 N, + direction
    (D) 1 N, − direction
    (E) 7 N, − direction

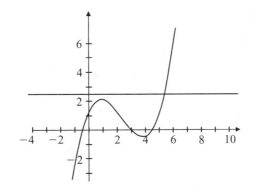

figure 13

8. An object with total energy 2.5 J moves under the influence of the potential in the figure. Which of the following is true about the motion?
    I.   The object will oscillate in the + x region.
    II. There is a point of stable equilibrium near $x = 3.5$.
    III. The force is 0 at $x = 3$.

    (A) I only   (B) II only   (C) III only   (D) II and III only   (E) I and III only

9. A 2-kg mass is moving in one dimension with a velocity given by $v(t) = \frac{1}{2}t^2$. At $t = 4$ s, the instantaneous power delivered by the net force is

(A) 8 W (B) 12 W (C) 32 W (D) 16 W (E) 64 W

10. A 3 kg mass is attached to a light string 2 m long and hung vertically to make a simple pendulum. The pendulum is displaced until the string is horizontal and then released. What is the approximate speed of the pendulum at its lowest point?

(A) 5 m/s
(B) 6 m/s
(C) 7 m/s
(D) 8 m/s
(E) cannot be determined because the tension is a nonconservative force

CHAPTER 4

PRACTICE EXERCISES

SECTION II FREE RESPONSE

figure 14

1. A 2-kg mass is pushed 0.5 m into a spring with spring constant 200 N/m on a frictionless horizontal surface. Upon release, the mass travels across the surface until it encounters a rough incline. The mass moves up the incline and stops at a height of 1 m above the horizontal surface.

    (a) How much work must be done to compress the spring initially?
    (b) Find the speed of the mass at the base of the incline.
    (c) How much work was done by friction on the incline?

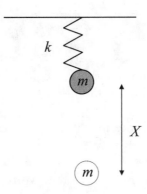

figure 15

2. A spring with spring constant k is hung vertically. A mass m is gently attached to it and released in such a way that the spring is unstretched upon release. The mass descends to a maximum spring extension X. Respond to the following in terms of m, k, and g.

(a) Determine X.
(b) Determine the speed of the mass at $\frac{1}{4}X$, where the mass has moved through $\frac{1}{4}$ the maximum extension.
(c) Determine the maximum speed of the mass.

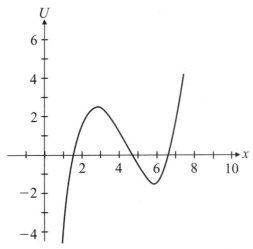

figure 16

3. A 2-kg mass moves under the influence of the potential energy $U(x) = \frac{1}{3}(x-4)^3 - \frac{x^2}{4} + 5$ shown in the figure.

(a) Find the force exerted on the mass at $x = 2$ m.
   The mass is placed at $x = 4$ and released, giving it a total energy of 1 J.
(b) Describe the subsequent motion qualitatively.
(c) Determine the approximate maximum speed of the mass.
(d) Write an equation that would allow you to determine where the mass will momentarily come to rest again (don't solve).

Answers and Explanations

MULTIPLE CHOICE

1. The answer is B. The component of the force in the direction of the displacement is $20\cos30 = 10\sqrt{3}$. The work done is $60\sqrt{3}$.

2. The answer is A. The work done is the area of the triangle $\frac{1}{2}Fx$. According to the work energy theorem; $\frac{1}{2}Fx = \Delta K \Rightarrow K = \frac{1}{2}Fx + \frac{1}{2}mv_0^2$

3. The answer is C. Using the work energy theorem, you get

$$W_{\text{total}} = \Delta K$$

$$W_{\text{grav}} + W_{\text{fric}} = \frac{1}{2}mv^2 - 0 \quad \Rightarrow \quad W_{\text{fric}} = -100 \text{ J}$$

$$(2)(10)(10) + W_{\text{fric}} = \frac{1}{2}(2)(10^2)$$

4. The answer is D. III is not true because there will always be two places where KE = PE, one on either side of the equilibrium point.

5. The answer is E. The tension force must equal 20 N, the weight, since there is no acceleration; then $P_T = Tv = (20)(3) = 60\text{W}$.

6. The answer is E. If nonconservative forces such as friction or tension are present, then the mechanical energy will, in general, not be conserved. An exception, however, is when the nonconservative forces don't do any work. One example of this is the tension force supplying centripetal force. It acts at right angles to the motion and so does no work.

7. The answer is B. $F = -\frac{dU}{dx} = 1 - 6x^2 \Rightarrow F(1) = -5\text{N}$

8. The answer is B. The energy is too large for the object to oscillate. If it is initially moving to the right, it will have a turning point at about $x = 5.3$ and will move off to the left without returning. The value of the potential is 0 at $x = 3$, but clearly the slope is not 0, so the force is also not 0. At x near 3.5, the curve bottoms out, and any small displacement from this point will tend to bring it back, making it a point of stable equilibrium.

9. The answer is E. $\quad a = \frac{dv}{dt} = t \qquad\qquad P = netFv = (2t)\left(\frac{1}{2}t^2\right)$

$$netF = ma = 2t \qquad\qquad P(4) = 64 \text{ W}$$

10. The answer is B. You can use energy conservation because the tension does no work.
$$E_i = E_f$$
$$mgh = \frac{1}{2}mv^2 \qquad\qquad \Rightarrow v = \sqrt{2gh} = \sqrt{40} = 6.3 \text{ m/s}$$

FREE RESPONSE

1. (a) $W = +\frac{1}{2}kx^2 = \frac{1}{2}(200)(0.5)^2 = 25$ J

    (b) Energy is conserved until the incline is encountered.

    $E_i = E_f$

    $25 = \frac{1}{2}mv^2 = \frac{1}{2}(2)v^2$

    $\Rightarrow v = 5$ m/s

    (c) You could use the work-energy theorem applied from the beginning where the KE is 0, to the end, where the KE is also 0. The spring, gravity, and friction do work, resulting in

    $W_{total} = \Delta K$

    $W_{spring} + W_{grav} + W_{fric} = 0$

    $+25 - (2)(10)(1) + W_{fric} = 0$

    $\Rightarrow W_{fric} = -5$ J

2. (a) Energy will be conserved throughout the motion. For part a, call the zero point for gravity the point of maximum extension.

    $E_0 = E_f$

    $mgX = \frac{1}{2}kX^2$

    $\Rightarrow X = \frac{2mg}{k}$

    (b) Now call $x = \frac{1}{4}X$ the zero point for gravity. Then, relative to this point:

    $E_0 = E_f$

    $mg\left(\frac{1}{4}X\right) = \frac{1}{2}mv^2 + \frac{1}{2}k\left(\frac{x}{4}\right)^2$

    plug in X: $v = \sqrt{\dfrac{7mg^2}{8k}}$

    (c) As the mass descends, it will gain speed until the spring force is large enough to start slowing it down, when the spring force is just equal to the gravity force: $kx = mg \Rightarrow x = \frac{mg}{k}$. Now you can use energy conservation again, with this point as the zero point for gravity.

    $E_0 = E_f$

    $mg(x) = \frac{1}{2}mv^2 + \frac{1}{2}k(x)^2$

    plug in for x: $v = \sqrt{\dfrac{mg^2}{k}}$

3. (a) $F = -\dfrac{dU}{dx} = -(x-4)^2 + \dfrac{x}{2}$

    $F(2) = -3\text{N}$

(b) The mass will oscillate between $x = 4$ and about $x = 6.8$, where the energy is all potential. The maximum speed will occur at the low point of the graph, at about $x = 5.7$.

(c) From the graph, the low point energy is about -1.5 J. This means the KE must be 2.5 J, the difference between the total energy and the PE at the low point. That leads to

$$\frac{1}{2}mv^2 = 2.5 \;\Rightarrow\; v \cong 1.6 \text{ m/s}$$

(d) You can explicitly equate the total energy of 1 J to the PE to determine the right-hand turning point.

$$1 = \frac{1}{3}(x-4)^3 - \frac{x^2}{4} + 5$$

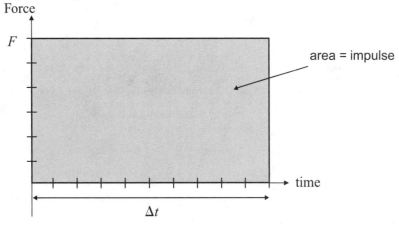

CHAPTER 5

Impulse and Momentum

This chapter introduces the concept of linear momentum. Unlike energy, momentum is a vector quantity, but like energy, momentum has a conservation law. The condition for momentum conservation is different than that for energy, and it's important to learn not only how to apply the law, but how to recognize when the law can be applied to a particular system.

Impulse

When a force acts on an object over a certain time period, the force has delivered an **impulse** to the object. For constant forces, the exact definition is:

$$\vec{J_F} = \vec{F}\Delta t$$

Here, $\vec{J_F}$ is the impulse delivered by the force F over the time Δt, a vector quantity. For a one-dimensional constant force, a graph (figure 1) of F vs. t over the interval leads to a simple interpretation of the impulse: It is the area under the curve.

Force

F

area = impulse

time

Δt

Figure 1

If the force varies over time, each component of the impulse is defined as the integral with respect to time of the corresponding component of the force

$$(J_F)_x = \int_{t_1}^{t_2} F_x \, dt \qquad (J_F)_y = \int_{t_1}^{t_2} F_y \, dt$$

Of course the area under the F_x vs. t graph is represented by the integral of the x-component with respect to time, so the interpretation of impulse as area under the force curve remains true.

Linear Momentum

On its own, impulse isn't that significant. But if you look at the impulse delivered by the net force, you can apply Newton's second law to get a useful relation. In one dimension with constant forces, you have

$$J_{netF} = netF\Delta t = ma\Delta t = m\left(\frac{v - v_0}{\Delta t}\right)\Delta t = mv - mv_0$$

If you define the **linear momentum** to be $\vec{p} = m\vec{v}$, then you have $J_{netF} = \Delta p$, or in two or more dimensions:

$$\vec{J}_{netF} = \Delta\vec{p}$$

This is sometimes called the impulse-momentum theorem. It's really a restatement of the second law in the language of impulse and momentum.

EXERCISE

Find the rebound speed of a 0.5 kg ball falling straight down that hits the floor moving at 5 m/s, if the average normal force exerted by the floor on the ball was 205 N for 0.02 s.

$$J_{netF} = \Delta p$$

$$(N - W)\Delta t = mv - mv_0$$

$$(205 - 5)(0.02) = 0.5v - 0.5(-5) \Rightarrow v = 3 \text{ m/s}$$

EXERCISE

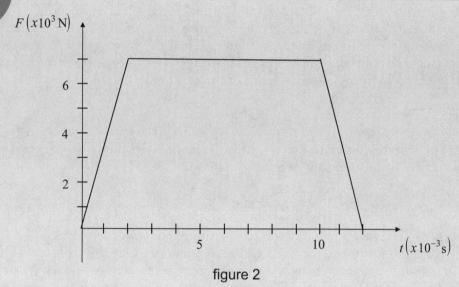

figure 2

A 5-kg mass moving at 10 m/s in the $+x$ direction is acted upon by a force acting in the $-x$ direction with magnitude given as a function of time by the graph (figure 2). Determine the speed and direction of the mass after the force has stopped acting.

The area under the graph is 70 N s (rectangle and two triangles), so this is the magnitude of the impulse delivered to the mass. Since the force acted in the $-x$ direction, the vector value is -70 N s. You can write:

$$J_{netF} = \Delta p$$

$$-70 = 5v - 5(10) \Rightarrow v = -4 \frac{m}{s}$$

Conservation of Momentum

Now let's look at systems that consist of several objects interacting with each other (for example, collisions). Allow for the possibility that there may be other forces acting on these objects besides the forces they exert on each other. For such a system with internal and external forces acting on it, you can define the total linear momentum as the vector sum of the momentum of each individual object:

$$\vec{P}_{total} = \vec{p_1} + \vec{p_2} + ...$$

In the Newton's laws chapter, you saw that when you're considering the net force acting on an entire system, you need to include only the forces external to the system. The internal forces that different parts of the system exert on each other always occur in action-reaction pairs that cancel out when added over the entire system. Since the impulse-momentum theorem is just a restatement of the second law, it's not surprising that there's an analogous result for the impulse delivered by the net force. When the entire system is considered, only the impulse delivered by the forces external to the system needs to be included. Internal impulses will cancel out in pairs as a result of the third law.

$$\Delta \vec{P}_{\text{total}} = \vec{J}_{\text{ext}}$$

If there are no external forces to the system or if the impulse they deliver is negligible, then the **conservation of momentum principle** applies:

$$\Delta \vec{P}_{\text{total}} = 0 \Rightarrow \vec{P}^{\,i}_{\text{total}} = \vec{P}^{\,f}_{\text{total}}$$

In the absence of external forces, the total linear momentum will stay the same. As individual objects in the system interact, their individual momenta change, but the sum of all remains constant. Keep in mind that this is a vector equation; if no external forces are present for a particular direction, the momentum component in that direction is conserved.

Notice the difference between the energy and momentum conservation conditions. For a system's energy to be conserved, external forces may be present, but they have to be of a particular type, the so-called conservative forces. For momentum conservation, no external forces can be present at all on the system.

It's worth mentioning that when the mechanical energy of a system isn't conserved, it doesn't simply disappear. The mechanical energy will be transferred to some other system, perhaps in some other form. For example, the kinetic energy lost by a mass sliding over a rough surface can be accounted for in the internal energy associated with the molecular motions within the mass and the surface. Similarly, when the linear momentum of a system isn't conserved, that linear momentum will be transferred to some other system. It's always possible, however, to extend the system to include all the momentum and energy transfers, so that in this larger sense, energy and linear momentum are always conserved. But if the system has to be extended too much, applying the conservation principles to solve problems may not be the most efficient technique.

Collisions

ONE DIMENSION

Collisions are a common application of this concept. Consider a one-dimensional example: a 4-kg mass moving in the $+x$ direction at 10 m/s collides head-on with a 2-kg mass moving at 6 m/s in the $-x$ direction. Determine the final speeds and directions of the masses.

$$P^i_{total} = P^f_{total}$$

$$m_1 v_{1i} + m_2 v_{2i} = m_1 v_{1f} + m_2 v_{2f}$$

$$4(10) + 2(-6) = 4v_{1f} + 2v_{2f}$$

$$14 = 2v_{1f} + v_{2f}$$

You can't proceed further, however, without more information. If you knew one of the final velocities, you could plug it in to get the other, but in general there are an infinite number of possibilities consistent with momentum conservation. The masses could be bouncy steel balls or mushy balls of clay; even with the same initial velocities, the results would obviously be much different.

Sometimes the extra information is provided as a condition on the kinetic energy in the collision. If the total kinetic energy is conserved, the collision is **elastic**. From the definition of KE you have

$$\frac{1}{2}m_1 v_{1i}^2 + \frac{1}{2}m_2 v_{2i}^2 = \frac{1}{2}m_1 v_{1f}^2 + \frac{1}{2}m_2 v_{2f}^2$$

You can combine this equation with momentum conservation, $m_1 v_{1i} + m_2 v_{2i} = m_1 v_{1f} + m_2 v_{2f}$ to derive a third equation that has a simple interpretation:

$$v_{1i} - v_{2i} = -(v_{1f} - v_{2f})$$

This simple equation says that the relative velocity of the two objects $v_1 - v_2$ changes direction but maintains the same magnitude in an elastic, one-dimensional collision.

EXAMPLE

Suppose the previous collision was elastic. What are the final velocities?

$$14 = 2v_{1f} + v_{2f}$$

$$v_{1i} - v_{2i} = -(v_{1f} - v_{2f})$$

$$10 - (-6) = v_{2f} - v_{1f}$$

$$16 = v_{2f} - v_{1f}$$

Solving simultaneously gives

$$v_{1f} = -0.67 \text{ m/s}$$

$$v_{2f} = 15.33 \text{ m/s}$$

It's possible for two objects to stick together in a collision. This is called a **totally inelastic collision**. Much of the kinetic energy initially in the bodies is lost and goes into the work done by internal forces within the objects as they deform and perhaps get warmer. Since there is only one common final velocity, the momentum conservation condition alone allows you to determine it.

EXAMPLE

Suppose the previous collision were totally inelastic. What is the final speed, and what fraction of the original kinetic energy is lost?

$$P^i_{\text{total}} = P^f_{\text{total}} \qquad\qquad KE_i = \frac{1}{2}(4)(10)^2 + \frac{1}{2}(2)(-6)^2 = 236 \text{ J}$$

$$4(10) + (2)(-6) = 6v \qquad\qquad KE_f = \frac{1}{2}(6)(4.67)^2 = 65.3 \text{ J}$$

$$v = 4.67 \, \frac{\text{m}}{\text{s}} \qquad\qquad \Delta KE = -170.7 \text{ J}$$

$$\text{Fraction lost} = \frac{170.7}{236} = 0.72$$

TWO DIMENSIONS

Momentum conservation involves a vector equation, equating the initial momentum of the system to the final momentum of the system.

$$\vec{P_i} = \vec{P_f}$$

Since two vectors can't be equal unless their components are separately equal, the law actually provides two separate conditions:

$$P_{xi} = P_{xf} \qquad\qquad P_{yi} = P_{yf}$$

To see how this works, consider a mass m_1 moving with velocity $\vec{v_1}$ colliding with a stationary mass m_2 (figure 3).

A Two-Dimensional Collision

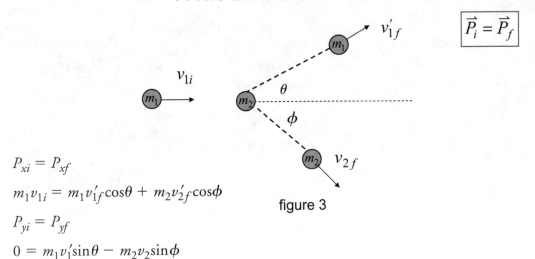

$$\boxed{\vec{P}_i = \vec{P}_f}$$

$P_{xi} = P_{xf}$

$m_1 v_{1i} = m_1 v'_{1f}\cos\theta + m_2 v'_{2f}\cos\phi$

$P_{yi} = P_{yf}$

$0 = m_1 v'_1 \sin\theta - m_2 v_2 \sin\phi$

figure 3

Even if you know the masses and initial velocity, there are still four unknowns, the final speeds and angles. Momentum conservation provides only two conditions, and an elastic collision provides only one more condition on the final velocities, so you need more information about the collision to completely determine the final velocities from the initial velocities. The situation is simplified if the collision is totally inelastic, because then there is only one final velocity, and once again momentum conservation gives all the information needed to obtain a solution.

EXAMPLE

A 4-kg mass moving at 10 m/s in the $-y$ direction collides and sticks to a 2-kg mass moving at 6 m/s in the $+x$ direction. Find the final velocity components.

$$P_{xi} = P_{xf} \qquad\qquad P_{yi} = P_{yf}$$

$$2(6) = 6v_x \qquad\qquad 4(-10) = 6v_y$$

$$v_x = 2\,\frac{m}{s} \qquad\qquad v_y = -6.67\,\frac{m}{s}$$

When the masses are equal, momentum conservation yields a condition on the velocities if one object is initially stationary:

$$m\vec{v}_{1i} = m\vec{v}_{1f} + m\vec{v}_{2f}$$

$$\vec{v}_{1i} = \vec{v}_{1f} + \vec{v}_{2f}$$
The three vectors then form a triangle (figure 4).

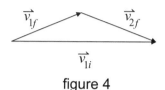

figure 4

If, in addition, the collision is elastic,

$$\frac{1}{2}mv_{1i}^2 = \frac{1}{2}mv_{1f}^2 + \frac{1}{2}mv_{2f}^2$$

$$v_{1i}^2 = v_{1f}^2 + v_{2f}^2$$
then the triangle is a right triangle $\theta + \phi = 90°$

Center of Mass

When a system consists of several objects, their motion can be quite complex. But one point associated with the system undergoes a particularly simple motion, the **center of mass** (CM). It is the average of each particle coordinate, weighted by the mass of each particle:

$$x_{CM} = \frac{m_1 x_1 + m_2 x_2 + ...}{m_1 + m_2 + ...} \qquad y_{CM} = \frac{m_1 y_1 + m_2 y_2 + ...}{m_1 + m_2 + ...}$$

Here's a simple example: Consider two masses on the x-axis, a 4-kg mass at $x = 18$ and a 2-kg mass at $x = 6$ (figure 5).

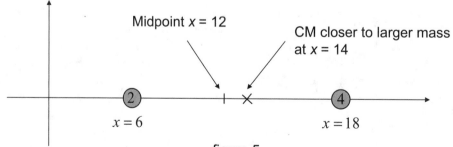

figure 5

$$x_{CM} = \frac{m_1 x_1 + m_2 x_2 + ...}{m_1 + m_2 + ...} = \frac{4(18) + 2(6)}{4 + 2} = 14$$

If the two masses were equal, the CM would have been halfway between them at $x = 12$. Since the 4-kg mass is twice the 2-kg mass, the CM is closer to the 4-kg mass, and the CM breaks the distance between the two masses into a 2-to-1 ratio, the same as the ratio of the masses. It's easy to see from the definition that uniform, symmetric objects will have their CM at the geometric center.

Now let's look at the velocity of the CM (in one dimension for simplicity). During a time Δt, the objects will undergo displacements Δx_1, Δx_2 ..., which will lead to a displacement in the CM: Δx_{CM}.

$$\Delta x_{CM} = \frac{m_1 \Delta x_1 + m_2 \Delta x_2 + ...}{m_1 + m_2 + ...} = \frac{m_1 \Delta x_1 + m_2 \Delta x_2 + ...}{M_{total}}$$

Divide by Δt and rearrange:

$$M_{total} v_{CM} = m_1 v_1 + m_2 v_2 + ... = p_1 + p_2 + ... = P_{total}$$

Since the total momentum of the system is the total mass multiplied by v_{CM}, it's as if the CM is moving as a point particle with mass M_{total} and velocity v_{CM}.

To see why the motion of the CM is simple, look at its acceleration and apply Newton's second law. For simplicity, use a one-dimensional situation.

$$a_{CM} = \frac{m_1 a_1 + m_2 a_2 + ...}{m_1 + m_2 + ...}$$

$$M_{total} a_{CM} = netF_1 + netF_2 + ...$$

As you add up all the forces on the system, the internal forces will cancel in action-reaction pairs, leaving only the net external force on the right-hand side.

$$M_{total} a_{CM} = netF^{ext}$$

Generalized to three dimensions, this means that the CM moves as a point particle with mass M_{total}, experiencing only the external forces. If there are no external forces, the CM initially at rest will remain at rest; if the CM initially is moving, it will continue to do so with a constant velocity.

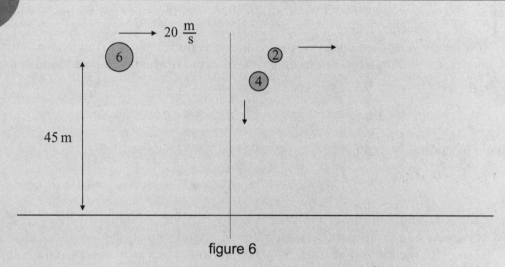

figure 6

A 6-kg spherical mass is currently moving horizontally at 20 m/s at a height of 45 m. A small explosion breaks the mass into a 2-kg and a 4-kg piece, with the 4-kg piece falling straight down with 0 initial speed (figure 6). How far does the 2-kg piece travel?

If the explosion had not occurred, the object and its CM would have traveled 60 m before hitting:

$$\Delta y = \frac{1}{2}gt^2 \qquad\qquad \Delta x = v_{x0}t$$

$$45 = 5t^2 \qquad\qquad \Delta x = 20(3)$$

$$t = 3\text{ s} \qquad\qquad \Delta x = 60\text{ m}$$

With the explosion occurring, the CM will still land here because it continues to move under only the influence of the external force of gravity; the explosion itself exerted only internal forces. Since the 4-kg piece lands 60 m to the left of the CM contact point, the 2-kg piece must land 120 m to the right of the same point. The 2-kg piece, then, travels 180 m horizontally from the explosion.

KEY FORMULAS

Impulse Delivered by a Force	$\vec{J}_F = \int_{t_1}^{t_2} \vec{F}\, dt$
Linear Momentum of Mass	$\vec{p} = m\vec{v}$
Impulse-Momentum Theorem	$\vec{J}_{netF} = \Delta\vec{p}$
Total Linear Momentum of System	$\vec{P} = \vec{p}_1 + \vec{p}_2 + \ldots$
Conservation of Momentum	$\vec{P}_i = \vec{P}_f$
Elastic Collision in One Dimension	$v_1 - v_2 = -(v_1' - v_2')$
Center of Mass	$x_{CM} = \dfrac{m_1 x_1 + m_2 x_2 + \ldots}{m_1 + m_2 + \ldots}$
	$y_{CM} = \dfrac{m_1 y_1 + m_2 y_2 + \ldots}{m_1 + m_2 + \ldots}$

CHAPTER 5

PRACTICE EXERCISES

SECTION I MULTIPLE CHOICE

1. A 2-kg mass moving at 3 m/s hits a vertical wall and rebounds with the same speed. If the contact time with the wall is 0.01 s, the magnitude of the force exerted on the mass is most nearly

(A) 6 N
(B) 600 N
(C) 1,200 N
(D) 12 N
(E) 300 N

2. A 1,000-kg vehicle moving at 3 m/s collides with a 2,000-kg stationary vehicle. After the collision, the two move together. The speed of the two just after collision is

(A) 1.5 m/s
(B) 1 m/s
(C) 2 m/s
(D) 0.5 m/s
(E) 0.67 m/s

3. A compressed spring is placed between two masses M and m resting on a smooth horizontal surface. When the spring is released, the two fly apart with M moving at velocity V. The velocity of m is

(A) $\frac{M}{m}V$ (B) $-\frac{M}{m}V$ (C) $\frac{m}{M}V$ (D) $-\frac{m}{M}V$ (E) $\frac{m}{m+M}V$

4. A mass m moving east with speed v on a smooth horizontal surface explodes into two pieces. After the explosion, one piece of mass $\frac{3}{4}m$ continues in the same direction with speed $\frac{4}{3}v$. Find the magnitude and direction for the velocity of the other piece.

(A) $\frac{1}{3}v$ to the left

(B) The piece is at rest.

(C) $\frac{1}{4}v$ to the left

(D) $\frac{3}{4}v$ to the left

(E) $\frac{1}{4}v$ to the right

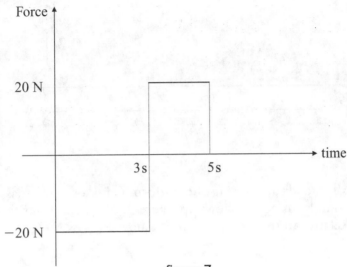

figure 7

5. A mass M moving with velocity v experiences the force shown in figure 7 for 5 seconds. The change in momentum of the mass is

    (A) $100 \ \frac{\text{kg} \cdot \text{m}}{\text{s}}$

    (B) $20 \ \frac{\text{kg} \cdot \text{m}}{\text{s}}$

    (C) not calculable until M and v are known

    (D) $-20 \ \frac{\text{kg} \cdot \text{m}}{\text{s}}$

    (E) $40 \ \frac{\text{kg} \cdot \text{m}}{\text{s}}$

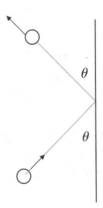

figure 8

6. A mass rebounds off a wall elastically as shown in figure 8. The vector that best represents the impulse delivered by the wall is

    (A) ↘ (B) ↘ (C) ← (D) ↗ (E) ↑

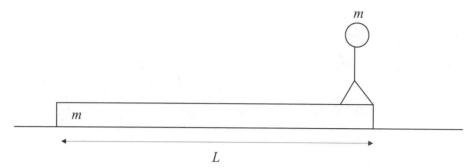

figure 9

7. A man of mass m stands at the rear of a uniform plank of equal mass and length L that rests on a frictionless surface as shown in figure 9. The man walks forward to the center of the plank. Relative to the ice, the man has moved

(A) $\frac{L}{2}$ (B) L (C) $\frac{L}{4}$ (D) $\frac{3L}{4}$ (E) $\frac{L}{3}$

8. A 0.5-kg mass moving north at 4 m/s collides head-on with a 10-kg stationary mass in an elastic collision. After the collision, the velocity of the 0.5-kg mass is most nearly

(A) 1 m/s north
(B) 2 m/s south
(C) 3.5 m/s south
(D) 0
(E) 4.5 m/s south

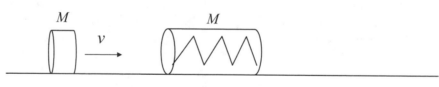

figure 10

Questions 9 and 10
A mass M moving with speed collides with a stationary spring gun of equal mass containing an uncompressed spring with spring constant K. Assume all surfaces are frictionless.

9. The maximum compression of the spring will be

(A) $v\sqrt{\frac{M}{K}}$ (B) $v\sqrt{\frac{2M}{K}}$ (C) $v\sqrt{\frac{M}{4K}}$ (D) $\frac{v}{2}\sqrt{\frac{M}{K}}$ (E) $v\sqrt{\frac{M}{2K}}$

10. After the collision, the gun will be moving with a speed most nearly

(A) $\frac{v}{2}$ (B) $\frac{v}{4}$ (C) v (D) $2v$ (E) $\frac{v}{3}$

PRACTICE EXERCISES

SECTION II FREE RESPONSE

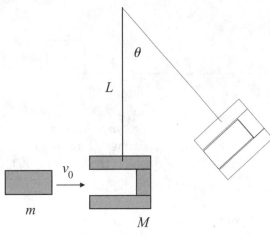

figure 11

1. A mass m is fired with speed v_0 into a pendulum of length L, mass M. The pendulum mass is specially shaped to catch the incoming mass so that the two move together after the collision. In terms of v_0, m, L, M, and g, determine

   (a) the speed of the two masses after the collision
   (b) an expression for the angle θ through which the pendulum moves after the collision
      Suppose the pendulum is hung so that it can move in a complete vertical circle.
   (c) What is the minimum value of v_0 that will ensure that the pendulum makes one complete revolution?

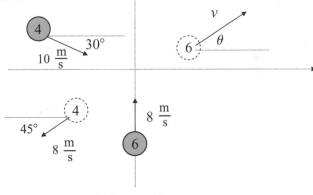

figure 12

2. A 4-kg mass moving at 10 m/s at an angle of 30° below the horizontal collides with a 6 kg mass moving vertically at 8 m/s. As a result of the collision, the 4-kg mass moves back at 45° below the $-x$-axis at 8 m/s.

   (a) Determine the magnitude and direction of the 6-kg mass velocity.
   (b) Was the collision elastic? Explain.

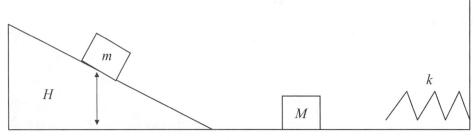

figure 13

3. A mass m slides down a smooth incline from a height H and collides with a stationary mass M sitting on a smooth horizontal surface. The two masses stick together and move to the right, where they encounter a spring with spring constant k.

(a) Find the speed of m at the bottom of the incline.
(b) Find the speed of the masses after the collision.
(c) Find the maximum compression of the spring.
(d) After the masses leave the spring moving to the left, a small explosion separates the two masses and causes the mass M to come to rest. How high will m go on the incline?

Answers and Explanations

MULTIPLE CHOICE

1. The answer is C. $\Delta p = 2(3) - 2(-3) = 12 \text{ N} \cdot \text{s}$

$$F\Delta t = \Delta p \Rightarrow F = \frac{\Delta p}{\Delta t} = \frac{12}{0.01} = 1{,}200 \text{ N}$$

2. The answer is B. $P_i = P_f$

$$3(1{,}000) = 3{,}000v \Rightarrow v = 1 \frac{\text{m}}{\text{s}}$$

3. The answer is B. $P_i = P_f$

$$0 = mv + MV \Rightarrow v = -\frac{M}{m}V$$

4. The answer is B. $P_i = P_f$

$$mv = \left(\frac{3}{4}m\right)\left(\frac{4}{3}v\right) + \left(\frac{1}{4}m\right)v' \Rightarrow v' = 0$$

5. The answer is D. The area under the graph is $-60 + 40 = -20 \frac{kg \cdot m}{s}$.

6. The answer is C. The vertical component of momentum doesn't change, so there is no vertical impulse component.

7. The answer is C. The CM is initially at rest and halfway between the man and the center of the plank $-\frac{L}{4}$ from the man. No external forces act, so the CM cannot move. When the man walks to the center of the plank, the CM of the system is directly underneath him, so he moved only $\frac{L}{4}$. As he walked to the left, the plank moved to the right as well.

8. The answer is C. An elastic collision reverses the direction of the relative speed. The initial relative speed is 4 m/s. The mass differences between the two objects imply that the 10-kg mass will not be moving fast and that the 0.5-kg mass will reverse direction, so C is the only answer that could work. D violates KE conservation. Of course, you could use equations to get the same result, but it would take longer.

9. The answer is E. At maximum compression, the two masses have the same speed as in a totally inelastic collision. Momentum conservation gives:

$$P_i = P_f$$

$$Mv = 2Mv' \Rightarrow v' = \frac{v}{2}$$

The KE lost, $\frac{1}{2}Mv^2 - \frac{1}{2}(2M)v'^2 = \frac{1}{4}Mv^2$ becomes PE in the spring:

$$\frac{1}{2}Kx^2 = \frac{1}{4}Mv^2 \Rightarrow x = v\sqrt{\frac{M}{2K}}$$

10. The answer is C. After the spring is uncompressed again, the collision is elastic. For equal masses, you can apply momentum conservation and the relative speed change formula:

$$P_i = P_f$$

$$Mv = Mv_1 + Mv_2 \qquad\qquad v = v_2 - v_1$$

$$v = v_1 + v_2$$

Combine to get $v_2 = v$

$$v_1 = 0$$

FREE RESPONSE

1. (a) $\qquad P_i = P_f$

$$mv_0 = (m + M)V$$

$$V = \frac{m}{m + M}v_0$$

(b) After the collision, energy is conserved:
$$E_i = E_f$$

$$\frac{1}{2}(m + M)V^2 = (m + M)gh$$

$$\frac{1}{2}\left(\frac{m}{m + M}v_0\right)^2 = g(L - L\cos\theta)$$

(c) At the top where the mass has risen $2L$, the centripetal force is supplied by the tension and gravity and will be a minimum when the tension is 0 (figure 16).

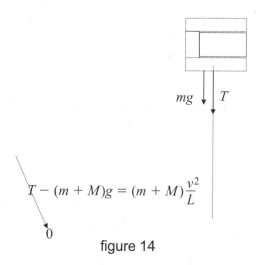

$$T - (m + M)g = (m + M)\frac{v^2}{L}$$

figure 14

You can then apply energy conservation from just after the collision to the top of the motion.

$$netF_{top} = (m + M)\frac{v^2}{L} \qquad E_i = E_{top}$$

$$(m + M)g = (m + M)\frac{v^2}{L} \qquad \frac{1}{2}(m + M)V^2 = \frac{1}{2}(m + M)v^2 + (m + M)g(2L)$$

$$v^2 = gL \qquad \frac{1}{2}\left(\frac{m}{m + M}v_0\right)^2 = \frac{1}{2}gL + g(2L)$$

$$v_0 = \frac{m + M}{m}\sqrt{5gL}$$

2. (a) $P_{xi} = P_{xf}$

   $(4)(10)\cos30 = -(4)(8)\cos45 + 6v_x$

   $v_x = 9.5 \frac{m}{s}$

   $P_{yi} = P_{yf}$

   $-(4)(10)\sin30 + (6)(8) = -(4)(8)\sin45 + 6v_y$

   $v_y = 8.4 \frac{m}{s}$

   $v = \sqrt{v^2_x + v^2_y} = 12.7 \frac{m}{s}$ $\tan\theta = \frac{v_y}{v_x} = 1.13 \Rightarrow \theta = 48.5°$ with respect to $+x$-axis

   (b) $KE_i = \frac{1}{2}(4)(10)^2 + \frac{1}{2}(6)(8)^2 = 392$ J

   $KE_f = \frac{1}{2}(4)(8)^2 + \frac{1}{2}(6)(12.7)^2 = 612$ J

   Kinetic energy increased as a result of the collision, so it clearly wasn't conserved, implying that the collision was not elastic.

3. (a) $E_i = E_f$ (b) $P_i = P_f$ (c) $E_i = E_f$

   $mgH = \frac{1}{2}mv^2$ $mv = (m + M)V$ $\frac{1}{2}(m + M)V^2 = \frac{1}{2}kx^2$

   $v = \sqrt{2gH}$ $V = \frac{m}{m + M}\sqrt{2gH}$ $x = \sqrt{\frac{m^2(2gH)}{k(m + M)}}$

   (d) $P_i = P_f$ $E_i = E_f$

   $(m + M)V = mv' + 0$ $mgH_f = \frac{1}{2}mv'^2 = \frac{1}{2}m(2gH)$

   $v' = \frac{m + M}{m}V = \sqrt{2gH}$ $H_f = H$

The system ends up with the same energy with which it began. Energy was lost in the first collision, with the lost energy perhaps appearing as internal energy in the masses. Then energy was added to the system with the explosion. Here, stored chemical energy became mechanical energy in the system, just enough to get the total mechanical energy back to its initial value.

CHAPTER 6

Rotational Motion and Angular Momentum

This chapter will describe rotational motion and explain its dynamics around a fixed axis and around an axis that isn't fixed. You'll see that there is a one-to-one correspondence between the description of rotation about a fixed axis and linear motion in one dimension. Although rotation about an axis that isn't fixed is a complicated subject, the AP C-level test is limited to rolling objects, which greatly simplifies things. Finally, we'll look at the concept of angular momentum and the conditions for its conservation.

Rotation About a Fixed Axis

DESCRIPTIVE VARIABLES
When a rigid object is pivoted at some point and allowed to rotate about the pivot point, the positions of all the particles making up the object change, with each particle moving in a circle (figure 1).

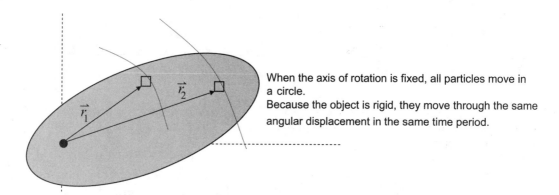

When the axis of rotation is fixed, all particles move in a circle.
Because the object is rigid, they move through the same angular displacement in the same time period.

figure 1

Since the object is rigid, however, the particles' positions with respect to each other don't change. If you know what angle any one particle has moved through, you know the positions of all the particles. That's why it makes sense to use the angle of rotation, the **angular displacement**, as the quantity to describe the object's position.

As each particle moves in its circular path, it has a linear displacement Δx as well as a linear velocity associated with it. If the particle is speeding up or slowing down, it will also have a tangential linear acceleration associated with it. You can relate the linear quantities to the angular quantities needed to describe the motion more easily, using radian measure for the angular displacement instead of degrees or some other unit (figure 2).

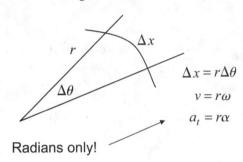

figure 2

You'll recall that the radian measure of an angle is the ratio of the arc length subtended by the angle to the radius of the arc. From this definition you get:

$$\Delta x = r\Delta\theta$$

Note that different particles have different r-values leading to different Δx-values, but they all have the same $\Delta\theta$. This fact makes fixed-axis rotation as simple as it sounds. If you imagine the displacement occurring in an infinitesimal time interval Δt, you can introduce velocity concepts:

$$\frac{\Delta x}{\Delta t} = r\frac{\Delta\theta}{\Delta t} \Rightarrow in \lim_{\Delta t \to 0}: \frac{dx}{dt} = r\frac{d\theta}{dt}$$

$$v = r\omega$$

Here $\omega = \frac{d\theta}{dt}$ is the **angular velocity** of the object. Once again, each particle with a different r has a different linear velocity, but all particles have the same angular velocity. You can differentiate the last equation to obtain

$$\frac{dv}{dt} = r\frac{d\omega}{dt}$$

$$a_t = r\alpha$$

Here a_t is the tangential acceleration, the component of the acceleration that is tangential to the circular path executed by the particle. The quantity $\alpha = \frac{d\omega}{dt}$ is the **angular acceleration**. All particles in the object have the same angular acceleration. Even if the linear speeds of the particles aren't changing, their velocities are still changing direction. This means that even if $\alpha = 0$, a component of the linear acceleration still acts toward the center—the centripetal acceleration $a_{cp} = \frac{v^2}{r} = \omega^2 r$, which is present any time circular motion occurs. In general, the total acceleration of any particle within the mass is

$$a = \sqrt{a_{cp}^2 + a_t^2} = \sqrt{(\omega^2 r)^2 + (r\alpha)^2}$$

EXERCISE

A disc rotates about an axis through its center according to the relation

$$\theta(t) = \frac{1}{3}t^3 - 6t$$

(a) Determine the angular velocity and acceleration for a general time t.
(b) Find the magnitude of the total linear acceleration of a point 0.5 m from the center at $t = 1$ s.
(c) Find the linear speed of a point on the disc 20 cm from the center at $t = 2$ s.

(a) Differentiating, you get

$$\omega = \frac{d\theta}{dt} = t^2 - 6 \qquad\qquad \alpha = \frac{dw}{dt} = 2t$$

(b) $\omega(1) = -5\frac{\text{rad}}{\text{s}}$ $\qquad\qquad$ $\alpha(1) = 2\frac{\text{rad}}{\text{s}^2}$

$$a = \sqrt{[(-5)^2(0.5)]^2 + [(0.5)(2)]^2} = 12.5\,\frac{\text{m}}{\text{s}^2}$$

$$\omega(2) = 2^2 - 6 = -2\frac{\text{rad}}{\text{s}}$$

(c) At $t = 2$ s,

$$v = r\omega = (0.2)(-2) = -0.4\,\frac{\text{m}}{\text{s}}$$

CONSTANT ANGULAR ACCELERATION EQUATIONS

You saw in Chapter 4 that when one-dimensional motion is described by a constant acceleration, then a set of four equations, two of them independent, relate the various quantities of the motion. The same is true for rotation about a fixed axis if the angular acceleration is constant. In a complete analogy, you can write:

Linear 1-D

$$v = v_0 + at$$

$$\Delta x = \frac{1}{2}(v + v_0)t$$

$$\Delta x = v_0 t + \frac{1}{2}at^2$$

$$v^2 = v_0^2 + 2a\Delta x$$

Rotation Fixed Axis

$$\omega = \omega_0 + \alpha t$$

$$\Delta \theta = \frac{1}{2}(\omega + \omega_0)t$$

$$\Delta \theta = \omega_0 t + \frac{1}{2}\alpha t^2$$

$$\omega^2 = \omega_0^2 + 2a\Delta \theta$$

EXERCISE

A stick pivoted about its center and rotating at 2.4 rad/s increases uniformly in angular velocity to 5.2 rad/s in the next 3 s. Find the angular acceleration and the angular displacement over the 3 s period.

You can make a table as you did in Chapter 4:

$$\omega_0 = 2.4 \, \frac{\text{rad}}{\text{s}}$$

$$\omega = 5.2 \, \frac{\text{rad}}{\text{s}} \quad \begin{matrix} \alpha = ? \\ \Delta\theta = ? \end{matrix}$$

$$t = 3 \text{ s}$$

Use the first equation to find α.

$$\omega = \omega_0 + \alpha t$$

$$5.2 = 2.4 + \alpha(3)$$

$$\alpha = 0.93 \, \frac{\text{rad}}{\text{s}^2}$$

Use the second equation to find $\Delta\theta$.

$$\Delta\theta = \frac{1}{2}(\omega + \omega_0)t$$

$$\Delta\theta = \frac{1}{2}(5.2 + 2.4)(3)$$

$$\Delta\theta = 11.4 \text{ rad}$$

A note about units: The equations relating angular and linear quantities

$$\Delta x = r\Delta\theta$$

$$v = r\omega$$

$$a_t = r\alpha$$

are derived from the definition of radian measure, so the quantities must use radians for the angle unit. The four kinematic equations follow from the basic definitions of the variables themselves, which means these equations will be true in any consistent system of units. The SI system using radian measure for angle has become the standard for the AP test.

ROTATIONAL KINETIC ENERGY AND MOMENT OF INERTIA

When an object rotates about a fixed axis, the ith particle within the object has kinetic energy $K_i = \frac{1}{2}m_i v_i^2$ (figure 3).

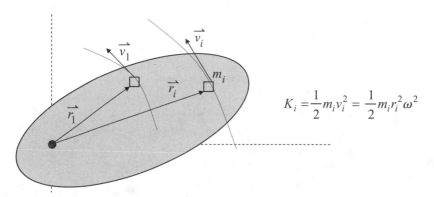

$$K_i = \frac{1}{2}m_i v_i^2 = \frac{1}{2}m_i r_i^2 \omega^2$$

figure 3

Conceptually, it's not difficult to imagine adding up all these contributions to obtain the total KE. In practice, it's more complex because particles that are different distances from the axis have different speeds. But because all particles have the same angular speed ω, the KE doesn't need a subscript to label it. You can derive a new equation and definition:

$$K_i = \frac{1}{2}m_i v_i^2 = \frac{1}{2}m_i r_i^2 \omega^2$$

Summing up all the particles, you get:

$$K = \sum K_i = \sum \frac{1}{2}m_i v_i^2 = \frac{1}{2}\left(\sum m_i r_i^2\right)\omega^2$$

Note that the ω is factored out of the summation. The summation quantity depends on the mass and how it's distributed over the object. It's called the **moment of inertia** about the particular axis:

$$I = \sum m_i r_i^2$$

With this definition, the rotational KE becomes

$$K_{\text{rot}} = \frac{1}{2}I\omega^2$$

Notice the analogy with translational KE, $K_{\text{tr}} = \frac{1}{2}mv^2$, with v replaced by ω and m replaced by I.

From the definition of the moment of inertia, you can directly calculate its value with an object that consists of several point masses. If the system doesn't consist of discrete point masses but instead is distributed continuously, the only simple object it can be is a hoop. In a hoop of radius R, all the mass is the same distance away, so it follows that

$$I_{\text{hoop}} = MR^2$$

For other continuous distributions, you'll need to integrate over the object to find I. On the AP test, the formula for I is often provided within the problem, but integrating to find I is expected and has appeared in past tests. You'll find an example of that process in Chapter 15.

EXAMPLE

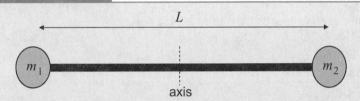

axis

figure 4

A uniform rod of length L and mass M that can pivot about its center of mass (its geometrical center) has two masses m_1 and m_2 placed at each end (figure 4). If it rotates with angular speed ω, find its rotational KE. The moment of inertia of a uniform rod about its center of mass is $\frac{1}{12}ML^2$.

Since $K_{\text{rot}} = \frac{1}{2}I\omega^2$, what you need to find is I, the moment of inertia of the system.

$$I_{\text{sys}} = I_{\text{rod}} + I_{\text{masses}}$$

Since I_{rod} is given, you just need I_{masses}. But treating these as point masses, you can easily get

$$I_{\text{masses}} = m_1\left(\frac{L}{2}\right)^2 + m_2\left(\frac{L}{2}\right)^2 = (m_1 + m_2)\frac{L^2}{4}$$

Then you have

$$K_{\text{rot}} = \frac{1}{2}\left(\frac{1}{12}ML^2 + (m_1 + m_2)\frac{L^2}{4}\right)\omega^2$$

In this exercise, the moment of inertia of the rod about its CM was given. The moment of inertia about another axis that doesn't pass through the CM but that is parallel to the first is given by the **parallel axis theorem** (figure 5):

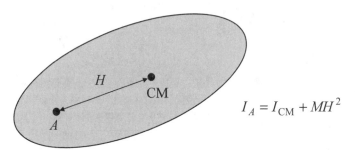

$$I_A = I_{CM} + MH^2$$

Axes at A and CM parallel

figure 5

$$I_A = I_{CM} + MH^2$$

Here M is the total mass of the object, and H is the distance between the two parallel axes, one passing through the CM. Note that since MH^2 is always positive, the axis with the minimum value for I always passes through the CM.

EXERCISE

Find the moment of inertia of a rod of mass M, length L about one end of the rod.

From the previous example, you have I_{CM}. Then you can write:

$$I_{end} = \frac{1}{12}ML^2 + M\left(\frac{L}{2}\right)^2 = \frac{1}{3}ML^2$$

TORQUE

You have seen that there is a one-to-one correspondence between the description of motion in one dimension and rotation about a fixed axis. Does this correspondence extend to dynamics as well? Is there an analogous quantity to force when we analyze rotation about a fixed axis? The answer is yes, and this quantity is called torque. To gain a conceptual understanding of torque, consider the following example.

Imagine a rigid rod pivoted about its left end so that it can rotate freely in a horizontal plane. You can apply a 10 N force (figure 6) in a variety of ways, and your intuition should tell you that not all of them are equally efficient in causing rotation to begin.

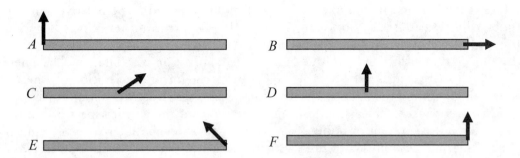

figure 6

A and B will not work at all, D is better than C, and F is the best, because it will most easily get the rod out of its rest state to begin rotating. You can see that a number of factors are involved in this analysis: how big the force is, how far from the pivot the force is applied, and the direction the force is applied. A quantity called **torque** reflects this information (figure 7).

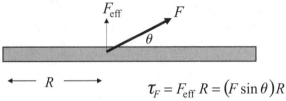

figure 7

$$\tau_F = (F\sin\theta)R = F_{\text{eff}}R$$

Here F_{eff} is the component of F that is effective in causing rotation. F_{eff} is perpendicular to the line drawn from the pivot to the point where the force acts. The length of this line is R.

There's another way to think of torque that can be useful in some problems. You can rearrange the formula for torque this way:

$$\tau_F = (F\sin\theta)R = F(R\sin\theta) = FR_{\text{eff}}$$

Here R_{eff}, also called the lever arm, is the perpendicular distance from the axis to the line of action (figure 8) of the force.

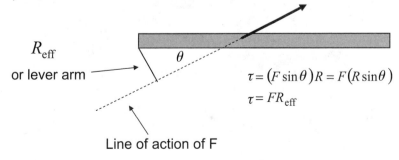

figure 8

Torques that tend to cause counterclockwise rotation are said to be positive, while negative torques will tend to cause clockwise rotation. In the preceding example, *A* and *B* had 0 torque, while *F* had the largest value, and in this case it was positive. When several forces act on an object, they all will exert torques about a given pivot or axis. There will be a net torque, and we shall see that just as the net force determines the linear acceleration of a mass, the net torque will determine the angular acceleration of an object rotating about a fixed axis.

When you consider linear motion in one dimension, the vector aspect of the force only shows itself in its sign, plus or minus. Similarly, for rotation about a fixed axis, a given torque will be either plus of minus. But just as force needs a full vector description in two or three dimensions, so does torque. The torque associated with a force and a given origin is a vector defined using the cross product (figure 9).

$$\vec{\tau} = \vec{r} \times \vec{F}$$

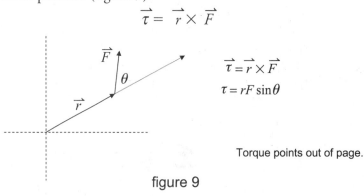

$$\vec{\tau} = \vec{r} \times \vec{F}$$
$$\tau = rF\sin\theta$$

Torque points out of page.

figure 9

The direction is determined by the right-hand rule. When you were concerned only with rotation about a fixed axis, the torques could affect the rotation only if they had components that were parallel or antiparallel to the axis; the two directions were labeled as positive and negative.

NEWTON'S SECOND LAW FOR FIXED AXIS ROTATION
You can apply Newton's second law to the rotating object (figure 10).

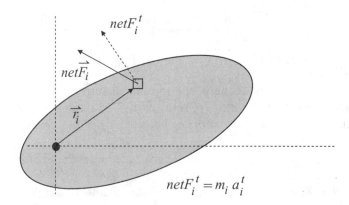

$$netF_i^t = m_i a_i^t$$

figure 10

Imagine looking at each particle, and break the forces acting on each into tangential and radial components. Focusing on the tangential component, you can write

$$netF_i^t = m_i a_i^t$$

By definition, $netF_i^t$ is perpendicular to r_i, so the torque on this piece is

$$net\tau_i = r_i \, netF_i^t = m_i r_i a_i^t \qquad \left(a_i^t = r_i \alpha \right)$$

$$net\tau_i = m_i r_i^2 \alpha$$

If you sum over the entire body, internal torques exerted within the object will cancel out due to the third law. Only the external torques will contribute, and you can write

$$net\tau^{ext} = \left(\sum m_i r_i^2 \right) \alpha$$

$$net\tau^{ext} = I\alpha$$

This is the dynamic equation for rotation about a fixed axis. It's the analog to $netF = ma$, with torque analogous to force and of course I and α continuing to be analogous to m and a. Given a system rotating about a fixed axis, you can apply this equation to relate the torques applied to the angular acceleration they create.

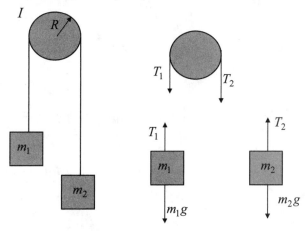

figure 11

EXAMPLE

Masses m_1 and m_2 are connected by a light string over a pulley of radius R and moment of inertia I (figure 11). Determine the acceleration of the masses.

As usual, you can begin with freebody diagrams, choosing clockwise rotation as the positive sense of the motion. Because the pulley has rotational inertia, the tension will be different on either side of it. Otherwise, there would be no torque exerted on it, and it couldn't accelerate. You can apply the second law in its usual form to each mass.

$$m_2 g - T_2 = m_2 a \qquad T_1 - m_1 g = m_1 a$$

Then apply the rotational dynamic equation to the pulley.

$$net\tau^{ext} = I\alpha$$

$$RT_2 - RT_1 = I\alpha$$

You now have three equations for the four quantities T_1, T_2, a, and α. You can obtain the fourth condition by noting that the linear acceleration of the masses is the same as the linear acceleration of a point on the rim of the pulley. You can write

$$a = R\alpha$$

If you substitute for α using this equation and divide by R, you get

$$T_2 - T_1 = \frac{I}{R^2}a$$

Adding this equation to the first two leads to the tensions canceling out, and you get

$$a = \frac{m_2 - m_1}{m_2 + m_1 + \dfrac{I}{R^2}}g$$

You can substitute back to solve for the tensions if you want to.

ROTATIONAL EQUILIBRIUM

A system is in **rotational equilibrium** if the net torque on it is zero *about any axis*: $net\tau = 0$. While the axis you choose could be anywhere in principle, in practice a given problem will usually have a clear best choice. If there is no clear pivot point, choose a place where several forces act. Since their distance from the axis will be 0, their contribution to the torque will be 0.

EXAMPLE

A uniform rod of mass 12 kg and length 6 m is pivoted at one end to a wall and is partially supported by a guy wire attached at the end as pictured (figure 12). A 20-kg mass is suspended by a rope wrapped around the rod, 4 m from the wall.
(a) Find the tension in the guy wire.
(b) Find the components of the force exerted by the pivot.

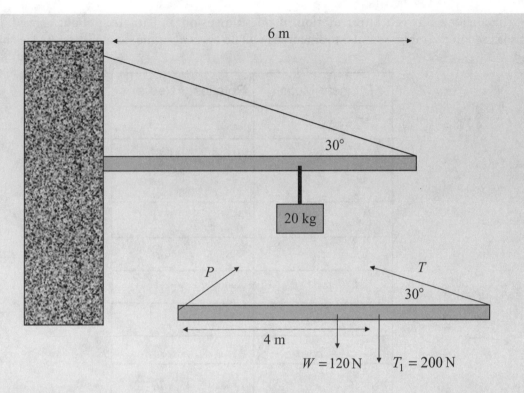

figure 12

(a) The strategy will be to analyze the rod, applying the condition of rotational equilibrium to it. You'll need to draw a freebody diagram (see figure 12). Notice that the diagram must reflect the different points where forces are applied. A single point is not enough to represent the object. A force $\vec{P}$, probably a result of normal and frictional forces, acts at the wall-rod connection, but if you choose this as your axis, it will exert 0 torque. For a uniform rod, the force of gravity can be considered as acting at the center of the rod. For this axis, you can write:

$$net\ \tau = (T \sin 30)(6) - 200(4) - 120(3) = 0$$

$$T = 387 \text{ N}$$

(b) Now apply the conditions of translational equilibrium.

$net F_x = 0 \Rightarrow P_x - T \cos 30 = 0$ $net F_y = 0 \Rightarrow P_y + T \sin 30 - 320 = 0$

$P_x = 335 \text{ N}$ $P_y = -127.5 \text{ N}$

The analogy between linear motion in one dimension and rotation about a fixed axis is summarized in the table. Angular momentum will be covered in more detail later in the chapter.

1-D Linear Motion	Rotation: Fixed axis
Δx	$\Delta \theta$
v	ω
a	α
m	$I = \sum mr^2$
$K = \dfrac{1}{2}mv^2$	$K = \dfrac{1}{2}I\omega^2$
F	τ
$F = ma$	$\tau = I\alpha$
$P = mv$	$L = I\omega$
$W = \int F dx$	$W = \int \tau d\theta$
$P = Fv$	$P = \tau \omega$

figure 13

Rolling

When an object rolls across a surface, the object's contact point with the surface is instantaneously at rest. If this weren't the case, the object would be skidding or slipping. Because the contact point is at rest, you can think of it as an instantaneous axis of rotation. Relative to the contact point, all points on the object have the same angular velocity even though they have different linear velocities (figure 14).

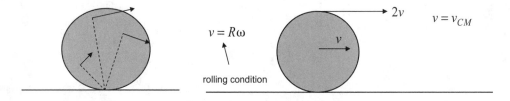

figure 14

In particular, if v is the velocity of the center of mass, a point on the rim opposite the contact point, twice as far away as the CM, will have a velocity $2v$. You can consider the motion a pure rotation about the contact point. Then, the KE of the object is

$$K_{roll} = \frac{1}{2}I_{CP}\omega^2 \qquad v = R\omega$$

Here I_{CP} refers to the moment of inertia about the contact point. The condition relating the CM speed to the angular velocity about the contact point, $v = R\omega$, must be satisfied for **rolling** to occur. You can then use the parallel axis theorem to relate I_{CP} to the moment of inertia about the center of mass

$$I_{CP} = I_{CM} + MR^2$$

Substituting, you obtain

$$K_{roll} = \frac{1}{2}(I_{CM} + MR^2)\omega^2$$
$$K_{roll} = \frac{1}{2}I_{CM}\omega^2 + \frac{1}{2}Mv^2$$

The first term is the KE for pure rotation about the CM with $\omega = \frac{v}{R}$. The second term is the translational KE of a point mass moving with speed v. You can think of rolling as a combination of a pure rotation *about* the CM and a pure translation *of* the CM.

EXERCISE

Find the linear speed of the CM of a disc with $I_{CM} = \frac{1}{2}MR^2$ after it has rolled down an incline from a height H, starting from rest.

You can use conservation of energy, equating the initial PE to the final KE.

$$E_i = E_f$$

$$MgH = \frac{1}{2}I_{CM}\omega^2 + \frac{1}{2}Mv^2$$

$$MgH = \frac{1}{2}\left(\frac{1}{2}MR^2\right)\left(\frac{v}{R}\right)^2 + \frac{1}{2}Mv^2$$

$$v = \sqrt{\frac{4}{3}gH}$$

If the object simply slid down the incline without acquiring any rotational KE, the speed at the bottom would be $v = \sqrt{2gH}$. Transferring energy into rotational motion causes the object to move more slowly.

Angular Momentum

A point particle located by position vector $\vec{r}$ and having momentum $\vec{p}$ has **angular momentum** $\vec{l}$ defined through the cross product (figure 15).

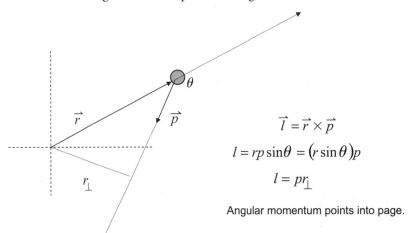

$$\vec{l} = \vec{r} \times \vec{p}$$

$$l = rp\sin\theta = (r\sin\theta)p$$

$$l = pr_{\perp}$$

Angular momentum points into page.

figure 15

$$\vec{l} = \vec{r} \times \vec{p}$$

Like torque, angular momentum is an origin-dependent quantity; its value depends on the origin it is referred to. Let's take the time derivative of $\vec{l}$:

$$\frac{d\vec{l}}{dt} = \frac{d}{dt}(\vec{r} \times \vec{p}) = \frac{d\vec{r}}{dt} \times \vec{p} + \vec{r} \times \frac{d\vec{p}}{dt}$$

Because $\vec{v} = \frac{d\vec{r}}{dt}$ is parallel to the momentum $\vec{p}$, their cross product is 0. Since $\frac{d\vec{p}}{dt} = net\vec{F}$, you can write

$$\frac{d\vec{l}}{dt} = 0 + \vec{r} \times \frac{d\vec{p}}{dt} = \vec{r} \times net\vec{F}$$

$$\frac{d\vec{l}}{dt} = net\vec{\tau}$$

In the last step, the vector definition of torque has been used. Just as the rate of change of linear momentum is determined by the net force, the rate of change of angular momentum is determined by the net torque.

For a system of particles, you can define the total angular momentum $\vec{L}$:

$$\vec{L} = \vec{l}_1 + \vec{l}_2 + \dots$$

If you take the time derivative of the total angular momentum, you'll find that the torques exerted by different parts of the system on each other cancel out in pairs due to Newton's third law. Only the external torques will make a contribution, so you have

$$\frac{d\vec{L}}{dt} = net\vec{\tau}^{\,ext}$$

Rolling Dynamics

Now let's use this equation for objects that are rolling along a straight line. (This is the subject area that the C-level test addresses.) If you choose the CM as the origin about which to calculate the total angular momentum, you'll greatly simplify the problem. Then, the magnitude of $\vec{L}$ will be

$$L = I_{CM}\omega$$

You can determine the direction of $\vec{L}$ by curling your right hand around the object in the rotation direction; your thumb will point in the direction of $\vec{L}$ (figure 16).

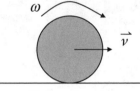
$\vec{L}$ points into page.

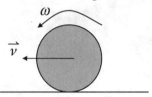
$\vec{L}$ points out of page.

figure 16

Then the dynamic equation becomes

$$\frac{dL}{dt} = net\tau^{ext} \qquad \Rightarrow \qquad net\tau^{ext} = I_{CM}\alpha$$

You'll notice that this equation has exactly the same form as the dynamic equation for fixed axis rotation. If you use the CM as the origin, you can treat rolling just like fixed axis rotation.

EXERCISE

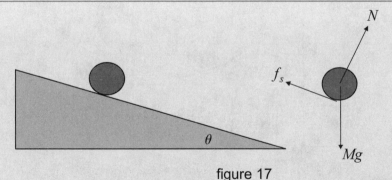

figure 17

A disc with $I_{CM} = \frac{1}{2}MR^2$ rolls down an incline with angle θ (figure 17). Determine the acceleration of the CM and the magnitude of the force of static friction.

Since the contact point is instantaneously at rest, static friction supplies the torque to set the disc into rotation. In general, its value will be less than the maximum value the surfaces can supply. When the maximum value is exceeded, the object will no longer roll but will slip, moving with a combination of rotation and translation.

From the freebody diagram, you can write the usual second law equation:

$$mg \sin \theta - f_s = ma$$

If you use the CM as your origin, gravity and the normal force exert 0 torque. The torque exerted by static friction is just Rf_s, so

$$net\,\tau^{ext} = I_{CM}\alpha$$

$$\text{rolling} \Rightarrow \alpha = \frac{a}{R}$$

$$Rf_s = \frac{1}{2}MR^2\alpha$$

$$\Rightarrow f_s = \frac{1}{2}Ma$$

You can then use the two dynamic equations to find

$$a = \frac{2}{3}g \sin \theta \qquad f_s = \frac{1}{3}mg \sin \theta$$

The maximum value of static friction is calculated as $f_s^{max} = \mu_s N = \mu_s mg \cos \theta$. This means slipping will occur when the following condition is satisfied:

$$f_s = \frac{1}{3}mg \sin \theta = \mu_s mg \cos \theta$$

$$\tan \theta = 3\mu_s$$

EXAMPLE

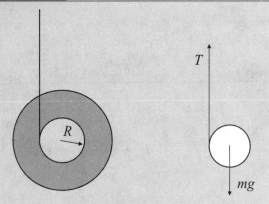

figure 18

A yo-yo with I_{CM}, mass M, and inner radius R is unwinding vertically, starting from rest (figure 18). Determine the linear acceleration of the CM, the tension in the string, and the kinetic energy at time t.

If you call the point where the string comes off the yo-yo the contact point, you can see that the contact point is instantaneously at rest with respect to the yo-yo, since the string here is at rest. Now you can consider the yo-yo a rolling object since $v = R\omega$.

From the freebody diagram you can write

$$mg - T = ma$$

About the CM you have

$$net\ \tau = RT \qquad \Rightarrow RT = I_{CM}\alpha = I_{CM}\frac{a}{R}$$

Combining the two equations, you find

$$a = \frac{mg}{m + \dfrac{I_{CM}}{R^2}} \qquad\qquad T = \frac{mg}{1 + \dfrac{mR^2}{I_{CM}}}$$

After a time t, $v = at$ and $\omega = \alpha t$. For the KE, you have

$$K = \frac{1}{2}mv^2 + \frac{1}{2}I_{CM}\omega^2$$

$$K = \frac{1}{2}m(at)^2 + \frac{1}{2}I_{CM}(\alpha t)^2$$

Then substitute for a and α.

Conservation of Angular Momentum

From the dynamic equation for the total angular momentum

$$\frac{d\vec{L}}{dt} = net\ \vec{\tau}^{ext}$$

you can infer that when there are no external torques on a system, the total angular momentum is conserved:

$$\vec{L}_i = \vec{L}_f$$

It's important to recognize that it's possible for external forces to be present and for angular momentum to still be conserved, when the external forces exert no torque. Choosing the best origin for an analysis is key here. There may be one particular origin that has 0 torque exerted about it by the external forces; using this origin, you can then apply the **angular momentum conservation law**.

EXAMPLE

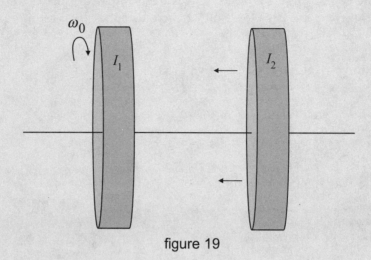

figure 19

A disc with moment of inertia I_1 about its center is rotating around an axis through its center with angular velocity ω_0. A second disc with moment I_2 that is not currently rotating is slid along the axis until it makes contact with the first disc (figure 19). If the two discs stick together, find the final angular velocity.

While the two discs exert forces on each other, there are no external torques, so angular momentum will be conserved. The final moment of inertia of the system will be the sum of the two individual values because they refer to the same axis.

$$L_i = L_f$$

$$I_1\omega_0 = I_f\omega_f = (I_1 + I_2)\omega_f$$

$$\omega_f = \omega_0\left(\frac{I_1}{I_1 + I_2}\right)$$

Notice that this problem is the fixed axis rotational analog to the one-dimensional totally inelastic collision of two masses with one mass initially at rest.

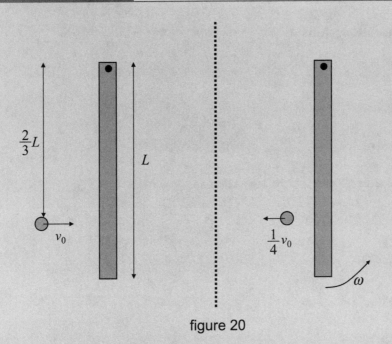

figure 20

A stick of length L, mass M, $I_{CM} = \frac{1}{12}ML^2$ is pivoted about one end as it rests on a frictionless horizontal table (figure 20). A second mass m_1 moving at a speed v_0 strikes the stick at a distance $\frac{2}{3}L$ from the pivot, rebounding with a speed $\frac{1}{4}v_0$. Find the angular velocity of the stick after the collision.

During the collision, the pivot exerts a force on the stick, so linear momentum is certainly not conserved. If you choose the pivot as the origin, however, this force exerts no torque, and you can apply conservation of angular momentum about that origin. You can use the parallel axis theorem to find I_{pivot}:

$$I_{pivot} = \frac{1}{12}ML^2 + M\left(\frac{L}{2}\right)^2 = \frac{1}{3}ML^2$$

$$L_0 = L_f$$

$$m_1 v_0\left(\frac{2}{3}L\right) = -m_1\left(\frac{v_0}{4}\right)\left(\frac{2}{3}L\right) + \frac{1}{3}ML^2\omega$$

$$\omega = \frac{5}{2}\frac{m_1}{M}\frac{v_0}{L}$$

KEY FORMULAS

Radian Measure Relations	$\Delta x = r\Delta\theta$
	$v = r\omega$
	$a_t = r\alpha$
Angular Velocity	$\omega = \dfrac{d\theta}{dt}$
Angular Acceleration	$\alpha = \dfrac{d\omega}{dt}$
Constant Angular Acceleration Equations	$\omega = \omega_0 + \alpha t$
	$\Delta\theta = \dfrac{1}{2}(\omega + \omega_0)t$
	$\Delta\theta = \omega_0 t + \dfrac{1}{2}\alpha t^2$
	$\omega^2 = \omega_0^2 + 2a\Delta\theta$
Moment of Inertia	$I = \sum m_i r_i^2$
Rotational Kinetic Energy	$K_{\text{rot}} = \dfrac{1}{2}I\omega^2$
Fixed Axis Instantaneous Power	$P = \tau\omega$
Parallel Axis Theorem	$I_A = I_{\text{CM}} + MH^2$
Fixed Axis Rotational Dynamics	$net\tau = I\alpha$
Torque	$\vec{\tau} = \vec{r} \times \vec{F}$
	$\tau = (F\sin\theta)R = F_{\text{eff}}R = FR_{\text{eff}}$
Rotational Equilibrium	$net\tau = 0$
Kinetic Energy of Rolling Object	$K_{\text{roll}} = \dfrac{1}{2}I_{\text{CM}}\omega^2 + \dfrac{1}{2}Mv^2$
Angular Momentum	$\vec{l} = \vec{r} \times \vec{p} \qquad L = I\omega$
Rotational Dynamics	$\dfrac{d\vec{L}}{dt} = net\vec{\tau}^{\,ext}$
Rolling Dynamics (about CM)	$net\tau^{\,ext} = I_{\text{CM}}\alpha$
Conservation of Angular Momentum	$\vec{L}_i = \vec{L}_f$

PRACTICE EXERCISES

SECTION I MULTIPLE CHOICE

Questions 1 and 2

A body with moment of inertia 20 kg • m² is rotating about a fixed axis with an angular velocity $\omega(t) = 3t^2 - 4$.

1. Through what angular displacement will the body move in the first 3 s?

   (A) 81 rad   (B) 69 rad   (C) 15 rad   (D) 23 rad   (E) 18 rad

2. What is the net torque exerted on the object at $t = 2$ s?

   (A) 240 N • m   (B) 12 N • m   (C) 8 N • m   (D) 160 N • m   (E) 0

figure 21

3. Masses m and $2m$ are connected by a rod of negligible mass. The rod can be pivoted about several positions along the rod. To obtain the greatest angular acceleration for a fixed torque applied, the system should be pivoted about an

   (A) axis through m (B) axis through $2m$ (C) axis through the center of the rod
   (D) axis through the rod $\frac{1}{3} L$ from m (E) axis through the rod $\frac{1}{3} L$ from $2m$

figure 22

4. A rod of negligible mass is pivoted about one end. Masses can be attached to the rod at various positions along the rod. Currently, there is a mass m attached a distance L from the pivot. To increase the moment of inertia about the pivot by a factor of 5, you must attach

   (A) $4m$ at $\frac{1}{4} L$ (B) m at $2L$ (C) m at $4L$ (D) $\frac{1}{4} m$ at L (E) $4m$ at $4L$

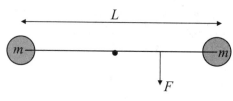

figure 23

5. Two equal masses m are connected by a light rod of length L that is pivoted about its center. A force F is applied to the rod as pictured, at a distance $\frac{L}{4}$ from the pivot. If you ignore gravity, the linear acceleration of the masses is

    (A) $\dfrac{F}{m}$ (B) $\dfrac{F}{2m}$ (C) $\dfrac{F}{4m}$ (D) $\dfrac{2F}{m}$ (E) $\dfrac{F}{8m}$

Questions 6 and 7

A hoop of mass 1 kg, radius 2 m is currently rotating about its center with an angular speed of 3 rad/s. A force of 10 N is applied tangentially at the rim.

6. The rotational kinetic energy of the hoop is

    (A) 4 J   (B) 6 J   (C) 12 J   (D) 18 J   (E) 20 J

7. The instantaneous rate at which the kinetic energy is changing is

    (A) 30 W   (B) 60 W   (C) 18 W   (D) 90 W   (E) 40 W

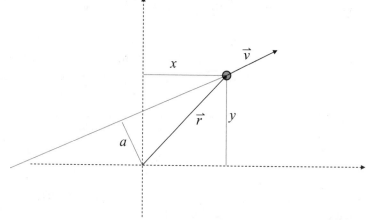

figure 24

8. A mass m is moving with velocity $\vec{v}$ as pictured. Relative to the origin, its angular momentum is

    (A) mvr (B) mvx (C) mvy (D) mva (E) $mv\sqrt{x^2 - y^2}$

9. A disc with moment of inertia I is rotating freely in a horizontal plane about its center with angular velocity ω. A bug of mass m lands at the center of the disc and then walks outward. When the bug has reached a distance R from the center, the angular velocity of the system will be

(A) ω (B) $\omega \dfrac{I}{I + mR^2}$ (C) $\omega \dfrac{I}{mR^2}$ (D) $\omega \dfrac{mR^2}{I}$ (E) $\omega \dfrac{I + mR^2}{I}$

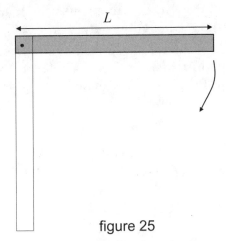

figure 25

10. A uniform stick of length L, mass M is pivoted about one end so that its moment of inertia about the pivot is $\frac{1}{3} ML^2$. The rod is raised to the horizontal and released. When the rod has rotated through $90°$, the angular speed of the stick will be

(A) $\sqrt{\dfrac{g}{3L}}$ (B) $\sqrt{\dfrac{g}{6L}}$ (C) $\sqrt{\dfrac{3g}{L}}$ (D) $\sqrt{\dfrac{6g}{L}}$ (E) $\sqrt{\dfrac{g}{L}}$

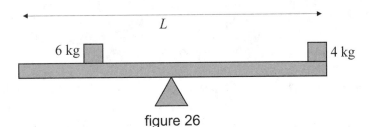

figure 26

11. A 10-kg uniform plank of length L is pivoted at its center. A 4-kg mass is to be placed on the right end. How far from the pivot must a 6-kg mass be placed to keep the plank in equilibrium?

(A) $\dfrac{L}{2}$ (B) $\dfrac{L}{4}$ (C) $\dfrac{3L}{4}$ (D) $\dfrac{L}{3}$ (E) $\dfrac{2L}{3}$

CHAPTER 6

PRACTICE EXERCISES

SECTION II FREE RESPONSE

1. The gate to a bullpen is open at a right angle to the fence, and the bull is rushing toward the opening to get out. The farmer/physicist estimates that the bull will reach the opening in 3 s, so he pushes at the end of the gate (always at a right angle) with a force of 100 N in an attempt to close it. The moment of inertia of the gate about the hinge axis is 1,000 kg m², and the gate length is 3 m.

   (a) What is the magnitude of the torque applied by the farmer?
   (b) What is the rotational kinetic energy of the gate after 3 s?
   (c) Through what angle will the gate have rotated after 3 s?
   (d) Will the gate be closed? Explain.

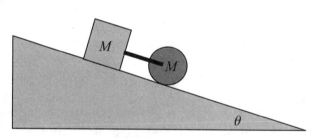

figure 27

2. A disc of mass M, radius R, $I_{CM} = \frac{1}{2}MR^2$ is rolling down an incline dragging a mass M attached with a light rod to a bearing at the center of the disc. The friction coefficients are the same for both masses, μ_s and μ_k.

   (a) Draw freebody diagrams for each mass.
   (b) Determine the linear acceleration of the mass M.
   (c) Determine the friction force acting on the disc.
   (d) Determine the tension in the rod.

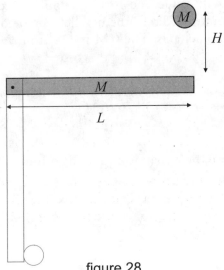

figure 28

3. A mass M is dropped from a height H onto one end of a stick of mass M, length L, pivoted about the opposite end. Assume the moment of inertia of the stick about the pivot is $\frac{1}{3}ML^2$. Upon collision, the mass adheres to the stick. Respond to the following in terms of M, L, H, and g.

(a) Find the speed of the mass just before impact.
(b) Find the angular speed of the system immediately after impact.
(c) Find the linear speed of the mass M at its lowest point.
(d) Determine the mechanical energy lost as a result of the collision.

Answers and Explanations

MULTIPLE CHOICE

1. The answer is C. Since $\omega = \frac{d\theta}{dt}$, you can integrate to find $\Delta\theta$:

$$\Delta\theta = \int_0^3 \omega\, dt = \int_0^3 (3t^2 - 4)\, dt$$

$$\Delta\theta = [t^3 - 4t]_0^3 = 15 \text{ rad}$$

2. The answer is A. Differentiate to get $\alpha = \frac{d\omega}{dt} = 6t$. Use the dynamic equation $net\tau = I\alpha$, evaluating at $t = 2$:

$$net\tau = (20)(12) = 240 \text{ N} \cdot \text{m}$$

3. The answer is E. For a fixed torque, the greatest angular acceleration will occur when the moment of inertia is minimized. From the parallel axis theorem, you can see that I_{CM} is smaller than any other parallel axis. The CM is $\frac{1}{3}L$ from $2m$.

4. The answer is B. The old moment of inertia is mL^2. Adding m at $2L$ adds $m(2L)^2 = 4mL^2$ to this. Then $I_{new} = I_{old} + 4mL^2 = 5mL^2 = 5I_{old}$.

5. The answer is C. First, use the dynamic equation to find α.

$$net\,\tau = I\alpha$$

$$F\left(\frac{L}{4}\right) = \left(2m\left(\frac{L}{2}\right)^2\right)\alpha \Rightarrow \alpha = \frac{F}{2mL}$$

Since $a_t = R\alpha$, you get $a_t = \frac{L}{2}\alpha = \frac{F}{4m}$.

6. The answer is D. A hoop has all mass the same distance from the center, so $I = mR^2$. Then $K_{rot} = \frac{1}{2}I\omega^2 = \frac{1}{2}(1 \cdot 2^2)3^2 = 18$ J

7. The answer is B. The instantaneous power delivered by the torque is

$$P = \tau\omega = [(10)(2)](3) = 60\,\text{W}$$

8. The answer is D. The magnitude of the angular momentum is given by

$$l = pr_\perp = mva$$

9. The answer is B. Conservation of angular momentum yields

$$L_i = L_f$$
$$I_w = I_f\omega_f = (I + mR^2)\omega_f$$
$$\Rightarrow \omega_f = \frac{I}{I + mR^2}$$

10. The answer is C. Use energy conservation. The CM falls only a height of $\frac{L}{2}$, and the final energy is all rotational KE.

$$E_i = E_f$$
$$Mg\frac{L}{2} = \frac{1}{2}\left(\frac{1}{3}ML^2\right)\omega^2$$
$$\Rightarrow \omega = \sqrt{\frac{3g}{L}}$$

11. The answer is D. Choose the center of the plank to calculate torques, because here the weight of the plank exerts no torque. Then $0 = net\,\tau = 40\frac{L}{2} - 60x \Rightarrow x = \frac{L}{3}$.

FREE RESPONSE

1. (a) Since the constant magnitude force is applied perpendicular to the gate at all times, the torque is a constant

$$\tau = RF \sin 90° = 3(100) = 300 \text{ N} \cdot \text{m}$$

(b) Find α from the dynamic equation, then use kinematics to determine the angular velocity after 3 s. Then, use the rotational KE formula:

$$net\tau = I\alpha$$

$$(100)(3) = 1{,}000\alpha \qquad\qquad \alpha = 0.3 \; \frac{\text{rad}}{\text{s}^2}$$

$$\omega(3) = \omega_0 + \alpha t = 0 + 0.3(3) = 0.9 \; \frac{\text{rad}}{\text{s}^2}$$

$$KE_{rot} = \tfrac{1}{2}I\omega^2 = \tfrac{1}{2}(1{,}000)(0.9)^2 = 405 \text{ J}$$

(c) Since you know the constant angular acceleration, you can use a kinematic equation to get $\Delta\theta$.

$$\Delta\theta = \tfrac{1}{2}\alpha t^2 \; (\omega_0 = 0)$$

$$\Delta\theta = \tfrac{1}{2}(0.3)(3)^2 = 1.35 \text{ rad}$$

(d) Since 1.35 rad is less than $90° = \frac{\pi}{2}$rad, the bull escapes.

2. (a) (figure 29)

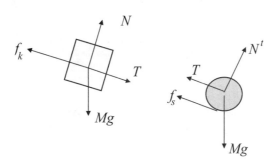

Figure 29

(b), (c), (d) From the freebody diagrams, you can apply the second law:

Sliding Mass
$$Mg \sin\theta + T - f_k = Ma$$
$$N - Mg \cos\theta = 0$$

Disc
$$Mg \sin\theta - T - f_s = Ma$$

The friction force on the sliding mass will be

$$f_k = \mu_k N = \mu_k Mg \cos\theta$$

Using the CM as the origin, you can apply the rolling dynamic equation. Only static friction exerts a torque about the CM.

$$net\tau = I_{CM}\alpha$$

$$Rf_s = \left(\frac{1}{2}MR^2\right)\frac{a}{R} \qquad \alpha = \frac{a}{R}$$

$$f_s = \frac{1}{2}Ma$$

You can now substitute for f_k and f_s in the first set of equations to solve for a and T.

$$Mg\sin\theta + T - \mu_k Mg\cos\theta = Ma \qquad Mg\sin\theta - T - \frac{1}{2}Ma = Ma$$

(Add these to eliminate T.)

$$T = Mg\sin\theta - \frac{3}{2}Ma$$

$$a = (4\sin\theta - 2\mu_k\cos\theta)\frac{g}{5}$$

$$T = \frac{Mg}{5}(3\mu_k\cos\theta - \sin\theta)$$

Then plug in for f_s:

$$f_s = \frac{1}{2}Ma = (2\sin\theta - \mu_k\cos\theta)\frac{Mg}{5}$$

3. (a) Use energy conservation.

$$E_i = E_f$$
$$MgH = \frac{1}{2}Mv^2 \qquad \Rightarrow \sqrt{2gH}$$

(b) Angular momentum during the collision will be conserved about the pivot because the pivot force exerts net torque about this origin.

$$L_i = L_f$$
$$MvL = I_f\omega_f = \left(\frac{1}{3}ML^2 + ML^2\right)\omega_f \qquad \Rightarrow \omega_f = \left(\frac{3v}{4L}\right) = \frac{3\sqrt{2gH}}{4L}$$

(c) Use energy conservation followed by the radian measure relation between linear and angular velocity. Notice that the CM of the stick falls $\frac{L}{2}$, while M at the end falls L.

$$E_i = E_f$$
$$\frac{1}{2}I_f\omega_f^2 + Mg\frac{L}{2} + MgL = \frac{1}{2}I_f\omega_f'^2$$
$$\frac{1}{2}I_f\omega_f^2 + \frac{3}{2}MgL = \frac{1}{2}I_f\left(\frac{v'}{L}\right)^2 \qquad I_f = \frac{4}{3}ML^2$$
$$v' = \frac{3}{2}\sqrt{\frac{1}{2}gH + gL}$$

(d) The change in energy due to the collision will be the difference between the energy just after the collision and the energy before the collision.

$$\Delta E = \frac{1}{2}I_f\omega_f^2 - MgH$$
$$\Delta E = \frac{1}{2}\left(\frac{4}{3}ML^2\right)\left(\frac{3\sqrt{2gH}}{4L}\right)^2 - MgH$$
$$\Delta E = -\frac{1}{4}MgH$$

7

Gravitation

This chapter focuses on the gravitational attraction between masses. After an introduction to the general force law, we'll look at applications to orbital motion of planets and satellites. Finally we'll cover the details of gravitational potential energy.

Newton's Law of Gravity

Isaac Newton hypothesized that any two masses exert an attractive force on each other. For point masses, this force is directed along the line connecting the masses. Its magnitude is directly proportional to the product of the two masses, and inversely proportional to the square of their separation. The equation for **Newton's law of gravity** (figure 1) summarizes this:

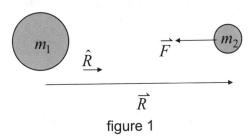

figure 1

$$\vec{F}_{1 \text{ on } 2} = -G \frac{m_1 m_2}{R^2} \hat{R} \qquad\qquad G = 6.67 \times 10^{-11} \frac{\text{N}}{\text{kg}^2 \cdot \text{m}^2}$$

Here $\vec{F}_{1 \text{ on } 2}$ is the force exerted on m_2 by m_1, and $\hat{R}$ is a unit vector directed along the line connecting the masses from m_1 to m_2. Since $\hat{R}$ and $\vec{F}_{1 \text{ on } 2}$ point in opposite directions, there is a minus sign in the equation. Of course, Newton's third law states that

$$\vec{F}_{1 \text{ on } 2} = -\vec{F}_{2 \text{ on } 1}$$

This equation is also true for spherical masses, where R is now the separation of the centers and $\hat{R}$ points along this line. To determine the effects of gravity, you can always imagine a spherical mass as a point mass with all its mass concentrated at its center.

Because of the R^2 in the denominator in the force law, Newton's law of gravity is said to be an **inverse square law**. As masses are separated, the force between them weakens. Should they increase their separation to twice the original value, the force becomes one-fourth its original value. Similarly, should the masses get closer so that they are separated by just one-third the original separation, the force increases to nine times the original value (figure 2).

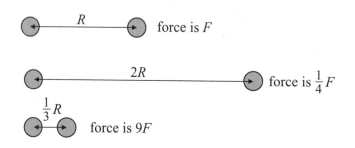

figure 2

The quantity G is called the **universal gravitational constant**. The fact that it is so small indicates that gravitational force is inherently weak. In fact, of all the basic forces of physics, the force of gravity is by far the weakest. That the weakest force in nature is responsible for planetary and galactic motions may seem like a contradiction, but gravity acts over large distances, and it's always attractive. Gravity can be the dominant force on the large scale because electric force gets contributions from equal numbers of positive and negative charges that cancel out.

EXERCISE

Find the attractive force between two 1 kg masses separated by 1 m.

Using the inverse square law, you get $F = G\frac{(1)(1)}{1^2} = 6.67 \times 10^{-11}$ N. Obviously, this weak force will have no noticeable effect on two masses sitting on a table.

EXERCISE

Find the force exerted on Earth by the Sun.

$M_e = 5.98 \times 10^{24}$ kg

$$F = G\frac{M_e M_s}{R^2} = 6.67 \times 10^{-11}\frac{(5.98 \times 10^{24})(1.99 \times 10^{30})}{(1.5 \times 10^{11})^2}$$

$M_s = 1.99 \times 10^{30}$ kg

$R = 1.5 \times 10^{11}$ m $\qquad\qquad F = 3.5 \times 10^{22}$ N

Because of the very large masses involved, you shouldn't be surprised that this large force has a very noticeable effect.

g vs. G

You've already seen one constant associated with gravity, the acceleration due to gravity near Earth's surface: $g = 9.8$ m/s^2. But if you think about it, this isn't a constant at all. If you traveled to another planet or even moved a fair distance from Earth's surface, the local acceleration due to gravity would be different. On the other hand, the G in Newton's law of gravity is a true constant. Its value is the same whether you measure the force between two bugs or two galaxies.

Remember, however, that G is not an acceleration. It is a very small number that sets the scale of the force when you express quantities in SI units. Since weight on Earth is just the force of gravity between an object and the entire Earth, you can combine the second law formula for weight, $W = mg$, with the law of gravity, recognizing that *close to Earth's surface* means a separation between Earth and the object of one Earth radius, R_e (figure 3).

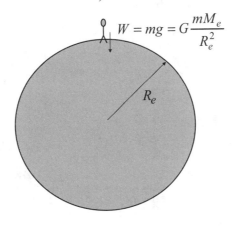

$$W = mg = G\frac{mM_e}{R_e^2}$$

$$mg = G\frac{mM_e}{R_e^2} \Rightarrow g = G\frac{M_e}{R_e^2}$$

figure 3

You can generalize this to any spherical planet with mass M_p and radius R_p:

$$g_p = G\frac{M_p}{R_p^2}$$

The local acceleration due to gravity, then, is determined by multiplying the universal G by a factor that depends on the mass and radius of the planet.

EXERCISE

If you weigh 800 N on Earth, what will you weigh on a planet with half the mass of Earth and a radius that is twice the radius of Earth?

Since the weight on the planet is $W_p = mg_p$, you can determine the overall factor of change using the relation for g_p. Halving the mass reduces g_p by $\frac{1}{2}$, while doubling the radius reduces g_p by a factor of $\frac{1}{4}$. The overall change is a factor of $\frac{1}{8}$, so your weight on the planet is 100 N.

Satellites

CIRCULAR ORBITS

Gravitational force can supply the centripetal force needed to cause an object to move in a circular orbit. Examples abound, from manmade communication satellites, to the Moon as it moves around Earth, to Earth itself as it moves around the Sun (figure 4). Let's apply the second law to a mass m circling another mass M.

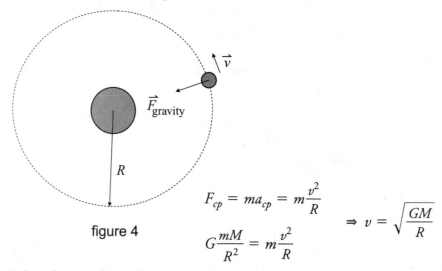

figure 4

$$F_{cp} = ma_{cp} = m\frac{v^2}{R}$$

$$G\frac{mM}{R^2} = m\frac{v^2}{R}$$

$$\Rightarrow v = \sqrt{\frac{GM}{R}}$$

Notice that the speed is independent of the orbiting mass and that the speed decreases by the square root of R as the radius gets bigger; at $4R$, the orbital speed is half the orbital speed at R.

EXERCISE

Communications satellites are often put into **geosynchronous** orbits. Such an orbit takes exactly one day to complete, so a satellite circling over the equator will always be above the same point on Earth. Determine the radius of a geosynchronous orbit.

The time it takes a satellite to travel one full circumference of its orbit is called the period T of the orbit. For a geosynchronous satellite, the period is one day, or 86,400 s. That means:

$$2\pi R = vT \Rightarrow v = \frac{2\pi R}{T}$$

Substitute into the relation for the orbital speed:

$$v = \sqrt{\frac{GM}{R}}$$

$$\frac{2\pi R}{T} = \sqrt{\frac{GM}{R}}$$

$$\Rightarrow R = \left(\frac{GMT^2}{4\pi^2}\right)^{\frac{1}{3}}$$

Substituting G, T, and $M = 6 \times 10^{24}$ kg, you get $R = 4.23 \times 10^7$ m, corresponding to a distance of a little more than 26,000 miles. Since Earth's radius is about 4,000 miles, this is more than 22,000 miles above Earth.

Elliptical Orbits

Orbits of satellites and planets can be elliptical. In fact, a circle is a "degenerate" ellipse. The ellipse of an orbit due to the gravitational attraction of a satellite to a large mass will always have the large mass at one of the foci of the ellipse (figure 5).

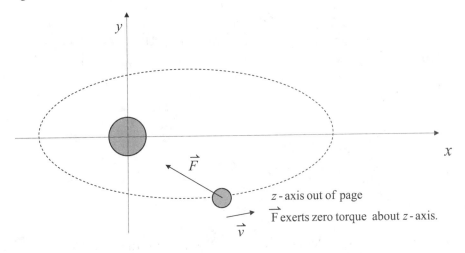

z-axis out of page

$\vec{F}$ exerts zero torque about z-axis.

figure 5

Whether the orbit is truly circular or elliptical, the force on the orbiting mass will always act directly toward the large mass. Let's describe the motion with the large mass at the origin and the *x-y* plane determined by the plane of the orbit. Because the gravitational force is acting directly at the origin, it will exert no torque about this point. This means the angular momentum of the satellite is conserved. This is a trivial statement for circular orbits since the speed is constant then, but for elliptical orbits it means that the object will change speed as its orbit distance varies.

EXAMPLE

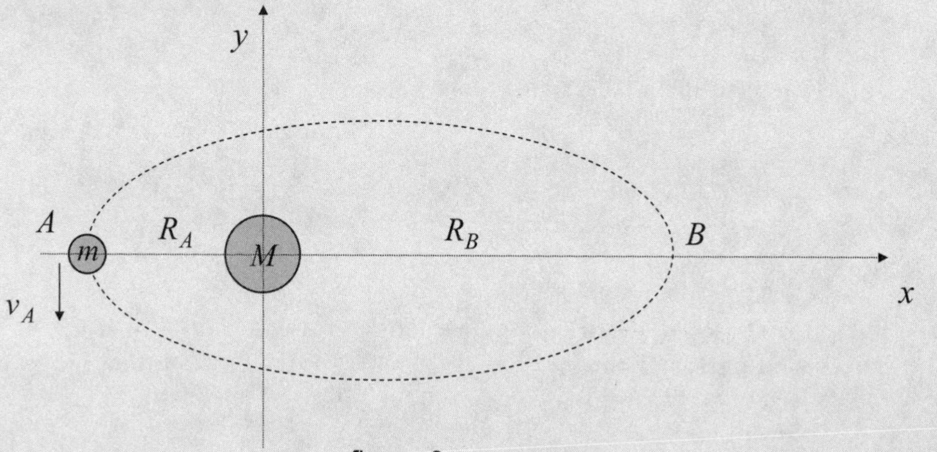

figure 6

Consider the elliptical orbit shown here (figure 6). At the points *A* and *B* where the object is closest and furthest from *M*, its velocity vector is perpendicular to the line connecting each point to the center of *M*, labeled R_A and R_B. If the speed of the object at *A* is v_A, what will be the speed at *B*?

Because the gravitational force exerts 0 torque about the axis of rotation, angular momentum is conserved. At any point in the motion $l = mvr_\perp$, and at *A* and *B*, $r_\perp$ is just the distance to *M*, so you get:

$$l_A = l_B$$

$$mv_AR_A = mv_BR_B$$

$$\Rightarrow v_B = \frac{R_A}{R_B}v_A$$

The object slows down as it moves from *A* to *B*.

Apparent Weight

Weight is the common name for the force of attraction between an object and Earth. In your everyday life, however, you probably identify your weight with the reading on a bathroom scale. When you stand motionless on the scale, the weight force acting down and the normal force exerted by the scale acting up are equal (figure 7). The reaction force to the normal force acts down on the scale, and the scale registers this force. If you jump around on the scale the reading will change, not because your weight has changed, but because the normal force has changed.

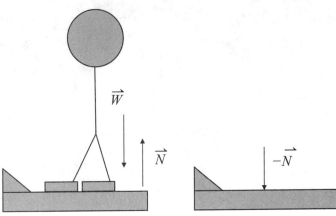

figure 7

Let's identify the **apparent weight** in several different situations. If you get on an elevator, for example, and it initially accelerates upward, the normal force of the floor must supply a force greater than your weight to accelerate you upward. A bathroom scale on the elevator would show a value larger than your weight, and your apparent weight would increase. The opposite would occur if you initially accelerated downward. If you were to jump out a window and go into free fall, a bathroom scale attached to your feet would read 0, since it too would be in free fall. In this case, your apparent weight is 0. But since $g = 9.8 \frac{m}{s^2}$ your true weight hasn't changed.

Now let's consider an astronaut aboard the space shuttle at a height of 300 miles above the Earth. This makes the orbit radius, measured to the Earth's center, about 6.9×10^6 m. The local value of g there is

$$g_{orbit} = G \frac{M_p}{R_{orbit}^2} = (6.67 \times 10^{-11}) \frac{6 \times 10^{24}}{(6.9 \times 10^6)^2} = 8.4 \frac{m}{s^2}$$

This is still 86 percent of the value at Earth's surface, so the astronauts are clearly not weightless. But they are in free fall, just like the situation described earlier. An astronaut who was simply raised to a height of 300 miles and released would fall straight down, just like the student jumping out a window. If the astronaut were given the right initial velocity perpendicular to the vertical, however, he would still fall but would keep missing Earth as he fell. A bathroom scale traveling with him would read 0 since it too was in free fall, moving under only the influence of gravity. Astronauts in orbit are definitely not weightless; the "weight force," the force of gravity, actually keeps them in orbit. If an astronaut were to travel far from the Earth and other gravitational influences, then he or she would indeed approach weightlessness.

Gravitational Potential Energy

You'll recall that the change in potential energy due to a conservative force $\vec{F}$ is

$$\Delta U = -W_F$$

Consider a mass M located at the origin. You could ask how much work is done by gravity on another mass m as it moves from infinity to a point where the masses are separated by R. If you call infinity the zero point of gravitational potential energy, then the negative of this work will be the potential energy at R. Symbolically, you can write (figure 8):

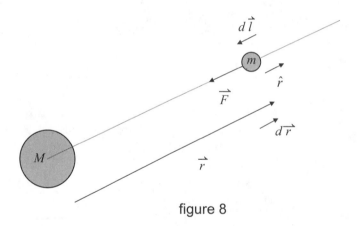

figure 8

$$\Delta U = U(R) - U(\infty) = U(R)$$

$$U(R) = -\int_{\infty}^{R} \vec{F} \cdot d\vec{l} = -\int_{\infty}^{R}\left(-G\frac{mM}{r^2}\hat{r}\right) \cdot d\vec{l} = -\int_{\infty}^{R} G\frac{mM}{r^2}\,dl \qquad \text{since } \hat{r} \cdot d\vec{l} = -dl$$

$$U(R) = +\int_{\infty}^{R} G\frac{mM}{r^2}\,dr \qquad \text{since } dl = -dr$$

$$U(R) = -G\frac{mM}{R}$$

Relative to infinity, the potential energy is negative. This means that you would have to do positive work to move the object slowly back to infinity, where the PE has arbitrarily been defined as 0.

Because the gravitational force is conservative, you can apply the energy conservation principle if only gravity is acting. The form for the total energy will be:

$$E = K + U$$

$$E = \frac{1}{2}mv^2 - G\frac{mM}{R}$$

In this formula, kinetic energy can never be negative, but both gravitational potential energy and the total energy can be negative. There's no deep significance to this; it's just a result of choosing infinity to be the zero point for gravitational PE.

EXAMPLE

What minimum initial speed must be given to a mass m at the surface of Earth so that it can completely escape the gravitational pull of Earth?

You're looking for the initial speed that will take the object from a separation of one Earth radius to infinity. This is called the **escape velocity**. To find it, you can use energy conservation. The minimum speed will get the object to infinity with 0 KE. By definition, it will also have 0 PE.

$$E_i = E_f$$

$$\frac{1}{2}mv^2_{escape} - G\frac{mM_e}{R_e} = K_\infty + U_\infty = 0$$

$$v_{escape} = \sqrt{\frac{2GM}{R_e}} = 1.12 \times 10^4 \frac{m}{s}$$

Finally, let's apply these ideas to determine the energy of a satellite m in a circular orbit of radius R about a large mass M. Recall that the orbit speed is $v = \sqrt{\frac{GM}{R}}$.

$$E = K + U = \frac{1}{2}mv^2 - G\frac{mM}{R} \qquad \Rightarrow E = -G\frac{mM}{2R}$$

$$E = \frac{1}{2}m\left(\sqrt{\frac{GM}{R}}\right)^2 - G\frac{mM}{R}$$

For circular orbits, the total energy is negative because the satellite cannot escape to infinity, and the value of the total energy is one-half the PE.

KEY FORMULAS

Newton's Law of Gravity

$$\vec{F}_{1 \text{ on } 2} = -G\,\frac{m_1 m_2}{r^2}\,\hat{r}$$

Local g

$$g_p = G\frac{M_p}{R_p^2}$$

Circular Orbit Speed

$$v = \sqrt{\frac{GM}{R}}$$

Gravitational PE

$$U(R) = -G\frac{mM}{R}$$

Escape Velocity

$$v_{\text{escape}} = \sqrt{\frac{2GM}{R}}$$

CHAPTER 7 PRACTICE EXERCISES

SECTION I MULTIPLE CHOICE

1. Two masses separated by a distance R exert a gravitational force F on each other. To triple the force, the separation must be changed to

   (A) $3R$ (B) $\frac{R}{3}$ (C) $\frac{R}{9}$ (D) $\sqrt{3}R$ (E) $\frac{R}{\sqrt{3}}$

2. A student with mass 60 kg imagines she travels to a planet with twice the mass of Earth and four times the radius of Earth. Her weight on this planet would be closest to

   (A) 7.5 N (B) 30 N (C) 75 N (D) 300 N (E) 4,800 N

3. A satellite is currently moving in a circular orbit of radius R with orbital speed v. With the aid of onboard rockets, it moves out of this orbit and eventually establishes a new circular orbit of radius $\frac{1}{2}R$. The orbital speed will be

   (A) $\sqrt{2}\,v$ (B) $2v$ (C) $\frac{v}{2}$ (D) $\frac{v}{\sqrt{2}}$ (E) $4v$

4. In an elliptical orbit about the Sun, which of the following planetary properties is conserved?
   I. mechanical energy
   II. linear momentum
   III. angular momentum

   (A) I and II only   (B) I and III only   (C) II and III only
   (D) I only   (E) I, II, and III

5. Astronauts float around inside the space shuttle as it orbits because

   (A) the effects of gravity are almost negligible
   (B) the net force on them is 0 because centrifugal force cancels out gravity
   (C) they are accelerating toward Earth's center at the same rate as the shuttle and everything within it
   (D) the buoyant force of air is comparable to the force of gravity
   (E) the gravitational attraction of the astronauts to each other and the shuttle is comparable to their attraction to Earth

6. When two masses separated by a distance R are brought closer, ending with a separation of $\frac{1}{2}R$, the gravitational potential energy of the system

(A) increases by 2   (B) increases by 4   (C) decreases by 2
(D) decreases by 4   (E) increases by $\sqrt{2}$

7. A satellite is placed in a circular Earth orbit with radius R. A second satellite is placed in a circular orbit of radius $2R$. Compared with the first satellite, the second will have

(A) less energy and less angular momentum
(B) more energy and less angular momentum
(C) less energy and more angular momentum
(D) more energy and more angular momentum
(E) the same energy and the same angular momentum

PRACTICE EXERCISES

SECTION II FREE RESPONSE

1. A 100-kg satellite is placed in a low Earth circular orbit with radius 1.2×10^7 m. An identical satellite is to be placed in circular orbit with twice the orbital period.
   (a) Find the speed of the first satellite.
   (b) Find the radius of the second satellite.
   (c) Onboard rockets on the first satellite are fired, and eventually the first satellite is moved into the same circular orbit as the second. How much work was done by the rocket engines?

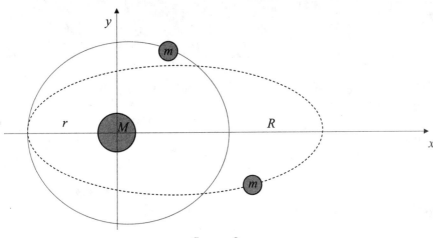

figure 9

2. A satellite of mass m moves in an elliptical orbit around Earth with r and R the closest and farthest distances from the center of Earth. An identical satellite moves in a circular orbit of radius r. The elliptical satellite has energy $E = -G\frac{mM}{6r}$. Respond to the following in terms of M, the mass of Earth, m, r, and G.
   (a) Determine the energy of the circular satellite.
   (b) Determine the speed of the elliptical satellite at the closest approach distance.
   (c) Derive an equation that would allow you to solve for R in terms of the given quantities (don't attempt to solve).

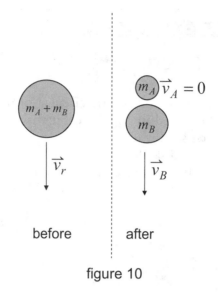

before   after

figure 10

(d) As the elliptical satellite passes the closest approach point on one orbit, an internal explosion occurs, splitting the satellite into two pieces. One piece m_A is instantaneously at rest just after the collision, while the other m_B continues in the same direction just after the collision (figure 10). Find ratio $\frac{m_A}{m_B}$ that will ensure that m_B eventually escapes the effects of Earth's gravity.

Answers and Explanations

MULTIPLE CHOICE

1. The answer is E. Since the force got larger, the separation got smaller. For the original separation, you can write $F \propto \frac{1}{R^2}$. Then for E, you have

$$F' \propto \frac{1}{\left(\frac{R}{\sqrt{3}}\right)^2} = \frac{3}{R^2} = 3F$$

2. The answer is C. Doubling the mass of the planet for a fixed radius doubles the weight. Quadrupling the radius for a fixed mass decreases the weight by $\frac{1}{16}$. Then the overall factor will be $2 \cdot \frac{1}{16} = \frac{1}{8}$. Since the weight on Earth is 600 N, C is correct.

3. The answer is A. For a circular orbit, $v = \sqrt{\frac{GM}{R}}$. As R becomes $\frac{1}{2}R$, v becomes bigger by $\sqrt{2}$.

4. The answer is B. Because gravity is an external force acting on the planet, its linear momentum isn't conserved. Gravity is a conservative force exerting 0 torque about the rotation axis, however, so energy and angular momentum are conserved.

5. The answer is C. From the point of view of the astronauts, the objects are just floating because the objects, the astronauts, and the shuttle itself are all accelerating at the same rate, the local g value, toward the Earth's center.

6. The answer is C. The PE formula is $U = -G\frac{mM}{R}$. As R decreases to $\frac{1}{2}R$, U becomes more negative; for example, smaller by a factor of 2.

7. The answer is D. For circular orbits, $E = -G\frac{mM}{2R}$, so increasing R makes E less negative, or larger. The angular momentum of the first satellite is $l = mvR = m\left(\sqrt{\frac{GM}{R}}\right)R$. For the second satellite, v decreases by $\frac{1}{\sqrt{2}}$ while R increases by 2, so overall the angular momentum increases by $\sqrt{2}$.

FREE RESPONSE

1. (a) Gravity supplies the centripetal force.

$$G\frac{mM}{R^2} = m\frac{v^2}{R}$$

$$\Rightarrow v = \sqrt{\frac{GM}{R}} = \sqrt{\frac{(6.67 \times 10^{-11})(5.98 \times 10^{24})}{1.2 \times 10^7}} = 5{,}765\ \frac{m}{s}$$

(b) The period of the first satellite satisfies

$$2\pi R = vT \Rightarrow T = \frac{2\pi R}{v} = \frac{2\pi(1.2 \times 10^7)}{5{,}765} = 1.31 \times 10^4\ s$$

You can relate the radius of circular orbits to their periods like this:

$$2\pi R = vT = \sqrt{\frac{GM}{R}}\,T \Rightarrow R = \left(\frac{GMT^2}{4\pi^2}\right)^{\frac{1}{3}}$$

$$R = \left(\frac{(6.67 \times 10^{-11})(5.98 \times 10^{24})(2.62 \times 10^4)^2}{4\pi^2}\right)^{\frac{1}{3}} = 1.91 \times 10^7\ m$$

(c) The work done will equal the change in the energy of the satellite. Since both orbits are circular, you can use the relation

$$E = \frac{1}{2}mv^2 - G\frac{mM}{R}$$

$$\Rightarrow E = -G\frac{mM}{2R}$$

$$E = \frac{1}{2}m\left(\sqrt{\frac{GM}{R}}\right)^2 - G\frac{mM}{R}$$

$$W = \Delta E = -G\frac{mM}{2}\left(\frac{1}{R_f} - \frac{1}{R_i}\right) = -(6.67 \times 10^{-11})\frac{(100)(5.98 \times 10^{24})}{2}\left(\frac{1}{1.91 \times 10^7} - \frac{1}{1.2 \times 10^7}\right)$$

$$W = 6.18 \times 10^8 \text{ J}$$

2. (a) Since the orbit is circular, you have (see part c above) $E = -G\frac{mM}{2r}$.

   (b) Equate the KE and PE at the closest approach point to the given energy.

$$\frac{1}{2}mv_r^2 - G\frac{mM}{r} = -\frac{GmM}{6r}$$

$$v_r = \sqrt{\frac{5GM}{3r}}$$

   (c) First use angular momentum conservation for the elliptical satellite. At the closest approach and farthest approach distances, the velocity is perpendicular to the position vector, so $l = mvr$.

$$l_r = l_R$$

$$\Rightarrow v_R = v_r\frac{r}{R} = \sqrt{\frac{5GMr}{3R^2}}$$

$$mv_r r = mv_R R$$

   Now equate the sum of the KE and PE at the farthest approach point to the total energy of the elliptical satellite.

$$\frac{1}{2}mv_R^2 - G\frac{mM}{R} = -G\frac{mM}{6r}$$

$$\frac{1}{2}m\left(\frac{5GMr}{3R^2}\right) - G\frac{mM}{R} = -G\frac{mM}{6r}$$

$$\frac{5r}{6R^2} - \frac{1}{R} = -\frac{1}{6r} \quad \text{solve for } R$$

   (d) Just after the explosion, the piece m_B located at r must have total energy 0 to escape.

$$\frac{1}{2}m_B v_B^2 - G\frac{m_B M}{r} = 0 \quad \Rightarrow \quad v_B = \sqrt{\frac{2GM}{r}}$$

   Then, use linear momentum conservation during the collision.

$$P_i = P_f$$

$$(m_A + m_B)v_r = 0 + m_B v_B \quad \Rightarrow \quad \frac{m_A}{m_B} = \frac{v_B}{v_r} - 1 = \frac{\sqrt{\frac{2GM}{r}}}{\sqrt{\frac{5GM}{3r}}} - 1 = 0.095$$

CHAPTER 8

Oscillations

This chapter focuses on the motion of objects that is repetitive. The special category of simple harmonic motion will be investigated in detail and the solution to the harmonic oscillator equation will be presented. The prototype for this analysis is the spring-mass system, which you've already seen as a model to illustrate energy concepts, but there are other systems you should be familiar witih, too.

Description

Consider a mass undergoing oscillations or vibrations, such as a spring-mass system oscillating on a frictionless, horizontal surface. The object moves under the influence of a **restoring force.** This force is 0 at the **equilibrium position**, and it tends to bring the mass back to the equilibrium position when the object is displaced from that point. To describe an oscillating system, you'll usually assume the origin is at the equilibrium position. This ensures that the position of the object is the same as the displacement from the origin. In fact, often "displacement" simply refers to the displacement from the origin.

For a spring-mass system, the spring force $F = -kx$ supplies the restoring force. The **amplitude** is the maximum value of the displacement. While displacement may be positive or negative, the amplitude is a positive quantity. The **period** is the time it takes for one complete oscillation, and the **frequency** is the number of oscillations in one second. If the frequency is 10 oscillations/s, then it takes $\frac{1}{10}$ s to complete just one vibration. Generally, you can say

$$T = \frac{1}{f}$$

where T is the period and f is the frequency. The unit for frequency is Hertz (Hz), which represents 1 oscillation/s.

Harmonic Oscillator Equation

Any repetitive motion can be described as harmonic motion. But if the restoring force satisfies a particularly simple relation, then the motion is **simple harmonic motion** (SHM).

For simple harmonic motion, the restoring force must be directly proportional to the displacement.

$$F_{\text{restore}} = -K(\text{displacement})$$

If the displacement doubles, for example, the magnitude of the force also doubles. The minus sign ensures that as the magnitude of the displacement increases, the speed decreases and vice versa.

Let's apply the second law to a spring-mass system, an obvious example of SHM. When the mass is displaced x from the equilibrium position, you have

$$ma = -kx$$
$$m\frac{d^2x}{dt^2} = -kx \qquad \Rightarrow \qquad \frac{d^2x}{dt^2} + \frac{k}{m}x = 0$$

This is a second-order differential equation for the function $x = x(t)$. It basically says that if you take two derivatives of the function and add them to the function itself, multiplied by $\frac{k}{m}$, you will always get 0, for any time. What functions have their second derivatives proportional to the functions themselves? The answer is sine and cosine. So it turns out that the most general solution of the preceding equation is

$$x(t) = A\cos(\omega t + \phi) \qquad \text{where } \omega = \sqrt{\frac{k}{m}}$$

If you plug this formula for into the differential equation, you get an identity:

$$\frac{d^2}{dt^2}(A\cos(\omega t + \phi)) + \frac{k}{m}A\cos(\omega t + \phi) = -\omega^2 A\cos(\omega t + \phi) + \frac{k}{m}A\cos(\omega t + \phi)$$
$$= -\frac{k}{m}A\cos(\omega t + \phi) + \frac{k}{m}A\cos(\omega t + \phi) = 0$$

The numerical values of A and ϕ are determined by the initial conditions of the system—the initial position and velocity of the mass. Since $\cos\theta$ always lies between ± 1, A is the maximum value of the displacement—the amplitude. The quantity "$\omega t + \phi$" is called the **phase** of the motion. Because sine and cosine differ in phase by $\frac{\pi}{2}$ rad, you could just as well have written the general solution in terms of the sine function rather than the cosine function. All it would involve is a redefinition of the constant ϕ.

$$\cos(\omega t + \phi) = \sin\left(\omega t + \phi + \frac{\pi}{2}\right) = \sin(\omega t + \phi') \qquad \phi' = \phi + \frac{\pi}{2}$$

From the discussion of the spring-mass system, you can see that

$$T_{\text{spring}} = 2\pi\sqrt{\frac{m}{k}} = \frac{2\pi}{\omega}$$

You can also see this independently of the previous discussion if you recognize that the cosine repeats every time its argument increases by 2π rad. Then it follows that

$$\omega(t + T) + \phi = \omega t + \phi + 2\pi$$

$$T = \frac{2\pi}{\omega}$$

The quantity ω is sometimes called the **angular frequency**. It differs from the frequency by a 2π factor: $\omega = 2\pi f$.

EXERCISE

A spring-mass system with $k = 20$ N/m and a mass of 0.5 kg is displaced 0.2 m from its equilibrium position on a smooth horizontal table and released from rest. Find its position at any later time.

You can use the general form of the solution to determine the values of A and ϕ.

$$x(t) = A \cos(\omega t + \phi) \qquad v(t) = \frac{dx}{dt} = -\omega A \sin(\omega t + \phi)$$

$$x(0) = 0.2 = A \cos\phi \qquad v(0) = 0 = -\omega A \sin\phi$$

The velocity condition tells you that $\phi = 0$, and then the position condition tells you that $A = 0.2$ m. Then, since $\omega = \sqrt{\frac{k}{m}} = 6.33 \, \frac{\text{rad}}{\text{s}}$, you have

$$x(t) = 0.2 \cos(6.33t)$$

You can generalize the definition of SHM to include any system that satisfies the following differential equation:

$$\frac{d^2X}{dt^2} + \omega^2 X = 0$$

This is called the **harmonic oscillator equation**. X may refer to a linear displacement, as in the spring-mass system, or it may refer to a more general variable. For example, X could be an angular displacement, or even the quantity of charge on a capacitor. A wide range of systems can oscillate, and the most basic types of oscillations satisfy this equation. Since you've already investigated the solution to this equation, you know immediately that

$$X(t) = A \cos(\omega t + \phi)$$

where A is the amplitude, and the period of the oscillation is given by $T = \frac{2\pi}{\omega}$.

VERTICAL SPRING-MASS

When the spring-mass system hangs vertically, two things happen. First, gravity is acting, so the total force acting on the mass is now $F = -kx + mg$. This would seem to destroy the SHM condition, because the gravity force isn't proportional to the displacement. A second change occurs, however: The equilibrium position of the mass shifts downward (figure 1).

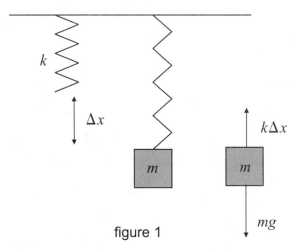

figure 1

If you attach a mass to a vertical spring and gently allow it to come to rest, the spring force up will just equal the weight:

$$k\Delta x = mg \implies \Delta x = \frac{mg}{k}$$

Here Δx is the displacement from the unstretched length of the spring. Left on its own, the mass will just sit at this position. If it's displaced further, it will oscillate and this point will be the new center of oscillation, the new equilibrium point. To see this, let x be the displacement from the new equilibrium point (figure 2).

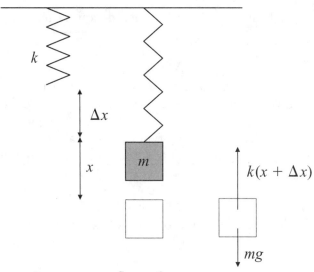

figure 2

The force acting on the mass is
$$F = -k(x + \Delta x) + mg = -k\left(x + \frac{mg}{k}\right) + mg$$
$$F = -kx$$
Now if you measure displacements from the new equilibrium point, the system behaves like a spring-mass system with the same k, m, and period, and gravity is eliminated from the problem.

An alternative approach to this analysis is to apply the second law directly.

$$netF = ma \Rightarrow mg - kx = m\frac{d^2x}{dt^2}$$

$$\frac{d^2x}{dt^2} + \frac{k}{m}x = g$$

Define a new variable x' to measure displacements from the new equilibrium position.

$$x' = x - \frac{mg}{k}$$

Since x and x' differ by only a constant, their derivatives will be the same. Then substituting for x you have

$$\frac{d^2x'}{dt^2} + \frac{k}{m}x' = 0$$

Thus, x' obeys a harmonic oscillator equation with a period that is unaffected by gravity. The moral of the story is that for vertical springs, find the new equilibrium point, measure displacements from there, and ignore the force of gravity.

EXERCISE

A spring with $k = 100$ N/m hangs vertically with a 2 kg mass at one end currently at rest. A 1 kg mass is gently added to the 2 kg mass, setting the system into oscillation. Determine the period, amplitude, and maximum speed of the oscillation.

The vertical motion doesn't affect the period. Since 3 kg is oscillating, you have

$$T_{spring} = 2\pi\sqrt{\frac{m}{k}} = 2\pi\sqrt{\frac{3}{100}} = 1.1 \text{ s}$$

The system will oscillate about an equilibrium point that's determined by how far the 1 kg mass would stretch the spring if it were allowed to reach equilibrium.

$$\Delta x = \frac{mg}{k} = \frac{(1)(10)}{100} = 0.1 \text{ m}$$

Because the 1 kg mass is added gently, the system has no KE when it returns to its highest point. But that means this is also the largest displacement from the new equilibrium point as well, so $A = 0.1$ m.

To find the maximum speed, use energy conservation for a spring-mass system oscillating about the new equilibrium point.

$$E_i = E_f$$

$$\frac{1}{2}kA^2 = \frac{1}{2}mv_0^2$$

$$(100)(0.1)^2 = (3)v_0^2 \Rightarrow v_0 = 0.58 \frac{\text{m}}{\text{s}}$$

SIMPLE PENDULUM

The motion of a simple pendulum is a common repetitive motion. It consists of a point mass m attached to a pivot by a light string of length L (figure 3).

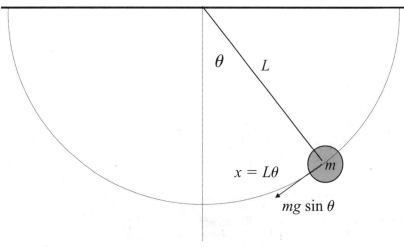

figure 3

Does it meet the SHM criterion? Clearly the equilibrium position is the point directly below the pivot. Since the mass is constrained to move on a circular arc, the displacement is the arc length. If you use radian measure for angle, then from the definition of radian measure you get

$$x = L\theta$$

The restoring force is supplied by the component of gravity that tends to bring the mass back along the arc to the equilibrium point. From the figure you can see that

$$F_{\text{restore}} = -mg \sin \theta$$

Because of $\sin\theta$, the SHM condition is not met:

$$F_{\text{restore}} \neq -Kx$$

Let's apply the rotational analog of the second law to this fixed axis problem.

$$\tau = -(mg \sin\theta)L = I\alpha = (mL^2)\frac{d^2\theta}{dt^2}$$

$$\frac{d^2\theta}{dt^2} + \frac{g}{L}\sin\theta = 0$$

This is *not* the harmonic oscillator equation. However, if θ doesn't get too big, then $\sin\theta \cong \theta$, which means you can replace the sine of the angle by the angle itself. If you don't believe this, try it on your calculator. Use radian mode and take the sine of 0.2 rad, about 11°. You get a value 0.199, obviously very close to the value of the angle itself. Replacing $\sin\theta$ by θ is called the small angle approximation. In this approximation, you have

$$\frac{d^2\theta}{dt^2} + \frac{g}{L}\theta = 0$$

This *is* a harmonic oscillator equation with

$$\omega^2 = \frac{g}{L} \Rightarrow T_{\text{pend}} = 2\pi\sqrt{\frac{L}{g}}$$

The end result is that a simple pendulum executes SHM in the small angle approximation.

EXAMPLE

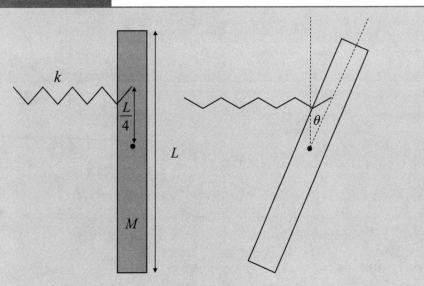

figure 4

A uniform stick of mass M and length L is pivoted at its center on a frictionless, horizontal table (figure 4). A spring with constant k is attached $\frac{1}{4}L$ from the pivot. Determine the period of small oscillations.

For small oscillations, you can approximate the stretch of the spring, equating it with the arc length subtended by θ.

$$x \cong \frac{L}{4}\theta \qquad \Rightarrow \quad F_{restore} = -k\frac{L}{4}\theta$$

Since this is a fixed-axis rotation problem, your approach should be to apply the dynamic equation and get it into the harmonic oscillator form. Then you can just read off the value of ω and get the period. The torque involves the effective component of $F_{restore}$, but in the small angle approximation, you replace $\cos\theta$ with 1.

$$F_{restore}^{eff} = F_{restore}\cos\theta \cong F_{restore}$$

For the torque about the pivot, you have

$$\tau = F_{restore}\frac{L}{4} = -k\frac{L^2}{16}\theta$$

Using $I = \frac{1}{12}ML^2$, you can apply the dynamic equation:

$$\tau = I\alpha$$

$$-k\frac{L^2}{16}\theta = \frac{1}{12}ML^2\frac{d^2\theta}{dt^2}$$

$$\frac{d^2\theta}{dt^2} + \frac{3k}{4M}\theta = 0$$

From the form of the equation, you can immediately see that $\omega = \sqrt{\frac{3k}{4M}}$, and so for the period you have

$$T = 2\pi\sqrt{\frac{4M}{3k}}$$

KEY FORMULAS

Period-Frequency	$T = \dfrac{1}{f}$
Harmonic Oscillator Equation	$\dfrac{d^2X}{dt^2} + \omega^2 X = 0$
Period, Angular Frequency	$T = \dfrac{2\pi}{\omega}$
Period, Spring-Mass	$T_{spring} = 2\pi\sqrt{\dfrac{m}{k}}$
Period, Simple Pendulum	$T_{spring} = 2\pi\sqrt{\dfrac{L}{g}}$

CHAPTER 8 PRACTICE EXERCISES

SECTION I MULTIPLE CHOICE

1. A mass is attached to a spring on a frictionless, horizontal surface. When it's set into oscillation, its period is T. An equal mass collides head-on with this mass, and the two masses stick together. The oscillation period is now

   (A) T (B) $\sqrt{2}T$ (C) $2T$ (D) $\dfrac{T}{\sqrt{2}}$ (E) $\dfrac{T}{2}$

2. A spring-mass system with parameters m and k is oscillating vertically. A second spring-mass system with 3 times the mass is set up beside the first. If the two systems are to oscillate in unison, the spring constant of the second system must be

   (A) $3k$ (B) $\dfrac{k}{3}$ (C) $\sqrt{3}k$ (D) $\dfrac{k}{\sqrt{3}}$ (E) $9k$

3. To increase the period of a simple pendulum by a factor of 2, you could
   I. double the mass
   II. double the length
   III. quadruple the length

   (A) I only   (B) II only   (C) III only   (D) I and II only   (E) I and III only

4. A given pendulum on Earth has a period T. On the Moon, where the acceleration due to gravity is $\frac{1}{6}$ that of Earth, the period will be

   (A) $\dfrac{1}{6}T$ (B) T (C) $\sqrt{6}T$ (D) $\dfrac{T}{6}$ (E) $\dfrac{T}{\sqrt{6}}$

5. A mass *M* is attached to a spring on a frictionless horizontal surface and set into oscillation. A smaller mass sits on top of the first and moves with it without slipping. The static friction force exerted on the smaller mass

    (A) is equal to $\mu_s N$ throughout the motion
    (B) reaches a maximum value as the masses reach their maximum speed
    (C) reaches a maximum value as the masses reach their minimum speed
    (D) reaches a maximum value at a point where the speed is between its maximum and minimum values
    (E) remains constant but is less than $\mu_s N$

Questions 6–8
A 2 kg mass oscillates vertically at the end of a spring according to

$$x(t) = 4\sin\left(\frac{\pi}{6}t + \frac{\pi}{8}\right)$$

6. The period of the oscillations is

    (A) 3 s   (B) $\frac{1}{3}$ s   (C) $\frac{1}{12}$ s   (D) 12 s   (E) $\frac{\pi}{6}$ s

7. The spring constant has a value in N/m of

    (A) $\frac{8\pi^2}{9}$ (B) $72\pi^2$ (C) $1{,}152\pi^2$ (D) $\frac{\pi^2}{18}$ (E) $\frac{81}{8\pi^2}$

8. The maximum kinetic energy of the mass is

    (A) 16 J   (B) $\frac{2}{3}\pi$ J   (C) 4 J   (D) 32 J   (E) $\frac{4\pi^2}{9}$ J

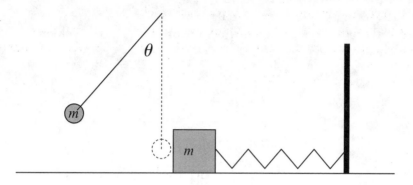

figure 5

1. A mass m is attached to a light string of length L, making a simple pendulum. It is displaced an angle θ from the vertical and released at $t = 0$. Directly below the pivot of the pendulum is a stationary second mass m equal to the first, attached to a spring of constant k on a frictionless, horizontal surface. When the first mass collides with the stationary mass, the first mass detaches from the string and sticks to the second mass.
    (a) At what time will the spring first reach its maximum compression?
    (b) Find the amplitude of the spring oscillations.

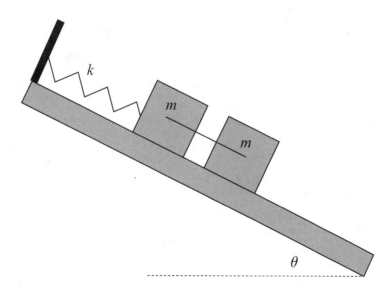

figure 6

2. Two equal masses m connected by a light string are currently at rest on a frictionless surface inclined at an angle θ. One of the masses is connected by a spring with constant k to a point at the top of the incline. At $t = 0$, the string is cut, and the mass connected to the spring begins to oscillate.
   (a) Determine the period of the oscillations.
   (b) Determine the amplitude of the oscillations.
   (c) In terms of the given quantities, write an expression for the velocity of the oscillating mass at an arbitrary time.

Answers and Explanations

MULTIPLE CHOICE

1. The answer is B. Since $T \propto \sqrt{m}$, it follows that doubling m increases the period by $\sqrt{2}$.

2. The answer is A. Oscillating vertically doesn't affect the period. Since $T \propto \sqrt{\frac{m}{k}}$, if the mass is tripled, then k must be tripled to keep the same period—which is what's required for unison oscillations.

3. The answer is C. The period is independent of the mass and $T \propto \sqrt{L}$, so increasing L by a factor of 4 will double the period.

4. The answer is C. Since $T \propto \frac{1}{\sqrt{g}}$, making g smaller by a factor of $\frac{1}{6}$ will increase the period by a factor of $\sqrt{6}$.

5. The answer is C. The static friction force must behave qualitatively like the spring force on the larger mass. Otherwise, the small mass wouldn't oscillate. This force reaches a maximum when the displacement is at its largest value, and here the speed is 0.

6. The answer is D. $\omega = \frac{\pi}{6} = \frac{2\pi}{T} \Rightarrow T = 12 \text{ s}$

$$T = 2\pi\sqrt{\frac{m}{k}} \Rightarrow k = 4\pi^2\sqrt{\frac{m}{T^2}}$$

7. The answer is D. $k = 4\pi^2\frac{2}{12^2} = \frac{\pi^2}{18}$

8. The answer is E. $v(t) = \frac{dx}{dt} = 4\frac{\pi}{6}\cos\left(\frac{\pi}{6}t + \frac{\pi}{8}\right)$ Then the maximum speed is $\frac{2\pi}{3}$, and

the maximum KE is $\frac{1}{2}(2)\left(\frac{2\pi}{3}\right)^2 = \frac{4\pi^2}{9} \text{ J}$.

FREE RESPONSE

1. (a) The total time will be $t = \frac{1}{4}T_{pend} + \frac{1}{4}T_{spring}$. For the pendulum, you have

$$T_{pend} = 2\pi\sqrt{\frac{L}{g}}$$

For the spring, $2m$ is oscillating, so you have

$$T_{spring} = 2\pi\sqrt{\frac{2m}{k}}$$

This means that $t = \frac{\pi}{2}\left(\sqrt{\frac{L}{g}} + \sqrt{\frac{2m}{k}}\right)$.

(b) The maximum compression of the spring will correspond to the amplitude of the oscillations. You can use energy conservation to find the speed of the pendulum mass just before collision.

$$E_i = E_f$$

$$mg(L - L\cos\theta) = \frac{1}{2}mv^2$$

$$v = \sqrt{2gL(1 - \cos\theta)}$$

Next, apply momentum conservation to find the speed of the masses just after collision.

$$P_i = P_f$$

$$mv = 2mV$$

$$V = \frac{1}{2}v = \frac{1}{2}\sqrt{2gL(1 - \cos\theta)}$$

Finally, use energy conservation to determine the maximum compression.

$$E_i = E_f$$

$$\frac{1}{2}(2m)V^2 = \frac{1}{2}kA^2$$

$$A = \sqrt{\frac{2m}{k}}V = \sqrt{\frac{mgL(1 - \cos\theta)}{k}}$$

2. (a) Gravity doesn't change the period. Since one mass is oscillating, you have

$$T = 2\pi\sqrt{\frac{m}{k}}$$

   (b) Initially, the two masses are at rest, so the spring force will just equal the component of gravity down the incline.

$$kx_0 = 2mg\sin\theta$$

$$x_0 = \frac{2mg\sin\theta}{k}$$

   After the string is cut, the single mass will oscillate about a new equilibrium point determined by just m.

$$x_0' = \frac{mg\sin\theta}{k}$$

   Since no initial speed is imparted to the mass when the string is cut, the difference in the two equilibrium positions will be the amplitude of the oscillation. When the mass returns to x_0, it will be instantaneously at rest again.

$$A = x_0 - x_0' = \frac{mg\sin\theta}{k}$$

   (c) The oscillating mass will satisfy $x(t) = A\cos(\omega t + \phi)$ for arbitrary times, with x measured relative to the new equilibrium point. At $t = 0$, $v = 0$, so you have

$$v(t) = -\omega A\sin(\omega t + \phi)$$

$$v(0) = 0 = -\omega A\sin\phi$$

$$\phi = 0$$

   Since $\omega = \sqrt{\frac{k}{m}}$, you can write

$$v(t) = -\sqrt{\frac{k}{m}}\left(\frac{mg\sin\theta}{k}\right)\sin\left(\sqrt{\frac{k}{m}}\,t\right)$$

$$v(t) = -\sqrt{\frac{m}{k}}\,(g\sin\theta)\sin\left(\sqrt{\frac{k}{m}}\,t\right)$$

9

Electric Force and Electric Field

As its name implies, **electrostatics** is the study of electric charges at rest. In this chapter, you'll look at how these charges exert forces on each other, and you'll explore the field concept. You'll also learn how to use Gauss's law to calculate the electric field produced by symmetric charge distributions.

Electric Charge

Electric charge is a fundamental property of many of the basic constituents of matter. There are two types of charge—positive and negative. Charge is a **quantized** entity, which means it has a fundamental unit that cannot be subdivided. The electron carries a negative charge equal to this basic unit, while the proton carries a positive charge equal to this unit. The value of this basic unit is

$$e = 1.6 \times 10^{-19} \text{ C}$$

Here C is short for **coulomb**, the SI unit of charge. Any macroscopic amount of charge must be an integral multiple of the basic unit.

Coulomb's Law

Electric charges exert forces on each other. Like charges ($++$ or $--$) will repel each other, and unlike charges ($+-$) will attract. For two point charges q_1 and q_2, this force acts along the line connecting the two charges, is directly proportional to the product of the two charges, and is inversely proportional to the square of the distance between the two. In symbols (figure 1), the force exerted on q_2 by q_1 is

$$\vec{F}_{1 \to 2} = \frac{1}{4\pi\varepsilon_0} \frac{q_1 q_2}{R^2} \hat{R}$$

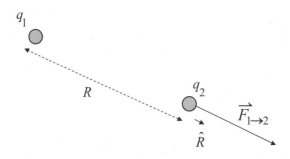

figure 1

$$\frac{1}{4\pi\varepsilon_0} = 9 \times 10^9 \ \frac{\text{N} \cdot \text{m}^2}{\text{C}^2} \qquad \varepsilon_0 = 8.85 \times 10^{-12} \ \frac{\text{C}^2}{\text{N} \cdot \text{m}^2}$$

Here $\hat{R}$ is a unit vector directed along the line connecting the two point charges. The force law, known as **Coulomb's law**, also describes the force between two spherical charges where R is the distance between the centers of the two charges.

EXERCISE

Three charges are arranged along the x-axis: $+3\mu C$ at the origin, $-2\mu C$ at $x = -2$ m, and $-4\mu C$ at $x = +3$ m. Find the net force on the charge at the origin (figure 2).

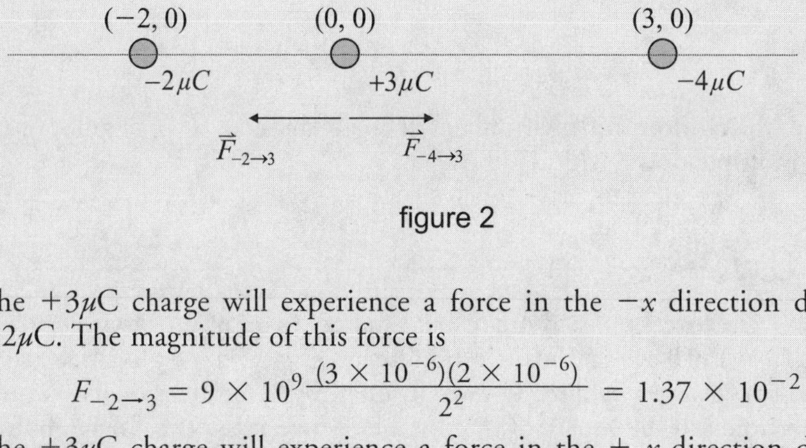

$$(-2, 0) \qquad (0, 0) \qquad (3, 0)$$
$$-2\,\mu C \qquad +3\,\mu C \qquad -4\,\mu C$$
$$\vec{F}_{-2 \to 3} \qquad \vec{F}_{-4 \to 3}$$

figure 2

The $+3\mu C$ charge will experience a force in the $-x$ direction due to the $-2\mu C$. The magnitude of this force is

$$F_{-2 \to 3} = 9 \times 10^9 \frac{(3 \times 10^{-6})(2 \times 10^{-6})}{2^2} = 1.37 \times 10^{-2} \ \text{N}$$

The $+3\mu C$ charge will experience a force in the $+x$ direction due to the $-4\mu C$. The magnitude of this force is

$$F_{-4 \to 3} = 9 \times 10^9 \frac{(3 \times 10^{-6})(4 \times 10^{-6})}{3^2} = 1.20 \times 10^{-2} \ \text{N}$$

The net force will point in the $-x$ direction and have a magnitude equal to the difference of the two contributions.

$$netF = (1.37 - 1.20) \times 10^{-2} = 1.7 \times 10^{-3} \ \text{N} \ (-x \ \text{direction})$$

Because both charges and vector components can carry a minus sign, it's easy to make sign errors in calculating electric forces. To guard against that, use the process from the example. First, find the magnitude of the force contribution, which is always positive, and then use your diagram to combine the different contributions with the correct signs.

Electric Field

How is it that two charges separated by a distance can exert forces on each other? How does one charge know about the presence of the other? The answer lies in the field concept. Each charge creates an **electric field** in the space surrounding it. Another charge placed at some point will experience the field created by the first charge at that point. But the field at that point exists whether a charge is there to experience it or not. The electric field created by a distribution of charges is defined in terms of the force that a test charge would experience if it were placed at some point. A **test charge** is defined as a positive charge that's so small that its presence doesn't change the original charge distribution. Specifically, that is

$$\vec{E} = \frac{\vec{F}}{q_t}$$

The SI units for electric field are $\frac{N}{C}$. When an electric field is created solely by charges at rest, it's called an **electrostatic field**. In principle, you can measure the field at any point in space by placing a small positive charge at that point and measuring the force exerted on it.

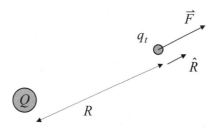

figure 3

You can use the definition of the field to determine the field created by various distributions of charge. The simplest and most important is the field created by a single point charge. Imagine a positive charge Q (figure 3). By symmetry, the magnitude of the field will depend only on the distance from the charge, and the direction will be radially outward. If you bring a test charge to some point a distance R away, for $\vec{E}$ you have

$$\vec{E} = \frac{\left(\frac{1}{4\pi\varepsilon_0} \frac{Qq_t}{R^2} \hat{R} \right)}{q_t} = \frac{1}{4\pi\varepsilon_0} \frac{Q}{R^2} \hat{R}$$

This is the formula for the field created by any point charge. It's also valid for the field created by a spherical charge for points outside of the charge. As mentioned earlier, the direction of the field is radially outward for a positive charge. If Q is negative, the field will be radially inward. The concept of **electric field lines** will help you visualize the field. These are continuous lines that begin on positive charges, end on negative charges, and satisfy two criteria:

    1. The electric field at a given point is tangent to the field line that passes through that point.

    2. The density of field lines at a point is proportional to the strength of the electric field at that point.

You'll find some examples in figure 4.

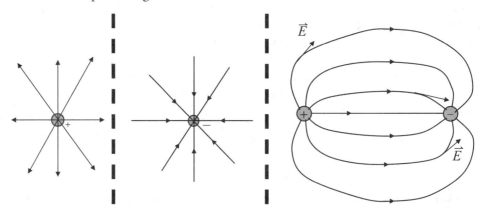

Field lines start on + charges and end on – charges.
The electric field is tangent to field lines.

figure 4

FIELD DUE TO POINT CHARGE DISTRIBUTIONS

If several point charges are present, you can calculate the total field using the **principle of superposition**. This principle states that the total field at a point can be determined by finding the contribution that each individual charge would make if it were the only charge present, then vector adding all the contributions. For the principle of superposition to apply to a theory, certain conditions must be met by the laws that underlie the theory. Without going into the mathematical detail of the conditions, let's simply say that this principle can be applied to both electricity and magnetism.

EXAMPLE

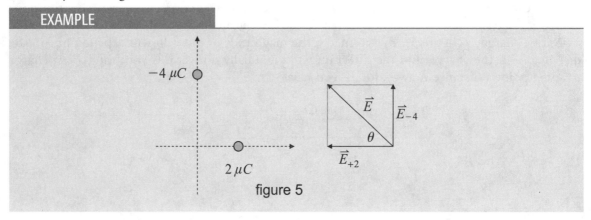

figure 5

A $-4\ \mu C$ charge is located at the point $(0, 3)$, and a $+2\ \mu C$ is located at the point $(2, 0)$. Find the total electric field, magnitude, and direction at the origin (figure 5).

You can find the field created by each charge separately, and then combine them using vector addition.

$$E_{-4} = 9 \times 10^9 \frac{4 \times 10^{-6}}{3^2} = 4 \times 10^3\ \frac{N}{C}\ (+y\ \text{direction})$$

$$E_{+2} = 9 \times 10^9 \frac{2 \times 10^{-6}}{2^2} = 4.5 \times 10^3\ \frac{N}{C}\ (-x\ \text{direction})$$

You can use basic trigonometry to find the magnitude and direction.

$$E = \sqrt{E_{-4}^2 + E_{+2}^2} = 6.02 \times 10^3\ \frac{N}{C} \qquad \tan\theta = \frac{E_{-4}}{E_{+2}} = \frac{4}{4.5}$$

$$\theta = 41.6°$$

MOTION OF A CHARGE IN A UNIFORM FIELD

If you happen to know the field at a given point, you can use the definition of an electric field to find the force on a charge that's placed at the point, assuming the introduction of the charge doesn't change the local charge distribution and the field.

$$\vec{F} = q\vec{E}$$

This equation gives you the force on a charge q placed at a point where the field is $\vec{E}$.

EXAMPLE

Find the acceleration of an electron placed at the origin in the previous example.

You can find the force from the electric field and then use Newton's second law.

$$F = qE = (1.6 \times 10^{-19})(6.02 \times 10^3) = 9.63 \times 10^{-16}\ N$$

$$F = ma$$

$$9.63 \times 10^{-16} = 9 \times 10^{-31}a$$

$$a = 1.1 \times 10^{15}\ \frac{m}{s^2}$$

FIELD DUE TO CONTINUOUS DISTRIBUTIONS

If the charge distribution doesn't consist of distinguishable point charges, you'll need to integrate to find the electric field. The basic technique is to identify an arbitrary piece of the distribution that you can treat as a point charge. Then, add up all the contributions. Because the electric field is a vector, this technique is difficult to do unless there's a lot of symmetry present.

EXAMPLE

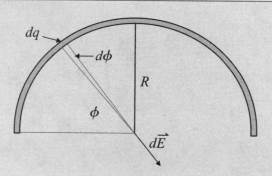

figure 6

A charge $+Q$ is uniformly distributed over a nonconducting material formed into a semicircle of radius R (figure 6). Find the magnitude and direction of the electric field at the center of the semicircle.

The charge per unit length along the arc is

$$\lambda = \frac{Q}{\pi R}$$

A little piece along the arc located at an angle ϕ and subtending an angle $d\phi$ carries a charge

$$dq = \lambda(Rd\phi) = \frac{Q}{\pi}d\phi$$

This piece contributes an amount $\vec{dE}$ to the field shown in the figure. The magnitude of this contribution is

$$dE = \frac{1}{4\pi\varepsilon_0}\frac{dq}{R^2} = \frac{1}{4\pi^2\varepsilon_0}\frac{Qd\phi}{R^2}$$

Symmetry tells you that the horizontal component of $\vec{dE}$ will be canceled out by a contribution from the other side of the arc. That means the only effective component is the vertical component, pointing downward.

$$dE_{\text{eff}} = dE\sin\phi = \frac{1}{4\pi^2\varepsilon_0}\frac{Qd\phi}{R^2}\sin\phi$$

Now you can integrate over ϕ, which varies from 0 to π.

$$E_{center} = \int dE_{eff} = \int_0^\pi \frac{1}{4\pi^2\varepsilon_0} \frac{Q\sin\phi}{R^2} d\phi$$

$$E_{center} = \frac{1}{4\pi^2\varepsilon_0} \frac{Q}{R^2}(-\cos\pi + \cos 0) = \frac{1}{2\pi^2\varepsilon_0} \frac{Q}{R^2}$$

The high degree of symmetry about the center of the semicircle caused the cancellation of the horizontal components and allowed for a straightforward addition of the vertical components.

Electric Flux

When electric field lines cut through a surface area, there is an **electric flux** through the area. Consider a planar area A (figure 7).

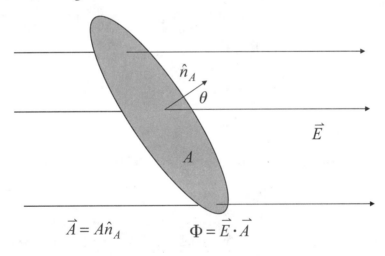

$$\vec{A} = A\hat{n}_A \qquad \Phi = \vec{E}\cdot\vec{A}$$

figure 7

Let's call a unit vector perpendicular to this area $\hat{n}_A$, and let's define an "area vector" $\vec{A}$, with magnitude equal to the area of the surface and direction along $\hat{n}_A$.

$$\vec{A} = A\hat{n}_A$$

For the planar area, there are actually two directions—opposite to each other—that are perpendicular to the area, so let's arbitrarily choose one of them. If you have a uniform electric field $\vec{E}$ in the region, you can define the electric flux Φ_E through the area as

$$\Phi_E = \vec{E}\cdot\vec{A} = EA\cos\theta$$

Notice that the flux is maximized when the electric field is parallel to $\hat{n}_A$ (which means the electric field is perpendicular to the area), and also notice that the flux is 0 if $\theta = 90°$, because the field lines don't cut through the surface. If the field isn't uniform or the area is more contorted, then you have to break up the surface into many little pieces, each of which can be treated as a planar surface if it is small enough. In the infinitesimal limit, you'll have an infinitesimal area $\vec{dA} = dA\hat{n}_{dA}$ where dA is the magnitude of the infinitesimal area and $\hat{n}_{dA}$ is the local unit vector perpendicular to the area element (figure 8).

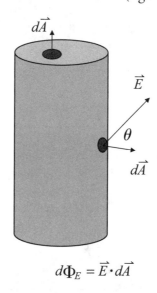

$$d\Phi_E = \vec{E} \cdot \vec{dA}$$

figure 8

You can then calculate the little bit of flux contributed by this piece and sum or integrate over the entire surface:

$$\Phi_E = \oint_{\text{surface}} d\Phi_E = \oint_{\text{surface}} \vec{E} \cdot \vec{dA}$$

If the surface is closed, such as a bag with no holes in it or a cylinder with the ends capped, then you can uniquely define the area vector for each area element as pointing outward.

EXERCISE

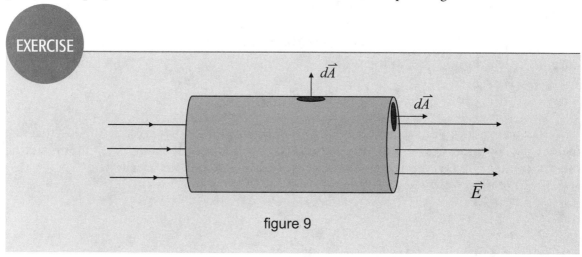

figure 9

Find the flux through a cylinder with its axis parallel to a uniform field $\vec{E}$ (figure 9).

The flux through the sheath of the cylinder will be 0 because the area elements are all perpendicular to $\vec{E}$. At the right cap, the flux is

$$\Phi_{E,\ \text{right}} = \vec{E} \cdot \vec{A}_{R\text{cap}} = EA_{\text{cap}}$$

At the left cap, the magnitude of the area and field are the same, but the area vector, pointing out of the surface, is in the opposite direction as the area vector at the right cap. That means

$$\Phi_{E,\ \text{left}} = \vec{E} \cdot \vec{A}_{L\text{cap}} = -EA_{\text{cap}}$$

Then the total flux is

$$\Phi_E = \Phi_{E,\ \text{sheath}} + \Phi_{E,\ \text{right}} + \Phi_{E,\ \text{left}}$$

$$\Phi_E = 0 + EA_{\text{cap}} - EA_{\text{cap}} = 0$$

Gauss's Law

Consider a closed surface like the cylinder in figure 9. A positive point charge located outside the surface will have field lines emanating out of it that cut through the surface.

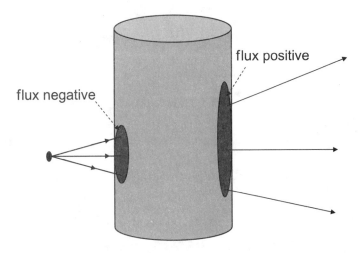

Charges outside a closed area
contribute a net zero flux.

figure 10

Where the charge is closest to the surface, the field has a relatively large magnitude as the field lines enter the surface. Notice that as the lines enter, the flux is negative, since the field is in the opposite direction of the outwardly directed area element. As the field lines leave the surface, the strength of the field has decreased, dropping off as $\frac{1}{R^2}$ where R measures the distance from the charge to the area element. The area that these same lines cut through, however, has now gotten larger, increasing as R^2. In fact, the magnitude of the flux entering and leaving is exactly the same, and since the leaving field lines create a positive flux, the overall electric flux is 0 for any charge outside the surface. The superposition principle then tells you that the flux due to any field created by a charge distribution that lies outside a surface will have 0 flux through the surface. Clearly, charges inside the surface won't have a 0 flux, since the field lines won't give canceling positive and negative contributions in that case (figure 11).

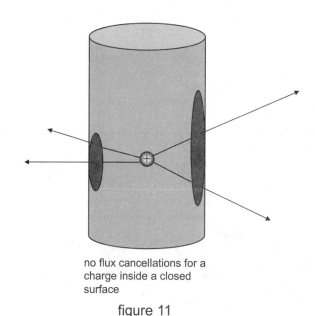

no flux cancellations for a
charge inside a closed
surface

figure 11

Gauss's law states that the total electric flux through any closed surface is directly proportional to the total charge inside the surface.

$$\Phi_E = \oint_{\text{surface}} \vec{E} \cdot d\vec{A} = \frac{Q_{\text{in}}}{\varepsilon_0}$$

EXAMPLE

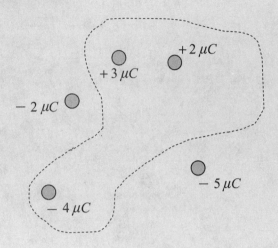

+3 µC

+2 µC

− 2 µC

− 5 µC

− 4 µC

figure 12

Consider the charge distribution shown in figure 12. What is the total electric flux through a closed surface with a cross section indicated by the outline?

The total charge inside the surface is $(3 + 2 - 4)$ µC. For the total electric flux, you have

$$\Phi_E = \oint_{surface} \vec{E} \cdot d\vec{A} = \frac{Q_{in}}{\varepsilon_0} = \frac{1 \times 10^{-6}}{\varepsilon_0} = 1.13 \times 10^5 \frac{N \cdot m^2}{C}$$

CONDUCTORS

A **conductor** is a material with many electrons within it that aren't tightly bound to any one atom. They will readily move in response to any electric field that might be present. Should a conductor happen to carry an overall charge because electrons have been added or taken away, Gauss's law allows you to say some very general things about the field and charge distribution associated with the conductor in the static situation when charges are no longer moving—the condition of **electrostatic equilibrium**. Consider a charged conductor in an electrostatic field (figure 13) with the cross section shown in the figure.

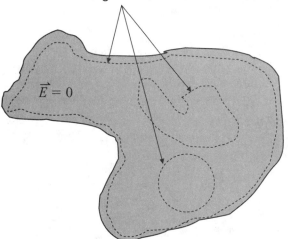

No charge can lie within these surfaces.

$\vec{E} = 0$

Excess charge resides on surface of a conductor.

figure 13

Let's assume there are no charges moving in the conductor, so they must feel no net force. This can only mean that the electric field is identically 0 inside the conductor after all charges have stopped moving and equilibrium is established.

$$\vec{E} = 0 \qquad \text{(inside a conductor in electrostatic equilibrium)}$$

Let's imagine drawing a series of closed surfaces within the conductor (dotted lines). Since we draw them to apply Gauss's law to the flux through them, they're called **Gaussian surfaces**. Because $\vec{E} \cdot d\vec{A} = 0$ everywhere within the conductor, the flux through any of these Gaussian surfaces is 0. From Gauss's law, this will mean that there can be no net charge residing within the conductor. You're left with the conclusion that any excess charge on a conductor in electrostatic equilibrium must lie on the surface of the conductor. The charge will distribute itself over the surface with some charge per unit area σ, measured in $\frac{\text{C}}{\text{m}^2}$. Once you look outside the conductor, the field will no longer be 0. But the mobility of charges on a conductor means that the field at the surface can have no component parallel to the surface. Such a component would move charges around on the surface, contrary to the assumption of equilibrium. So $\vec{E}$ must end or begin at the surface, directed perpendicular to the surface.

Imagine a very small cylindrical Gaussian surface oriented with its axis perpendicular to the surface, with one cap inside and one cap outside (figure 14).

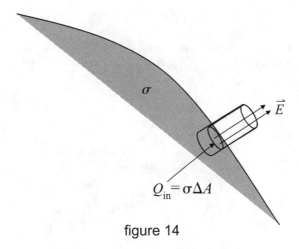

figure 14

The magnitude of $\vec{E}$ won't change much over the small area, and the only contribution to the flux comes from the outer cap, since the inner cap is inside the conductor where the field is 0. Gauss's law gives you

$$\oint_{\text{Gaussian}} \vec{E} \cdot d\vec{A} = \frac{Q_{\text{in}}}{\varepsilon_0}$$

$$\Rightarrow E = \frac{\sigma}{\varepsilon_0} \quad \text{(just outside a charged conductor)}$$

$$E\Delta A = \frac{\sigma \Delta A}{\varepsilon_0}$$

Choosing the appropriate Gaussian surface made the calculation simple. Had you chosen a cylinder with the axis in another direction, Gauss's law would still be true, but you wouldn't have ended up with a simple expression for $\vec{E}$. For the C-level test, this is an important lesson. You should usually choose a Gaussian surface that will respect the symmetry of a given charge distribution. If you do this, E will factor out of the integral and you can solve for it.

$$\oint_{\text{Gaussian}} \vec{E} \cdot d\vec{A} = \frac{Q_{\text{in}}}{\varepsilon_0}$$

$$EA_{\text{sym}} = \frac{Q_{\text{in}}}{\varepsilon_0}$$

$$E = \frac{Q_{\text{in}}}{\varepsilon_0 A_{\text{sym}}}$$

Here A_{sym} refers to the area of the Gaussian surface you are using. In the next few sections, we'll look at some examples of this.

SPHERICAL SYMMETRY

Charge distributions that exhibit spherical symmetry include a single point charge, charged conducting and nonconducting spheres, and concentrically placed charged spheres. In each case, to determine the field created at a given distance from the center of symmetry, you'll need to introduce a spherical Gaussian surface (figure 15).

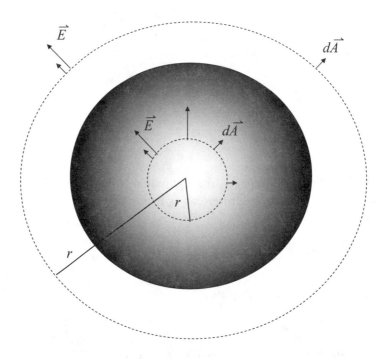

figure 15

You can draw the surface inside or outside the charge distribution, depending on where you want to calculate the field. In either case, since $\vec{E}$ and $d\vec{A}$ are parallel over the entire surface, and the magnitude of is constant over the surface, it follows that

$$\oint_{\text{Gaussian}} \vec{E} \cdot d\vec{A} = \oint_{\text{Gaussian}} E \, dA = E \oint_{\text{Gaussian}} dA = E(4\pi r^2)$$

For any spherically symmetric charge distribution, $\vec{E}$ will point radially and its magnitude will be given by

$$E(4\pi r^2) = \frac{Q_{\text{in}}}{\varepsilon_0} \quad \Rightarrow \quad E = \frac{Q_{\text{in}}}{4\pi\varepsilon_0 r^2}$$

The result indicates that the field is the same as if all the charge inside the surface were concentrated at the center of symmetry.

EXAMPLE

Find the field inside and outside a nonconducting sphere of radius R carrying a uniformly distributed charge Q.

Outside the distribution, $Q_{in} = Q$ and you have

$$E = \frac{Q}{4\pi\varepsilon_0 r^2} \quad r > R$$

Inside the distribution, you need to know how much of the charge is inside a radius r. Since the charge density is

$$\rho = \frac{Q}{\frac{4}{3}\pi R^3}$$

it follows that

$$Q_{in} = \rho\left(\frac{4}{3}\pi r^3\right)$$

Then you have

$$E = \frac{\rho\left(\frac{4}{3}\pi r^3\right)}{4\pi\varepsilon_0 r^2} = \frac{\rho r}{3\varepsilon_0} = \frac{Qr}{4\pi\varepsilon_0 R^3} \quad r < R$$

Notice that E rises linearly as r increases until the boundary is reached, and then it drops off as $\frac{1}{r^2}$ (figure 16).

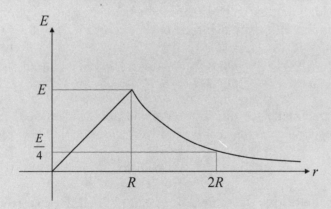

figure 16

CYLINDRICAL SYMMETRY

Charge distributions that exhibit cylindrical symmetry include a long line of charge, charged conducting and nonconducting cylinders, and concentrically placed charged cylinders. Such configurations will produce fields that point radially from the axis of symmetry if the distribution can be treated as being infinitely long. To determine the field created at a given distance from the axis of symmetry, let's introduce a cylindrical Gaussian surface (figure 17).

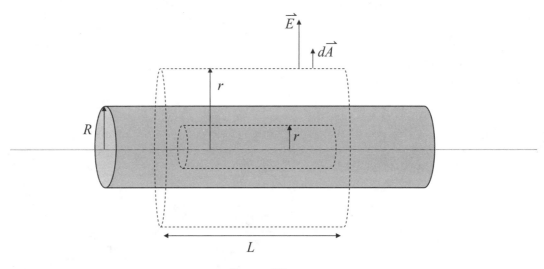

figure 17

You can draw the surface inside or outside the charge distribution, depending on where you want to calculate the field. The flux will be 0 through the caps of the cylinder, and over the sheath, $\vec{E}$ and $d\vec{A}$ are parallel with the magnitude of $\vec{E}$ is constant. It follows that

$$\underset{\text{Gaussian}}{\oint \vec{E} \cdot d\vec{A}} \;=\; \underset{\text{Gaussian}}{\oint E dA} = E \underset{\text{Gaussian}}{\oint dA} = E(2\pi rL)$$

For any cylindrically symmetric charge distribution, $\vec{E}$ will point radially, either toward or away from the cylinder axis depending on the charge, and its magnitude will be

$$E(2\pi rL) = \frac{Q_{\text{in}}}{\varepsilon_0} \;\Rightarrow\; E = \frac{Q_{\text{in}}}{2\pi \varepsilon_0 rL}$$

The result indicates that the field is the same as it would be if all the charge inside the surface were concentrated along the axis of symmetry.

EXAMPLE

A long cylinder of radius R carries a uniform positive charge density ρ. Determine the magnitude of the field both inside and outside the charge distribution.

Outside the distribution, $r > R$, the charge enclosed by the Gaussian surface is

$$Q_{in} = \rho(\pi R^2 L)$$

Notice that R appears here because there is no charge outside the distribution. Then you have

$$E = \frac{\rho(\pi R^2 L)}{2\pi\varepsilon_0 rL} = \frac{\rho}{2\varepsilon_0 r} \qquad r > R$$

You'll see that L, the length of the Gaussian surface, canceled out. This shouldn't be surprising, because it would be strange if the result depended on an arbitrarily drawn length. The quantity $\rho\pi R^2$ is the charge per unit length of the distribution and is often written as λ. In terms of this, the field takes the form

$$E = \frac{\lambda}{2\pi\varepsilon_0 r} \qquad r > R$$

For points inside the distribution, $r < R$, the charge inside is

$$Q_{in} = \rho(\pi r^2 L)$$

Then the field will be

$$E = \frac{\rho(\pi r^2 L)}{2\pi\varepsilon_0 rL} = \frac{\rho r}{2\varepsilon_0} \qquad r > R$$

The magnitude of the field will rise linearly as r increases until the boundary of the distribution is reached. Then it falls off as $\frac{1}{r}$ (figure 18), not as quickly as a point charge because of the unphysical infinite extent of the distribution.

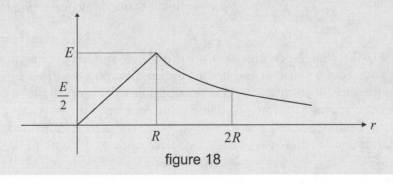

figure 18

PLANAR SYMMETRY

Large (ideally infinite) conducting and nonconducting charged sheets will exhibit planar symmetry. Such distributions will create a field that will point perpendicular to the planar surface, either toward it or away from it, depending on the charge. Let's first look at the case of an infinite nonconducting planar sheet of thickness t carrying a uniform positive charge density ρ (figure 19).

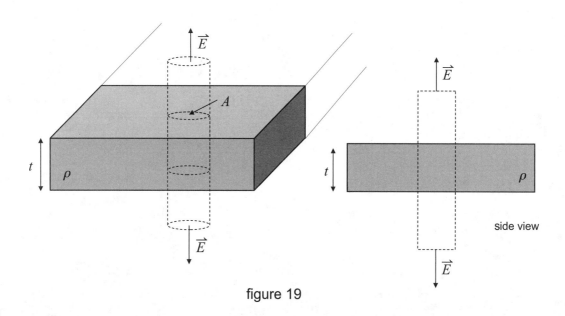

figure 19

To determine the field outside the distribution, you can use a cylindrical Gaussian surface that extends out of the distribution equal distances on each side. At each cap, the flux is positive because the field points out of the surface. If you designate the cap area as A, then

$$\Phi_E = 2EA = \frac{Q_{in}}{\varepsilon_0} = \frac{\rho A t}{\varepsilon_0}$$

$$E = \frac{\rho t}{2\varepsilon_0} = \frac{\sigma}{2\varepsilon_0}$$

field outside nonconducting sheet

The quantity $\sigma = \rho t$ is the charge per unit area on the planar surface. Notice that the field outside an infinite planar sheet is constant and doesn't decrease as you get further away. This too is a result of treating the sheet as infinite; any real distribution will eventually look like a point charge if you get far enough away, but the preceding result will be valid for points close to the sheet. To find the field inside the sheet, draw a similar Gaussian surface contained completely within the material but extending an equal amount x on either side of the center line (figure 20).

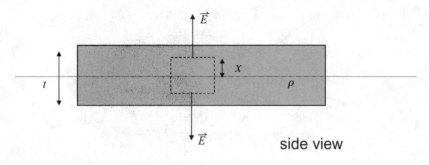

side view

figure 20

Applying Gauss's law, you get

$$\Phi_E = 2EA = \frac{Q_{in}}{\varepsilon_0} = \frac{\rho(2xA)}{\varepsilon_0}$$

$$E = \frac{2\rho x}{\varepsilon_0}$$

field inside nonconducting sheet

If you're dealing with a conducting planar sheet, there will be no field inside. If the conductor carries a charge distributed over its surface, you can take advantage of the properties of a conductor in choosing a Gaussian surface. If you place one cap of a Gaussian cylinder inside the conductor, you're assured that the flux through this cap is 0. For example, suppose you have a planar conductor with equal amounts of charge distributed uniformly over the two planes (figure 21).

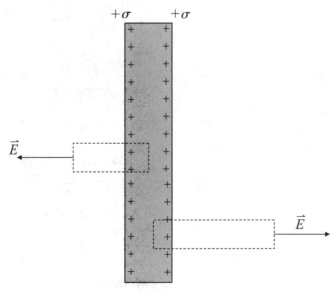

figure 21

You can determine the field on the left by using a Gaussian cylinder (shown in cross section in the figure) of cap area A. For this surface, you have

$$\Phi_E = EA = \frac{Q_{in}}{\varepsilon_0} = \frac{\sigma A}{\varepsilon_0}$$

$$E = \frac{\sigma}{\varepsilon_0}$$

You can apply similar considerations to get the field on the right, which will have the same magnitude if the surface charges are equal on both sides of the sheet.

It's often advantageous to put part of your Gaussian surface inside a conductor if there is one in a problem. The fact that the electrostatic field is always 0 there ensures a 0 flux for this part of the surface.

KEY FORMULAS

Coulomb's Law	$\vec{F}_{1 \to 2} = \frac{1}{4\pi\varepsilon_0} \frac{q_1 q_2}{R^2} \hat{R}$
Electric Field	$\vec{E} = \frac{\vec{F}}{q_t}$
Field of Point Charge	$\vec{E} = \frac{1}{4\pi\varepsilon_0} \frac{Q}{R^2} \hat{R}$
Electric Flux	$\Phi_E = \int_{surface} \vec{E} \cdot d\vec{A}$
Gauss's Law	$\int_{surface} \vec{E} \cdot d\vec{A} = \frac{Q_{in}}{\varepsilon_0}$

PRACTICE EXERCISES

SECTION I MULTIPLE CHOICE

Questions 1 and 2. Two charges are arranged on the corners of a square as pictured.

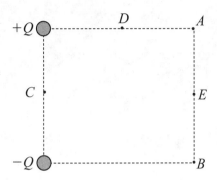

figure 22

1. The direction of the net electric field at the center of the square is

   (A) ↑   (B) →   (C) ↓   (D) ↙   (E) ↗

2. The magnitude of the field will be strongest at
   (A) *A*   (B) *B*   (C) *C*   (D) *D*   (E) *E*

figure 23

3. The figure shows an isolated negative charge fixed in position. Point *R* is 3 times as far away as point *S*. The ratio of the field strength at *S* to the field strength at *R* is

   (A) 9 to 1   (B) 3 to 1   (C) 1 to 9   (D) 1 to 3   (E) 1 to 1

4. A 2 μC charge with mass 0.1 kg accelerates at 2 m/s² in a uniform electric field. The magnitude of the field is most nearly

(A) $10^5 \dfrac{N}{C}$ (B) $10^{-5} \dfrac{N}{C}$ (C) $2 \dfrac{N}{C}$ (D) $0.2 \dfrac{N}{C}$ (E) $0.1 \dfrac{N}{C}$

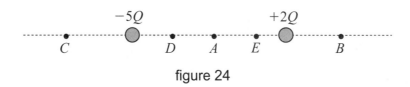

figure 24

5. Charges $+2Q$ and $-5Q$ are situated as shown. At what point could the electric field be equal to 0?

(A) A (B) B (C) C (D) D (E) E

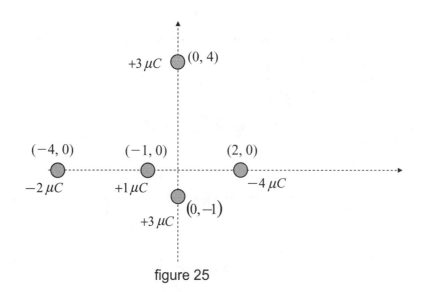

figure 25

6. Charges are distributed along the *x*- and *y*-axes as shown in the figure. The total electric flux through a sphere of radius 3 m centered on the origin is

(A) $1\dfrac{\mu C}{\varepsilon_0}$ (B) 0   (C) $4\dfrac{\mu C}{\varepsilon_0}$ (D) $-6\dfrac{\mu C}{\varepsilon_0}$ (E) $5\dfrac{\mu C}{\varepsilon_0}$

7. A spherical conductor of radius R carries a total charge $+ Q$. Which of the following statements is correct?
   I. The electric field just outside the surface of the conductor is the same as the field just outside a uniformly charged spherical nonconductor of the same radius and charge.
   II. The electric field just inside the surface of the conductor is the same as the field just inside a uniformly charged spherical nonconductor of the same radius and charge.
   III. A nonspherical Gaussian surface drawn completely within the conductor will have a net electric flux through it.

   (A) I only   (B) II only   (C) III only   (D) I and II   (E) I and III

8. Gauss's law could easily be used to solve for the electric field outside of all of the following charge distributions except a

   (A) charged nonconducting sphere
   (B) long straight line of charge
   (C) long charged conducting cylinder
   (D) charged nonconducting cube
   (E) charged nonconducting plane

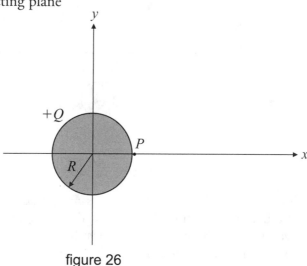

figure 26

9. A uniformly charged nonconducting sphere of radius R, charge $+ Q$, is centered at the origin. The field strength at point P with coordinates $(R, 0)$ just outside the surface will double if which of the following occurs?
   I. Add a point charge $+ Q$ at the origin.
   II. Add a point charge $- Q$ at the point $(2R, 0)$.
   III. Add a uniformly charged nonconducting sphere with charge $- Q$ and radius $\frac{1}{2} R$ with its center at the point $(2R, 0)$.

   (A) I only   (B) I and II only   (C) I and III only   (D) II and III only   (E) I, II, and III

CHAPTER 9

PRACTICE EXERCISES

Section II Free Response

1. Two charges are located along the x-axis, $-3\,\mu C$ at the origin and $+6\,\mu C$ at the point $(2, 0)$.
   (a) Determine the electric field at the point $(-1, 0)$.
   (b) Find the magnitude and direction of the force on an electron placed at $(-1, 0)$.
   (c) Determine the point on the x-axis where the electric field is 0.

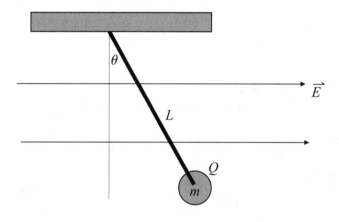

figure 27

2. A nonconducting sphere of charge $+Q$ and mass m is attached to a string of length L and hangs from a ceiling. When a uniform electric field directed horizontally is introduced, equilibrium is eventually established with the mass hanging at an angle θ with respect to the vertical. In terms of g and the given quantities, find the strength of the electric field and the tension in the string.

3. A nonconducting hoop of radius R carries a positive charge Q distributed evenly over the circumference. Determine the electric field along the axis of the hoop.

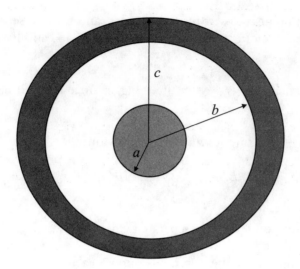

figure 28

4. A uniformly charged nonconducting sphere of radius *a* and charge *Q* is concentrically placed inside a conducting spherical shell of inner radius *b* and outer radius *c* that carries no excess charge.
    (a) Determine the electric field in the following regions:
        (i) $r < a$
        (ii) $a < r < b$
        (iii) $b < r < c$
        (iv) $r > c$
    (b) Determine the surface charge density on the inner and outer surfaces of the conducting shell.

Answers and Explanations

MULTIPLE CHOICE

1. The answer is C. At the center, the field created by the top left charge is directed along the diagonal away from that charge, while the field created by the bottom left charge is directed toward it along the other diagonal. Since the two fields have the same strength, the horizontal components cancel out.

2. The answer is C. This point is closest to both charges, and the two separate fields created by each charge are in the same direction—down—so there is no cancellation.

3. The answer is A. The field at S is $3^2 = 9$ times bigger since R is 3 times farther away.

4. The answer is A. *netF* = *ma* implies $qE = ma$. Substituting, you get

$$E = \frac{(0.1)(2)}{2 \times 10^{-6}} = 10^5 \, \frac{\text{N}}{\text{C}}$$

5. The answer is B. At this point, the two separate fields oppose each other. Because B is closer to the smaller charge, the effect of the smaller charge can be large enough to offset the field due to the bigger charge. At C, the two fields oppose each other but can never cancel out due to the proximity to the larger charge. At A, D, and E, the fields reinforce each other.

6. The answer is B. A 3 m radius includes only 3 charges. Their total charge adds to 0, so Gauss's law says the electric flux must be 0 as well.

7. The answer is A. Outside a spherical distribution, Gauss's law says the field is exactly the same as that of a point charge at the center. That means both the spherical conductor and the spherical nonconductor will have identical fields outside. Choice II is not true because $E = 0$ in a conductor but not in a charged nonconductor. The flux through any Gaussian surface completely within the conductor will be 0 since $E = 0$ here. This eliminates III.

8. The answer is D. While you can apply Gauss's law to this distribution, there's no simple Gaussian surface that you could draw that would allow you to factor E out of the surface integral. Gauss's law is true for any closed surface, but this will lead to a solution for E only if there is enough symmetry to perform this factoring.

9. The answer is E. You can think of the original sphere as a point charge at the origin. It produces a field at P equal to $\frac{Q}{4\pi\varepsilon_0 R^2}$ in the $+x$ direction. Choices I, II, and III each produce an identical field at P, so by the superposition principle each will double the original field. Notice that the size of the added charge in choice III is irrelevant as long its radius is smaller than R.

FREE RESPONSE

1. (a) The field due to the $-3\ \mu C$ charge points in the $+x$ direction and has magnitude

$$E^{-3} = 9 \times 10^9\ \frac{3 \times 10^{-6}}{1^2} = 2.7 \times 10^4\ \frac{N}{C}$$

The field due to the other charge points in the $-x$ direction with magnitude

$$E^{+6} = 9 \times 10^9\ \frac{6 \times 10^{-6}}{3^2} = 0.6 \times 10^4\ \frac{N}{C}$$

The overall field points in the $+x$ direction with magnitude

$$E = (2.7 - 0.6) \times 10^4 = 2.1 \times 10^4\ \frac{N}{C}$$

(b) An electron placed at this point will feel a force on the opposite direction to the field, the $-x$ direction. The magnitude will be

$$F = qE = (1.6 \times 10^{-19})(2.1 \times 10^4) = 3.4 \times 10^{-15}\ N$$

(c) Between the two charges on the x-axis, the two fields will reinforce each other. To the left of the origin, closer to the smaller charge, the fields tend to cancel out, and if the point is chosen properly, the two contributions will cancel out. This will occur at some point $x < 0$.

$$(9 \times 10^9)\frac{3 \times 10^{-6}}{x^2} = (9 \times 10^9)\frac{6 \times 10^{-6}}{(2-x)^2}$$

$$\frac{(2-x)^2}{x^2} = 2 \Rightarrow \frac{2-x}{x} = \pm\sqrt{2} \Rightarrow x = \frac{2}{1 - \sqrt{2}} = -4.83\ m$$

Only the $-$ root gives a negative x-value.

2. This is an equilibrium problem. You can find the net force components in each direction and set them equal to 0 to get the two unknowns. From the freebody diagram (figure 29), you have

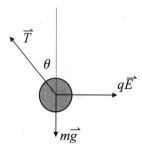

figure 29

$$netF_x = 0 \qquad\qquad netF_y = 0$$

$$T\sin\theta - qE = 0 \qquad\qquad T\cos\theta - mg = 0$$

$$T\sin\theta = qE \qquad\qquad T\cos\theta = mg$$

Dividing the two equations gives you

$$E = \frac{mg}{q}\tan\theta$$

The tension is given directly from the y-components:

$$T = \frac{mg}{\cos\theta}$$

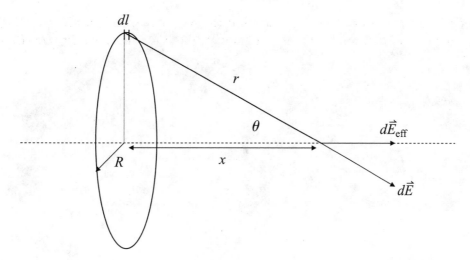

figure 30

3. You can look at a point x along the axis and find the contribution of a small element on the loop to the field at this point. From the figure, you can see that

$$dE = \frac{1}{4\pi\varepsilon_0} \frac{dQ}{r^2}$$

where dQ is the charge on the loop element. By symmetry, the elements on the opposite sides of the loop will contribute a components perpendicular to the axis that cancel out, so you only need to add up the components that lie along the axis, $d\vec{E}_{\text{eff}}$.

$$dE_{\text{eff}} = \frac{1}{4\pi\varepsilon_0} \frac{dQ}{r^2} \cos\theta$$

$$dE_{\text{eff}} = \frac{1}{4\pi\varepsilon_0} \frac{dQ}{r^2} \frac{x}{r}$$

$$dE_{\text{eff}} = \frac{1}{4\pi\varepsilon_0} \frac{xdQ}{r^3}$$

You can now add up, or integrate, all the contributions. As you do this, x and r remain constant; they're the same for each element of the loop. The integration becomes a simple summation of all the charge on the loop, so

$$E = \int_{\text{loop}} dE_{\text{eff}} = \int_{\text{loop}} \frac{1}{4\pi\varepsilon_0} \frac{xdQ}{r^3} = \frac{1}{4\pi\varepsilon_0} \frac{x}{r^3} \int_{\text{loop}} dQ$$

$$E = \frac{1}{4\pi\varepsilon_0} \frac{xQ}{r^3} = \frac{1}{4\pi\varepsilon_0} \frac{xQ}{(x^2 + R^2)^{\frac{3}{2}}}$$

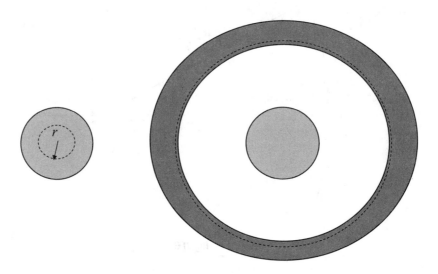

figure 31

4. (a) (i) You can draw a spherical Gaussian surface within the inner sphere. Gauss's law says

$$\int_{\text{Gaussian}} \vec{E} \cdot d\vec{A} = \frac{Q_{\text{in}}}{\varepsilon_0}$$

$$E(4\pi r^2) = \frac{Q}{\varepsilon_0}\left(\frac{\frac{4}{3}\pi r^3}{\frac{4}{3}\pi a^3}\right)$$

$$E = \frac{Qr}{4\pi\varepsilon_0 a^3} \quad r < a$$

In the second step, the charge inside the Gaussian surface is determined by the fraction of the volume inside the surface. Notice that the charge density is $\rho = \frac{Q}{\frac{4}{3}\pi a^3}$

(ii) Between the spheres, the inner sphere acts like a point charge, so

$$E = \frac{Q}{4\pi\varepsilon_0 r^2} \quad a < r < b$$

(iii) Inside the conductor, the field is 0:

$$E = 0 \quad b < r < c$$

(iv) Outside of both spheres, the total charge inside, Q, behaves like a point charge.

$$E = \frac{Q}{4\pi\varepsilon_0 r^2} \quad r > c$$

(b) Even though the conductor carries no excess charge, the field of the inner sphere will cause charge to separate on the conductor. In equilibrium, you can find charge on the inner and outer surfaces by using the Gaussian surface drawn within the conductor as shown in the figure. For this surface, the flux must be 0 since the field is 0 inside the conductor. Let's call Q_b the charge on the inner surface and Q_c the charge on the outer surface. If you apply Gauss's law to the inner surface, you have

$$\Phi_E = \frac{Q_{in}}{\varepsilon_0}$$

$$0 = Q + Q_b$$

$$Q_b = -Q$$

This means $-Q$ is drawn in, producing a surface charge density $\sigma_b = \frac{-Q}{4\pi b^2}$.

Because the conductor was neutral to begin with, $+Q$ must be distributed on the outer surface, since charge distributed on conductors in equilibrium must reside on the surface. That means

$$Q_c = +Q \quad \Rightarrow \quad \sigma_c = \frac{+Q}{4\pi c^2}$$

Electric Potential and Electric Potential Energy

When you're studying mechanics, you can often simplify problems by introducing the energy concept. Because it's a scalar, energy is easier to work with than vector quantities like force and acceleration. In this chapter, you'll learn how electrostatics lends itself to a scalar description as well. The concept of electric potential gives you a tool to describe the energy of any charge placed in a region where an electric field is present. As you develop the concept of electric potential, you'll also learn about important properties of conductors. The concept of capacitance will be developed as a particular application of electric potential.

Electric Potential

Suppose that several point charges are distributed through a given region (figure 1). At every point in space, an electric field $\vec{E}$ is present. To move a charge slowly from A to B will take work because the agent moving the charge will have to provide a force just equal to the electric force $\vec{F} = q\vec{E}$.

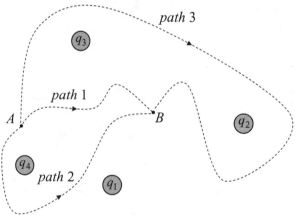

figure 1

For an electrostatic field, this force is conservative; the work done in slowly moving the charge between A and B is independent of the path taken. This means that the work done along the three different paths in the figure is the same for each path. But the work will depend on the magnitude of the charge moved, since the force is directly proportional to this charge. If you moved a $+2\ \mu C$ charge, for example, it would take twice the work as a $+1\ \mu C$ charge. It's useful to define a quantity that's closely related to this work but which doesn't depend on the charge moved. The **electric potential difference** between A and B is defined as

$$\Delta V_{A\to B} = \frac{W_{A\to B}^{agent}}{q}$$

Here $W_{A\to B}^{agent}$ is the work an agent must do to slowly move the charge q from A to B. Since this is done slowly, the work done by the agent is just the opposite of the work done by the field.

$$W_{A\to B}^{agent} = -W_{A\to B}^{field}$$

For the potential difference, you can write

$$\Delta V_{A\to B} = -\frac{W_{A\to B}^{field}}{q}$$

By dividing by q, you make the value of ΔV independent of the charge moved. It will depend only on the two points chosen and, of course, the distribution of charge creating the field in the first place. The units of electric potential difference are $\frac{J}{C}$, called a **volt** (V).

EXAMPLE

It takes $+5\ \mu J$ of work for an agent to move a $+2\ \mu C$ charge from A to B. Determine the potential difference between A and B and the amount of work that would be required to move a $-3\ \mu C$ charge between A and B.

From the definition of potential difference, you have

$$\Delta V_{A\to B} = \frac{W_{A\to B}^{field}}{q} = \frac{5\times 10^{-6}}{2\times 10^{-6}} = 2.5\ V$$

To move a $-3\ \mu C$ charge through the same potential difference, you have

$$2.5 = \frac{W}{-3\times 10^{-6}} \Rightarrow W = -7.5\ \mu J$$

You can obtain a general expression for the potential difference between two points in terms of the electric field in the region. Remembering that the force an agent must supply to move a charge slowly is just the opposite of the force exerted by the field.

$$\Delta V_{A\to B} = \frac{W_{A\to B}^{agent}}{q} = \frac{1}{q}\int_{\vec{r}_A}^{\vec{r}_B}\vec{F}^{agent}\cdot d\vec{l} = \frac{1}{q}\int_{\vec{r}_A}^{\vec{r}_B}(-q\vec{E})\cdot d\vec{l}$$

$$\Delta V_{A\to B} = -\int_{\vec{r}_A}^{\vec{r}_B}\vec{E}\cdot d\vec{l}$$

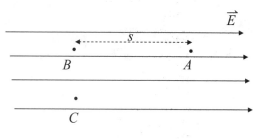

figure 2

If the field is uniform, this integral is particularly simple. To find the potential difference between the points A and B shown in figure 2.

$$\Delta V_{A \rightarrow B} = -\int_{\vec{r_A}}^{\vec{r_B}} \vec{E} \cdot d\vec{l} = E \int_0^s ds$$

$$\Delta V_{A \rightarrow B} = Es$$

Note that ΔV is positive as you proceed against the field lines since an agent would have to do positive work to move a test charge this way.

You'll need to be careful in using the $\Delta V = Es$ formula. It's exact only if the magnitude of the field is constant along the field line. If the field isn't uniform, this relation will be true if E is interpreted as the average field strength along the field line followed. The s in the formula refers to the distance along the field lines. This means that point C in the figure is at the same potential as B even though it is a greater physical distance from A.

Only the change in electric potential has physical significance. You can choose the zero point anywhere that's convenient. If you choose A as the zero point, then you can refer to the potential at B and write it as

$$V_B = Es$$

Whenever you refer to the potential at some point, what you're really talking about is the potential difference between that point and the zero point. It is common to choose infinity as the point of zero potential. In this case one has for some arbitrary point P

$$V_P = -\int_{\infty}^{P} \vec{E} \cdot d\vec{l}$$

POTENTIAL DUE TO POINT CHARGE DISTRIBUTIONS

The simplest charge distribution is a single point charge. For example, you could ask what the electric potential is at a distance R from the charge Q. Let's arbitrarily define the 0 of potential to be at infinity, far away from the charge. You can set up an integration to determine the total potential difference between infinity and the point in question.

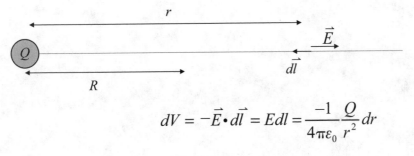

$$dV = -\vec{E} \cdot \vec{dl} = Edl = \frac{-1}{4\pi\varepsilon_0}\frac{Q}{r^2}dr$$

figure 3

From figure 3 you can see that the tiny bit of potential difference associated with displacement $\vec{dl}$ is

$$dV = \frac{-1}{4\pi\varepsilon_0}\frac{Q}{r^2}dr \qquad\qquad dl = -dr$$

Then you can integrate from infinity to R:

$$V = \int_{\infty}^{R}\frac{-1}{4\pi\varepsilon_0}\frac{Q}{r^2}dr$$

$$V = \frac{1}{4\pi\varepsilon_0}\frac{Q}{R}$$

This is the electric potential a distance R from a point charge Q. It will also be valid for a spherical charge with R measured from the center.

When several point charges are present, the potential at a point can be determined using the superposition principle. You can find the potential due to each charge individually as if none of the others are present and then add the individual values. Symbolically, you can write

$$V = \frac{1}{4\pi\varepsilon_0}\frac{q_1}{r_1} + \frac{1}{4\pi\varepsilon_0}\frac{q_2}{r_2} + \ldots$$

Because the potential is a scalar, this is an easy operation. Unlike using superposition with the electric field, there are no directions to worry about.

EXAMPLE

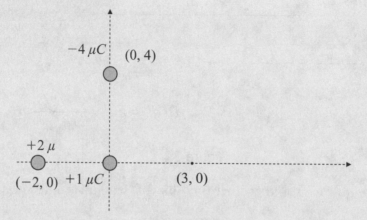

figure 4

Three charges are distributed as shown in figure 4. Determine the electric potential at the point (3, 0).

To get the total, just add the individual potentials contributed by each charge. Be sure to include the proper sign with each charge as you calculate.

$$V = V_{+2} + V_{+1} + V_{-4}$$

$$V = (9 \times 10^9) \left[\frac{2 \times 10^{-6}}{4} + \frac{1 \times 10^{-6}}{3} + \frac{-4 \times 10^{-6}}{5} \right]$$

$$V = 600 \text{ V}$$

POTENTIAL DUE TO CONTINUOUS CHARGE DISTRIBUTIONS

For continuous distributions of charge, you can use two approaches to determine the potential at a given point.

1. Suppose $\vec{E}$ is known or is easy to calculate, perhaps using Gauss's law. In this case, you can apply the basic definition of the electric potential in terms of the field.

$$V_P = -\int_{\infty}^{P} \vec{E} \cdot d\vec{l}$$

Remembering that the electrostatic force is conservative, you can just sum up all the $(-\vec{E} \cdot d\vec{l})$ contributions along a path where it's easy to calculate the integral.

2. If the distribution isn't too complex, treat each element of the distribution as a point charge contributing an infinitesimal amount to the potential at P, and use superposition to find the total contribution. This approach has the benefit of never having to use the vector $\vec{E}$.

Let's look at examples of each approach.

EXAMPLE

Find the electric potential for points both inside and outside a uniformly charged nonconducting sphere of radius R and total charge Q.

For $r > R$, the sphere acts like a point charge. Then

$$V(r) = -\int_{\infty}^{r} \vec{E}_{\text{out}} \cdot d\vec{l} = -\int_{\infty}^{r} \frac{Q}{4\pi\varepsilon_0 r^2} \hat{r} \cdot d\vec{l} = \frac{Q}{4\pi\varepsilon_0 r} \quad r > R$$

For $r < R$, you'll have to integrate all the way into the sphere. From your work on Gauss's law in the last chapter, you know the field inside the sphere is given by

$$\vec{E}_{\text{in}} = \frac{Qr}{4\pi\varepsilon_0 R^3}$$

Then, using the definition of the potential, you have

$$V(r) = -\int_{\infty}^{r} \vec{E} \cdot d\vec{l} = -\int_{\infty}^{R} \vec{E}_{\text{out}} \cdot d\vec{l} - \int_{R}^{r} \vec{E}_{\text{in}} \cdot d\vec{l}$$

Notice that you break up the integral into two parts because of the different functional form of $\vec{E}$ in the two regions. The first integral is just the potential of a point charge at R, since outside the sphere the charge behaves as a point charge. For the second integral, you have to use your form for $\vec{E}_{\text{in}}$.

$$V(r) = \frac{Q}{4\pi\varepsilon_0 R} - \int_{R}^{r} \frac{Qr'}{4\pi\varepsilon_0 R^3} \, dr' = \frac{Q}{4\pi\varepsilon_0 R} + \frac{Q}{4\pi\varepsilon_0 R^3}\left(\frac{1}{2}R^2 - \frac{1}{2}r^2\right)$$

$$V(r) = \frac{Q}{8\pi\varepsilon_0 R}\left\{3 - \frac{r^2}{R^2}\right\}$$

You can see that even though the field is 0 at the center of the sphere, the value of the electric potential is not. You chose infinity to be the zero point, and it takes work to bring a charge to the center from infinity.

EXAMPLE

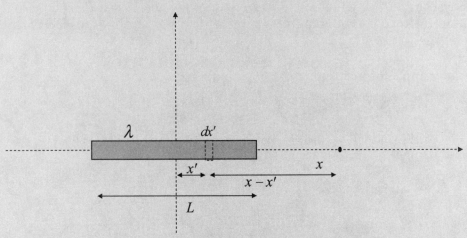

figure 5

A length L of nonconducting material carrying a uniform charge per unit length λ is symmetrically placed on the x-axis (figure 5). Determine the potential at an arbitrary point on the x-axis outside the distribution.

A little element of the material will carry a charge $dq = \lambda dx'$ where dx' is the length of the element located at the point x'. This element contributes an amount to the potential:

$$dV = \frac{dq}{4\pi\varepsilon_0(x - x')} = \frac{\lambda dx'}{4\pi\varepsilon_0(x - x')}$$

Integrating over the distribution gives you

$$V(x) \int_{-\frac{L}{2}}^{\frac{L}{2}} \frac{\lambda dx'}{4\pi\varepsilon_0(x - x')} = \frac{-\lambda}{4\pi\varepsilon_0} \ln\left(\frac{x - \frac{L}{2}}{x + \frac{L}{2}}\right)$$

Determining the Field from the Potential

Imagine a charge moving along a path. As it displaces by $\vec{dl}$ (figure 6), it undergoes a change in electric potential:

$$dV = -\vec{E} \cdot \vec{dl} = -E\cos\theta\, dl$$

$$dV = -E_l dl$$

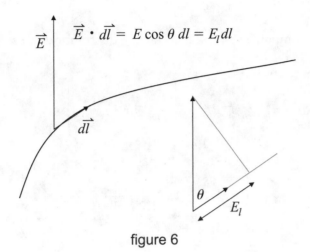

figure 6

Here E_l refers to the component of the field along the displacement $\vec{dl}$. Then you can write

$$E_l = -\frac{dV}{dl}$$

This states that the electric field component in any direction can be determined from the scalar electric potential by differentiation with respect to displacements in the desired direction. For example, the potential due to a point charge is

$$V(r) = \frac{Q}{4\pi\varepsilon_0 r}$$

Differentiating with respect to r will give you the component of the field pointing radially away from the charge

$$E_r = -\frac{dV}{dr} = \frac{Q}{4\pi\varepsilon_0 r^2}$$

Of course, this is the only nonzero component of the field because of the symmetry.

EXERCISE

Find the *x*-component of the field for the distribution in example 2.

You only need to find $-\frac{dV}{dx}$.

$$E_x = -\frac{dV}{dx} = -\frac{d}{dx}\left\{\frac{-\lambda}{4\pi\varepsilon_0}\ln\left(\frac{x-\frac{L}{2}}{x+\frac{L}{2}}\right)\right\}$$

$$E_x = \frac{\lambda}{4\pi\varepsilon_0}\frac{x+\frac{L}{2}}{x-\frac{L}{2}}\left\{\frac{1}{x+\frac{L}{2}} - \frac{x-\frac{L}{2}}{\left(x+\frac{L}{2}\right)^2}\right\}$$

$$E_x = \frac{\lambda}{4\pi\varepsilon_0}\frac{L}{\left(x-\frac{L}{2}\right)\left(x+\frac{L}{2}\right)}$$

Equipotential Surfaces and Conductors

Looking back at figure 2, you can see that it will take no work to move a charge from *B* to *C*. That's because the field and the force are always at right angles to the displacement along such a path. It follows that there will be no potential difference between *B* and *C* either. In fact, any planar surface that's perpendicular to the field lines in figure 2 will have the property that any two points on the surface have no potential difference between them because moving along such a surface will always involve moving at right angles to the field. A connected surface where all points have 0 potential difference between them is called an **equipotential surface**. Each surface can be labeled by a unique voltage value with respect to the zero point, and the electric field will always be perpendicular to the equipotential surfaces. For a point charge or spherical distribution, the equipotential surfaces are concentric spheres centered on the charge (figure 7). For more complicated distributions, the surfaces can contort quite a bit.

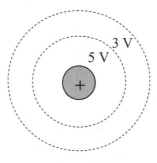

figure 7

A **conductor** is a material that contains many charges that are free to move. For example, many of the electrons in a metal are not specifically bound to any one atom and can move freely throughout the material. Should they experience an electric field, these mobile electrons will move and redistribute themselves. If the electric field applied is static, not changing in time, then the condition of **electrostatic equilibrium** will be achieved quite quickly. In this state, charges no longer move, and this can only mean that the net electric field inside the conductor is 0. The redistributed charges lie along the surface of the conductor and create their own field that exactly cancels out the original field within the conductor. At the surface of the conductor, the electric field lines enter or leave at right angles to the surface, since any parallel component would cause charges on the surface to move.

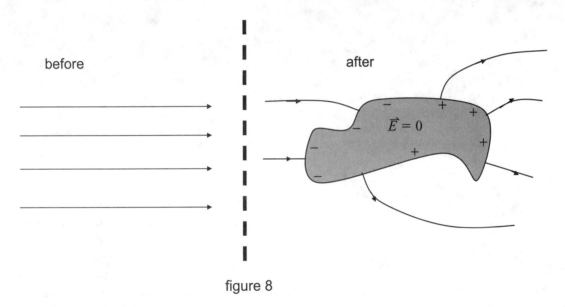

figure 8

Figure 8 depicts what happens when a conducting shape is placed in a uniform static field. Notice the distortion of the field outside of the conductor. This is a result of the superposition of the original uniform field and the field due to the charges on the conductor that moved to the surface in response to it.

If a test charge is moved along the surface of the conductor, the electric field will do no work on it because the field is at right angles to the displacement of the charge. This means that the surface is an equipotential surface. In fact, it takes no work to move a charge anywhere within the material since the field is 0 inside, so the entire conductor is characterized by a single value of electric potential.

EXERCISE

Two identical spherical conductors labeled A and B with radius R are separated by a distance d that's very large compared with R. Conductor A has a charge Q on it, while B is neutral. The two conductors are brought together so that they touch, and then they are moved back to their original positions. Find the potential at a point just outside the surface of A

(a) before they are brought together

(b) after they are touched and returned to their positions

(a) Initially A behaves as a point charge just outside of its radius. Since it carries a charge Q, the potential is

$$V_{\text{before}} = \frac{Q}{4\pi\varepsilon_0 R}$$

(b) When they touch, the charge will distribute itself equally over both spheres as the combined surface of the two conductors becomes one large equipotential surface. Each sphere will then carry $\frac{1}{2}Q$. When they are returned to their initial positions, you can find the potential at the surface of A using superposition.

$$V_{\text{after}} = \frac{\frac{1}{2}Q}{4\pi\varepsilon_0 R} + \frac{\frac{1}{2}Q}{4\pi\varepsilon_0 d}$$

Capacitance

Imagine two conductors placed near each other. You could remove electrons from one of them, leaving it with charge $+Q$, and transfer the electrons to the other, so that it would have charge $-Q$. Such a device is called a **capacitor** (figure 9).

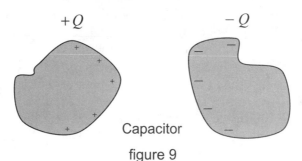

$+Q$ $-Q$

Capacitor

figure 9

Because each conductor is an equipotential surface, there is a unique potential difference V between the two conductors. The ratio of the charge separated to the potential difference created by the separation is called the **capacitance** of the system.

$$C = \frac{Q}{V}$$

The units of capacitance are $\frac{C}{V}$, called a **farad** (F). When more charge is transferred, the potential difference increases by the same factor so that the ratio stays the same. In fact, the value of the capacitance depends on only the geometry of the conductors. You can use the basic definition to calculate the capacitance of various configurations. The basic steps are:

1. Imagine the two conductors are charged to $+Q$ and $-Q$.
2. Use Gauss's law to find $\vec{E}$ in the region between the conductors.
3. Calculate V from $V = -\int \vec{E} \cdot d\vec{l}$.
4. Plug into $C = \frac{Q}{V}$.

EXAMPLE

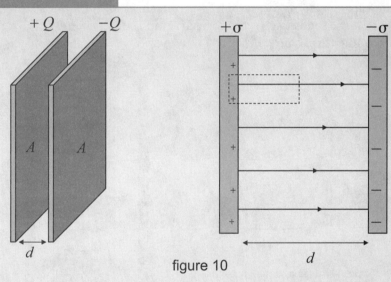

figure 10

Find the capacitance of two parallel conducting plates of area A separated by distance d (figure 10).

The charges will reside on the inner surfaces of the conductors, creating a surface charge density $\pm\sigma = \frac{\pm Q}{A}$. A Gaussian cylinder with one cap embedded in the left conductor will have flux through the other cap $\Phi_E = Ea$ where a is the cap area. Then, from Gauss's law you have

$$Ea = \frac{Q_{\text{in}}}{\varepsilon_0} = \frac{\sigma a}{\varepsilon_0} = \frac{Qa}{\varepsilon_0 A}$$

$$E = \frac{Q}{\varepsilon_0 A}$$

Next, calculate V from this $\vec{E}$. Since the field is uniform, the integral is simple:

$$V = -\int \vec{E} \cdot d\vec{l} = Ed = \frac{Qd}{\varepsilon_0 A}$$

Finally, use the definition of the capacitance.

$$C = \frac{Q}{V} = \frac{\varepsilon_0 A}{d}$$

Capacitance is the amount of charge that can be "stored" on one of the conductors per potential difference created by the storage. The preceding example indicates that capacitance is increased with wider plates, making the surface environment "roomier" for the charges. If the separation is made smaller, this too increases the capacitance, because the nearby opposite charges will help hold the surfaces charges in place.

Capacitors and Dielectrics

A **dielectric** is a nonconducting material. When such a material is inserted between the conductors of a capacitor, the capacitance of the system is increased. A simple model to explain why this happens proposes that the molecules of the dielectric molecules become polarized in the electric field between the conductors (figure 11).

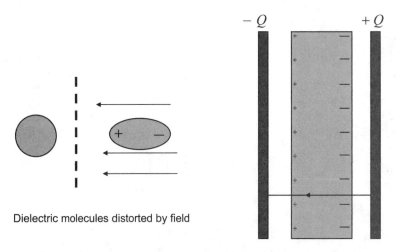

Dielectric molecules distorted by field

Surface charge induced on dielectric

figure 11

This creates a surface charge density at each surface of the dielectric as the molecules near the surface distort. Notice that the **induced surface charge** is of the opposite sign to the original charge on the nearest conductor. For points within the dielectric, this will weaken the electric field because these points will "see" effectively less charge on each plate. Assume the dielectric fills the space between the two conductors, and then consider these two cases:

Case I: The capacitor is connected to a device (such as a battery) that maintains a fixed voltage between the two conductors. In this case, the weakening of the field by the induced charge screening leads to a momentary lowering of the potential difference between the conductors, since $V = Ed$. The battery will then separate more charge until a new equilibrium is established at the original voltage. Now you have more charge separated for the same potential difference, so the capacitance is larger. You can define the dielectric constant of the material as the ratio of the old to the new capacitance:

$$C' = \kappa C$$

When the dielectric is introduced with a battery attached, capacitance goes up and more charge is stored, but the potential difference and electric field remain the same.

Case II: The charged capacitor is isolated before the dielectric is inserted. Now there's no battery attached and the charge on each conductor won't change. A surface charge will still be induced, however, and this will then decrease the electric field and potential difference. Since the same charge is now stored at a smaller potential difference, the capacitance has again increased. You can write

$$C' = \kappa C$$

$$\frac{Q}{V'} = \kappa \frac{Q}{V} \qquad \Rightarrow V' = \frac{V}{\kappa}$$

Similarly, $E' = \frac{E}{\kappa}$.

You can see that when a dielectric is inserted into an isolated capacitor, both E and V decrease, Q stays the same, and the capacitance increases.

EXAMPLE

A parallel plate capacitor with area A, separation d is charged so that $\pm Q$ is on the two plates. The battery is then removed, isolating the capacitor, and a dielectric with constant κ is inserted, completely filling the space between the plates. Determine the charge density induced at each surface of the dielectric.

From the earlier analysis of the parallel plate capacitor, you can infer that before the dielectric is inserted, the electric field is

$$E = \frac{Q}{\varepsilon_0 A} = \frac{\sigma}{\varepsilon_0}$$

When the capacitor is isolated, Q doesn't change, but surface charge is induced and the field decreases by $\frac{1}{\kappa}$, as shown earlier. You can introduce a Gaussian surface, as in figure 12.

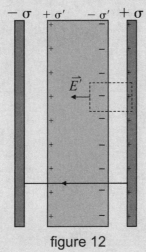

figure 12

The cap with area a in the conductor will have no flux, so the only contribution comes from the cap in the dielectric, where the field is $\vec{E'}$. Notice that the surface encloses charge on the conductor with density σ and induced charge with density σ'. Applying Gauss's law, you have

$$E'a = \frac{(\sigma - \sigma')a}{\varepsilon_0} \Rightarrow E' = \frac{(\sigma - \sigma')}{\varepsilon_0}$$

Since $E' = \frac{E}{\kappa}$, you can use the relation for E to determine σ'.

$$\frac{\sigma}{\kappa\varepsilon_0} = \frac{(\sigma - \sigma')}{\varepsilon_0} \Rightarrow \sigma' = \sigma\left(1 - \frac{1}{\kappa}\right)$$

Notice that large dielectric constants imply large induced charge densities, which leads to very effective screening of the conductor charge for points inside the dielectric.

Electric Potential Energy

As you've already learned, electric potential at a given point was originally defined as the negative of the work done by the field in slowly moving a charge from the zero point to the chosen point. The electric force associated with static fields is conservative (the work is independent of path), so you can identify the negative work with the change in the **electric potential energy**. In symbols, you have

$$\Delta V = \frac{-W_{\text{field}}}{q} = \frac{\Delta U}{q} \Rightarrow \Delta U = q\Delta V$$

For a positive charge to decrease in potential energy, $\Delta U < 0$, the charge must move downhill from higher to lower electric potential. But for a negative charge to decrease in potential energy, it must move from lower to higher electric potential, or uphill. If this seems confusing, remember that electric potential is a property of the point in space, independent of any charge placed there; electric potential energy is a specific property of a charge. You can look at this behavior concretely in figure 13.

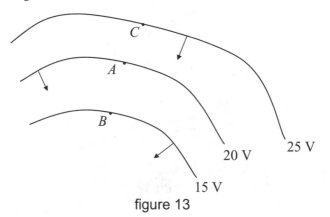

figure 13

Here, you can see three equipotential surfaces, labeled with their voltage levels. The electric field is perpendicular to the surfaces and points toward lower electric potential. A positive charge placed at A would be forced by the field toward B, where the electric potential is lower and where the charge will have less potential energy. A negative charge placed at A would be forced toward C, where the electric potential is higher but where the charge will have lower potential energy.

EXAMPLE

A -2 μC charge with mass 5×10^{-8} kg is released from rest at point A in figure 13. How fast will it be moving if it eventually passes through C?

The charge will decrease in PE and gain KE, $\Delta K = -\Delta U$.

$$\frac{1}{2}mv^2 = -q\Delta V = -(-2 \times 10^{-6})(25 - 20) = +10 \times 10^{-6}$$

$$V = \sqrt{\frac{20 \times 10^{-6}}{5 \times 10^{-8}}} = 20\ \frac{m}{s}$$

When several point charges are present in a given region, each charge has potential energy. Since you can easily calculate the electric potential due to a configuration of point charges, you can just as easily calculate the PE of a charge placed in the region.

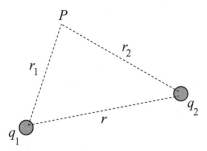

figure 14

For example, in figure 14, the two charges q_1 and q_2 create an electric potential at P (0 at infinity) given by

$$V_P = \frac{1}{4\pi\varepsilon_0}\frac{q_1}{r_1} + \frac{1}{4\pi\varepsilon_0}\frac{q_2}{r_2}$$

If a third charge q_3 is placed at P, it will have potential energy, measured with respect to 0 at infinity, given by

$$U = q_3 V_P = \frac{1}{4\pi\varepsilon_0}\frac{q_3 q_1}{r_1} + \frac{1}{4\pi\varepsilon_0}\frac{q_3 q_2}{r_2}$$

EXAMPLE

What is the total potential energy of the system of three charges after q_3 has been placed at P?

The answer isn't just the previous result, because there's potential energy in the system of q_1 and q_2 even before q_3 is introduced. To sort this out, imagine constructing the system from scratch with all the charges out at infinity. The PE of the system will be the PE gained by everything as the charges are placed in position. Let's say you bring in q_1 first. This takes no work because there are no charges present yet to move against. Next, you bring in q_2. Since q_1 creates a potential at the position of q_2, it gains an amount of PE written as

$$U_{12} = q_2 V_1 = \frac{1}{4\pi\varepsilon_0} \frac{q_2 q_1}{r}$$

Finally, q_3 is placed so that the total gain in PE is

$$U_{total} = \frac{1}{4\pi\varepsilon_0} \left(\frac{q_2 q_1}{r} + \frac{q_3 q_1}{r_1} + \frac{q_3 q_2}{r_2} \right)$$

Sometimes this total PE is called the **energy of assembly**, for obvious reasons.

Electric Energy and Capacitors

When a capacitor is charged, energy has to be supplied to separate the charge on the conductors. You can think of this as energy stored in the position of the separated charges, which can be recovered by allowing the charges to move. This means that you can think of the work supplied in charging the capacitor as potential energy. How much energy is stored in a capacitor carrying charge Q? Imagine the capacitor partially charged to some value q. Then, to separate the next little bit dq, it must move through the potential difference created by q, so

$$dU = dq V(q) = dq \frac{q}{C}$$

Integrating, you get

$$U = \int_0^Q \frac{q}{C} dq = \frac{1}{2} \frac{Q^2}{C}$$

Using the definition of capacitance, you can also write this relation as

$$U = \frac{1}{2} CV^2 = \frac{1}{2} QV$$

EXAMPLE

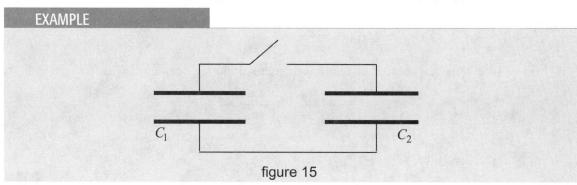

figure 15

Capacitor C_1 is charged to a voltage V_0 and isolated. A second capacitor C_2 is connected to C_1 through a switch as shown in figure 15. The switch is then thrown, allowing charge to redistribute. Find the final charge and voltage distributions on the two capacitors and the energy lost as a result of the movement of charge.

The initial charge on C_1 is $Q = C_1 V_0$. Assume $+ Q$ is on the top plate and $- Q$ is on the bottom. The energy stored is

$$U_0 = \frac{1}{2} C_1 V_0^2$$

When the switch is closed, charge will be redistributed until the two top plates are an equipotential surface and the two bottom plates are also an equipotential surface. This means the potential difference across each capacitor is the same. If you call q_1 and q_2 the respective final charges on the two top plates, you have

$$\frac{q_1}{C_1} = \frac{q_2}{C_2}$$

The charge $+ Q$ on the C_1 top plate initially can only stay on the two top plates; there's no other place it can move to, so

$$Q = q_1 + q_2$$

Solving these two equations results in

$$q_1 = Q \frac{C_1}{C_1 + C_2} \quad q_2 = Q \frac{C_2}{C_1 + C_2}$$

Using $Q = C_1 V_0$ and the fact that $V = \frac{q}{C}$ for each capacitor, you can find that the final voltage across each capacitor is

$$V_f = V_0 \frac{C_1}{C_1 + C_2}$$

The final energy stored will be

$$U_f = \frac{1}{2} C_1 V_f^2 + \frac{1}{2} C_2 V_f^2 = \frac{1}{2} C_1 V_0^2 \left(\frac{C_1}{(C_1 + C_2)} \right)$$

The energy lost during the transfer will be

$$U_f - U_0 = \frac{1}{2} C_1 V_0^2 \left(\frac{C_1}{(C_1 + C_2)} - 1 \right)$$

$$\Delta U = -\frac{1}{2} C_1 V_0^2 \left(\frac{C_2}{(C_1 + C_2)} \right) = -U_0 \left(\frac{C_2}{(C_1 + C_2)} \right)$$

The energy lost would appear as thermal energy in the connecting circuit.

If you look at the specific case of a parallel plate capacitor, you can derive a formula for the energy density associated with an electric field. Since the electric field within a parallel plate capacitor ideally is completely contained in the space between the plates and since this space has a volume of Ad, you can write

$$U = \frac{1}{2}CV^2 = \frac{1}{2}\left(\frac{\varepsilon_0 A}{d}\right)\left(Ed\right)^2 = \left(\frac{1}{2}\varepsilon_0 E^2\right)\left(Ad\right)$$

Dividing by the volume between the plates, you have the energy density:

$$u_E = \frac{1}{2}\varepsilon_0 E^2$$

At any point within the capacitor, you can think of a certain energy per volume that's stored in the electric field. Although it's derived for the special case of the parallel plate capacitor, this relation is valid in vacuum for any configuration of charges creating the field.

KEY FORMULAS

Definition of Electric Potential	$\Delta V = \dfrac{-W_{field}}{q} = -\displaystyle\int_{P_1}^{P_2} \vec{E} \cdot d\vec{l}$
Potential Difference in Uniform Field	$\Delta V = Es$
Potential Due to a Point Charge	$V = \dfrac{1}{4\pi\varepsilon_0}\dfrac{Q}{R}$
Potential Due to Several Point Charges	$V = \dfrac{1}{4\pi\varepsilon_0}\dfrac{q_1}{r_1} + \dfrac{1}{4\pi\varepsilon_0}\dfrac{q_2}{r_2} + \ldots$
Electric Potential at P	$V_P = -\displaystyle\int_{\infty}^{P} \vec{E} \cdot d\vec{l}$
Field from Potential	$E_l = -\dfrac{dV}{dl}$
Capacitance	$C = \dfrac{Q}{V}$
Parallel Plate Capacitor	$C = \dfrac{\varepsilon_0 A}{d}$
Dielectric Inserted into Capacitor	$C' = \kappa C$
Electric Potential Energy	$\Delta U = q\Delta V$
Electric PE of Two Point Charges	$U = \dfrac{1}{4\pi\varepsilon_0}\dfrac{q_1 q_2}{R}$
Energy Stored in Capacitor	$U = \dfrac{1}{2}\dfrac{Q^2}{C} = \dfrac{1}{2}CV^2 = \dfrac{1}{2}QV$
Energy Density in Electric Field	$u_E = \dfrac{1}{2}\varepsilon_0 E^2$

PRACTICE EXERCISES

SECTION I MULTIPLE CHOICE

Questions 1–3

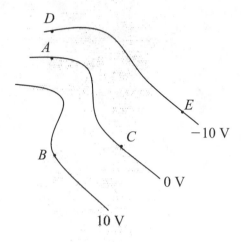

figure 16

1. The direction of the electric field at A is

   (A) →   (B) ↑   (C) ↓   (D) ↗   (E) ↙

2. An electron placed at C and released would most likely pass closest to

   (A) A (B) B (C) C (D) D (E) E

3. The distance between D and A is 10^{-2} m. The strength of the electric field at A is most nearly

   (A) $10 \frac{V}{m}$ (B) $10^2 \frac{V}{m}$ (C) $10^{-1}\frac{V}{m}$ (D) $10^3\frac{V}{m}$ (E) $10^{-2}\frac{V}{m}$

4. A positive charge Q is a distance R from a point P. The electric potential at P could be doubled by
   I. placing an identical charge Q at another point a distance R from P
   II. placing charge $2Q$ at a distance $2R$ from P
   III. placing charge $4Q$ at a distance $2R$ from P

   (A) I only   (B) II only   (C) III only   (D) I and II only   (E) I and III only

advantage™

Questions 5 and 6
Two equal positive charges are fixed on the *x*-axis at equal distances from the origin.

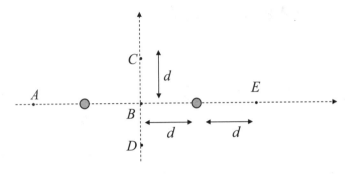

figure 17

5. The electric potential is a maximum at

   (A) *A*   (B) *B*   (C) *C*   (D) *D*   (E) *E*

6. It would take 0 work to move a charge from

   (A) *A* to *B*   (B) *C* to *B*   (C) *B* to *D*   (D) *A* to *E*   (E) *C* to *E*

7. An isolated conductor has a charge *Q* placed on it. When equilibrium is established,

   (A) excess charge will reside on the surface, and the electric field will be 0 outside the conductor
   (B) the charge will spread throughout the conducting material, making the electric field 0 inside the conductor
   (C) all points of the conductor will be at the same potential, with electric field lines tangential to the surface
   (D) the excess charge will move to the surface, and all points of the conductor will be at the same potential
   (E) the excess charge will move to the surface, making the electric field inside the conductor equal to the field just outside the conductor

8. A charge distribution creates an electric potential that varies along the *x*-axis as $V(x) = 2x^2 - 5x$. The *x*-component of the electric field at $x = 1$ is

   (A) $-3\frac{\text{V}}{\text{m}}$ (B) $3\frac{\text{V}}{\text{m}}$ (C) $-1\frac{\text{V}}{\text{m}}$ (D) $1\frac{\text{V}}{\text{m}}$ (E) 0

9. A parallel plate capacitor with capacitance C is charged to a value Q and then isolated. The separation between the plates is then tripled. The work required to separate the plates was

(A) $\dfrac{1}{2}\dfrac{Q^2}{C}$ (B) $\dfrac{3}{2}\dfrac{Q^2}{C}$ (C) $\dfrac{9}{2}\dfrac{Q^2}{C}$ (D) $\dfrac{Q^2}{C}$ (E) $\dfrac{1}{6}\dfrac{Q^2}{C}$

10. A parallel plate capacitor with capacitance C is connected to a battery, causing charge $+Q$ and $-Q$ to reside on the two plates. With the battery connected, a dielectric material with constant κ is inserted between the plates. Which of the following is true when equilibrium is established?

(A) The dielectric develops a $+$ surface charge near the $-$ plate, reducing the potential difference between the plates.

(B) The dielectric develops a $+$ surface charge near the $-$ plate, which will now carry a charge a negative charge greater than $-Q$.

(C) The dielectric develops a $+$ surface charge near the $-$ plate, reducing the capacitance of the system

(D) The dielectric develops a $-$ surface charge near the $-$ plate, and the potential difference between the plates remains the same.

(E) The dielectric develops a $-$ surface charge near the $-$ plate, which will now carry a charge greater than $-Q$.

11. A spherical capacitor consisting of two concentric spherical conducting shells is charged so that an electric field $\vec{E}$ exists in the space between the conductors. More charge is added until the magnitude of the field has doubled at every point within the capacitor. If the initial energy stored was U_0, the work it took to add the extra charge was

(A) U_0 (B) $2U_0$ (C) $3U_0$ (D) $4U_0$ (E) $\dfrac{1}{2}U_0$

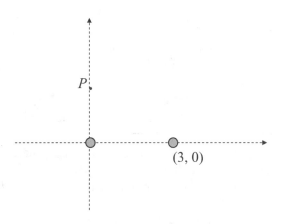

figure 18

1. Two identical $+ 6 \ \mu C$ charges with mass 10^{-6} kg are placed as shown in figure 18.
    (a) Determine the electric potential at P, with position $(0, 3)$.
    (b) An identical third charge is brought slowly from far away to P. How much work did this take?
    (c) All three charges are released simultaneously. What is the maximum speed attained by each of them?

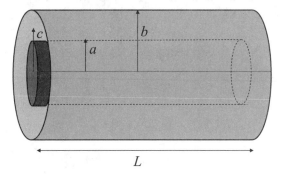

figure 19

2. An isolated cylindrical capacitor consists of two concentric conducting cylinders of length L and radii a and b. The inner and outer conductors carry $+ Q$ and $- Q$, respectively.
    (a) Determine the electric field between the conductors.
    (b) Determine the electric potential difference between the two conductors.
    (c) What is the capacitance of this device?
    (d) A dielectric material with constant κ is introduced, filling the region $a < r < c$, with $c < b$. What will be the final potential difference between the two conductors?

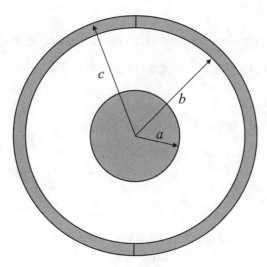

figure 20

3. A spherical nonconductor of radius a carries a charge $+Q$ uniformly spread over its volume. Two hemispherical conducting shells of inner radii b and outer radii c are brought together concentrically, with the nonconductor forming a single conducting sphere. The outer sphere is momentarily connected by a wire to 0 potential (grounded), and then the wire is removed. Determine the electric potential at the position $r = b$ just outside the conducting shell
   (a) before the conductor is introduced
   (b) after the conductor is introduced but before it is grounded
   (c) after the conductor is grounded

Answers and Explanations

MULTIPLE CHOICE

1. The answer is B. The electric field is perpendicular to the equipotentials, pointing toward lower potential.

2. The answer is B. Electrons are negative and will move toward higher potential, which would take the electron from 0 V toward the $+10$ V surface.

3. The answer is D. The average field in the region between A and D is $E = \dfrac{\Delta V}{s} = \dfrac{10}{10^{-2}}$

4. The answer is D. For several point charges, just add the contribution of each. The contribution from I is $\dfrac{1}{4\pi\varepsilon_0}\dfrac{Q}{R}$, the same as the original, so the potential is doubled. The contribution from II is also the same. Choice III, however, gives $k\dfrac{4Q}{2R}$, which is twice the original.

5. The answer is B. At any point, the two charges contribute $V = \frac{1}{4\pi\varepsilon_0}\left(\frac{q}{r_1} + \frac{q}{r_2}\right)$. By making both r_1 and r_2 as small as possible you get the biggest value of V. This occurs at B.

6. The answer is D. A and E are both at the potential $V = \frac{1}{4\pi\varepsilon_0}\left(\frac{q}{R} + \frac{q}{3R}\right)$, so there's no potential difference between the two points. This means it takes no net work to move a charge between the points. Notice that C and D are also at the same potential, but they weren't given together as a choice.

7. The answer is D. In electrostatic equilibrium, excess charge on a conductor lies on the surface. Since the field is 0 inside and enters at right angles at the surface, it takes no work to move a charge anywhere on or in the conductor, so the entire object is at the same potential.

8. The answer is D. $E_x = -\frac{dV}{dx} = -4x + 5$. At $x = 1$, you get 1 V/m.

9. The answer is D. The initial energy stored is $\frac{1}{2}\frac{Q^2}{C}$. Q remains fixed, but separation of the plates decreases the capacitance to $\frac{1}{3}C$. Then the final energy stored is

$$\frac{1}{2}\frac{Q^2}{\frac{1}{3}C} = 3\left(\frac{1}{2}\frac{Q^2}{C}\right)$$

The difference between final and initial stored energy is the work needed to separate the plates, leading to D.

10. The answer is B. The induced charge will always be of opposite sign to the nearest plate. The screening that this creates for points inside the dielectric will decrease the electric potential drop across the dielectric. Since the battery is connected, more charge will be separated, so the final charge on the negative plate is greater than $-Q$.

11. The answer is C. Doubling the magnitude of $\vec{E}$ will quadruple the energy density, since $u_E \propto E^2$. This means that the final energy stored in the capacitor is $4U_0$. The work needed to add the extra charge is the difference between the final and initial energy stored, $3U_0$.

FREE RESPONSE

1. (a) Superpositions allows you to add the potentials of each charge as if the other weren't present.

$$V_P = 9 \times 10^9 \left(\frac{6 \times 10^{-6}}{3} + \frac{6 \times 10^{-6}}{3\sqrt{2}} \right) = 3.1 \times 10^4 \text{ V}$$

(b) The work follows from the definition of electric potential.

$$W = qV_P = (6 \times 10^{-6})(3.1 \times 10^4) = 0.19 \text{ J}$$

(c) By symmetry, each charge will end up with the same KE when the charges have moved out to infinity. This KE will be $\frac{1}{3}$ the initial stored PE in the configuration of the three charges. To the answer to b, you'll need to add the PE stored in the initial positions of the first two charges. This is

$$U_{12} = 9 \times 10^9 \frac{(6 \times 10^{-6})^2}{3} = 0.11 \text{ J}$$

The initial PE is $U_0 = 0.11 + 0.19 = 0.30$ J. Then you can find the final speed of one charge this way:

$$K_f = \frac{1}{3} U_0 = 0.1 \text{ J}$$

$$\frac{1}{2}mv^2 = \frac{1}{2}(10^{-6})v^2 = 0.1$$

$$v = 450 \frac{\text{m}}{\text{s}}$$

2. (a) Drawing a cylindrical Gaussian surface of length L with radius r between the two conductors, you can apply Gauss's law. This surface encloses all the charge on the inner conductor, and the only flux is through the sheath.

$$E(2\pi rL) = \frac{Q}{\varepsilon_0} \quad \Rightarrow E = \frac{Q}{2\pi\varepsilon_0 rL}$$

(b) Using the definition of electric potential difference, integrate $\vec{E}$ between the two conductors.

$$V = -\int_b^a \vec{E} \cdot d\vec{r} = -\int_b^a \frac{Q}{2\pi\varepsilon_0 Lr} \, dr$$

$$V = \frac{Q}{2\pi\varepsilon_0 rL} \ln \frac{b}{a}$$

(c) From the definition of capacitance, you get

$$C = \frac{Q}{V} = \frac{Q}{\frac{Q}{2\pi\varepsilon_0 L} \ln \frac{b}{a}} = \frac{2\pi\varepsilon_0 L}{\ln \frac{b}{a}}$$

(d) For the isolated capacitor, the electric field outside the dielectric remains the same, while within the dielectric it decreases by $\frac{1}{\kappa}$. Then you can use the definition of potential difference again, but break the integration into two parts since $\vec{E}$ changes.

$$V = \int_b^a \vec{E} \cdot d\vec{l} = -\int_b^c \vec{E}_{out} \cdot d\vec{l} - \int_c^a \vec{E}_{in} \cdot d\vec{l}$$

$$V = \int_b^c \frac{Q\,dr}{2\pi\varepsilon_0 L r} - \int_c^a \frac{Q\,dr}{2\pi\varepsilon_0 \kappa L r}$$

$$V = \frac{Q}{2\pi\varepsilon_0 L}\left(\ln\frac{b}{c} + \frac{1}{\kappa}\ln\frac{c}{a}\right)$$

3. (a) Before the conductor is introduced, the nonconductor acts as a point charge for points outside of it. At $r = b$, you have

$$V_b = \frac{Q}{4\pi\varepsilon_0 b}$$

(b) After the conductor is introduced, charge will separate to the inner and outer surfaces of the conductor, with $-Q$ drawn inward, leaving $+Q$ on the outer surface. If you aren't convinced of this, draw a spherical Gaussian surface just inside the conductor at $r = b$. The flux through this must be 0 since the field is 0, so it must contain 0 charge as well. Since $+Q$ of the nonconductor is inside, there must be $-Q$ on the conductor inner surface as well. For points outside the conductor, the total charge inside is still $+Q$. At $r = c$, the potential is

$$V_c = \frac{Q}{4\pi\varepsilon_0 c}$$

But moving a test charge to b takes no further work because $\vec{E}$ is 0 in the conductor. Now,

$$V_b = \frac{Q}{4\pi\varepsilon_0 c}$$

(c) With the conductor grounded, the $+Q$ on the outer surface can move to infinity or 0 potential. The $-Q$ on the inner surface must remain to ensure that the field in the conductor remains 0. With the wire removed, points outside the conductor will see 0 charge. The result is that it takes no work to move a test charge from infinity all the way to the inner conducting surface. As the test charge emerges into the space between the conductors, it sees the effective point charge $+Q$, so

$$V_b = \frac{Q}{4\pi\varepsilon_0 b}$$

Electric Circuits

Electrostatics deals with electrical effects when all charges have stopped moving. In this chapter, you'll look at the effects of organized motion of charges. Charges can be agents for energy transfer, and electric circuits can facilitate energy transfer to various elements of the circuit. You'll also study resistors and capacitors in detail as examples of circuit elements.

Conductors and Electric Current

A conductor contains many charges, usually electrons, that aren't tightly bound to any one atom. A lump of metal sitting on a table contains many trillions of electrons undergoing random motion due to the thermal energy the material possesses. The speeds associated with these thermal motions are quite large, on the order of 10^6 m/s, but the motion is random. And with many collisions occurring every second, there will always be equal numbers of electrons moving in opposite directions, so there's never a net movement of electrons in any one direction.

An **electric current** is a flow of electric charge. To get an electric current in a conductor, you need to get the electrons, which carry electric charge, to move in an organized manner. You can do this by introducing an electric field into the conductor. The mobile electrons will continue to execute their rapid thermal motion, but they'll have a tendency to drift up the field lines because there's a net force on the electrons opposite the field direction (figure 1).

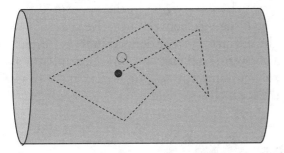

Thermal motion: electrons move rapidly but on average have zero displacement.

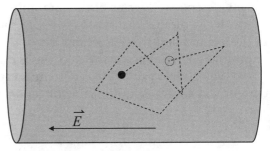

Electric field causes electrons to drift slowly opposite the field lines.

figure 1

The rate at which electrons move along the field lines is called the **drift speed**, typically about 10^{-4} m/s, which is quite small. But so many electrons are moving in a typical conductor that the currents can be quite large. Electric current is defined quantitatively as the rate at which charge crosses an area.

$$i = \frac{dq}{dt}$$

The unit for electric current is $\frac{C}{s}$, called an **Ampere** (A). Sometimes it's useful to define the **current density** $\vec{j}$ within a conductor. The flux of the current density over an area will be the current flowing through the area:

$$i = \oint \vec{j} \cdot \vec{dA}$$

The most common situation for the AP test occurs in straight wires with a uniform current density. Here the area is the cross-sectional area of the wire, and $\vec{j}$ and $\vec{dA}$ are parallel. In this case, you have

$$i = \oint \vec{j} \cdot \vec{dA} = \oint j\,dA = j \oint dA = jA$$

For a uniform current distribution, the current density is $j = \frac{i}{A}$, directed along the local current flow direction.

EXERCISE

Find the electric current established when 10^{20} electrons move through a cross section of a copper wire in 30 seconds.

Since each electron carries 1.6×10^{-19} C, you have

$$i = \frac{1.6 \times 10^{-19}(10^{20})}{30} = 0.53 \text{ A}$$

While the negative electrons actually move through the wires in common circuits, circuits are usually described in terms of the motion of positive charges moving in the opposite direction. Only precise measurements on a wire can show the difference between negative charges moving to the left and positive charges moving to the right. Electric current defined in terms of the flow of positive charge opposite the electrons is called **conventional current**, but unless it's otherwise stated, you should assume that current means conventional current (figure 2). In this way, the current will always be in the same direction as the local electric field.

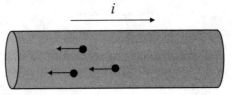

Conventional current: electron drift to the left
is equivalent to positive charge drift to the
right

figure 2

Batteries

When a conductor is placed in an external electric field, the charges will move in response to the field. The presence of the electric field creates a potential difference between points on the conductor, and positive charge tends to move to lower potential. If the conductor is just sitting in an external field, the charges will quickly be redistributed and eliminate any potential differences, as you saw in the discussion about equipotential surfaces.

But if you connect to the conductor a device that will maintain a potential difference between points on the conductor, equilibrium won't be established, and charges will continue to move from higher to lower potential. For this process to continue, the charges that have moved to lower potential must be raised back to higher potential again. Otherwise, the redistributed charges will change the potential difference impressed upon the conductor by the device. This means that the device must be able to add energy to charges and raise them to higher electric potential.

A battery is one example of such a device. The nature of the chemical reaction within the battery determines the potential difference between the terminals. In essence, the battery maintains a charge separation between the terminals (figure 3).

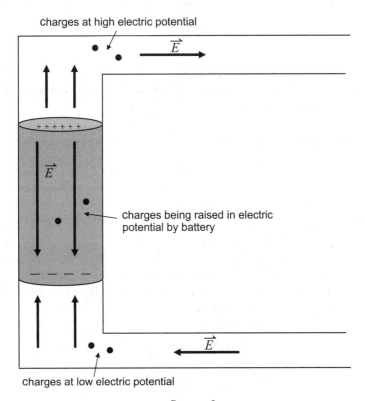

charges at high electric potential

$\vec{E}$

$\vec{E}$

charges being raised in electric potential by battery

$\vec{E}$

charges at low electric potential

figure 3

When the terminals are connected to a conductor, an electric field is set up in the wire very quickly, and mobile charges begin to move immediately. After a (usually) brief period of time, a **steady state** is established; the current flowing at any point in the circuit doesn't change. As the charges move around the circuit, they transfer the potential energy they gained from the battery to the circuit elements through which they pass. When they enter the battery at the negative terminal, positive charges are faced with an electric field that opposes their movement to the positive terminal. The energy required to move these charges through so that they can re-enter the circuit at the positive terminal is supplied by the chemical energy derived from the reacting chemicals. The symbol for a battery is displayed in figure 4; the positive terminal is the longer line.

figure 4

Electrical Resistance and Ohm's Law

When a potential difference is applied across a conductor, the current established is directly proportional to the impressed voltage difference. This empirical fact is known as **Ohm's law**.

$$\Delta V \propto I$$

A plot of ΔV vs. I will be a straight line, and its slope is called the **electrical resistance** of the conductor. The name "resistance" is justified. Consider figure 5, which depicts the graphs for two different conductors. You can see that the steeper slope has less current established for the same applied potential difference; this conductor resists current flow more than the conductor with smaller slope.

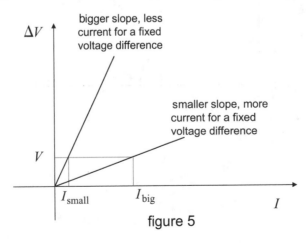

figure 5

If you call the resistance R, Ohm's law is written as

$$\Delta V = IR$$

The SI units of resistance are $\frac{V}{I}$, called **ohms** (Ω). The resistance of a conductor will depend on a number of factors. For example, let's consider a cylindrical length L of conductor with cross-sectional area A and a fixed potential difference ΔV between the ends (figure 6).

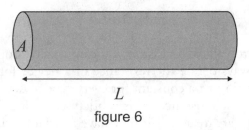

figure 6

As the charges move through the material, collisions will slow them down. More collisions mean less current and greater resistance. So you might expect that a long, narrow conductor would have more resistance than a short, wide one. You might also suspect that different materials would have an effect as well. These ideas can be summed up in the relation

$$R = \rho\frac{L}{A}$$

The dependence on geometry comes from the $\frac{L}{A}$ factor. The dependence on material is contained in ρ, called the resistivity of the material.

EXERCISE

A 0.3 m length of wire with uniform cross-sectional area 8×10^{-5} m^2 has a potential difference of 5 V applied across it, producing a current of 2 A. Find the resistance of the wire and the resistivity of the material.

You can find the resistance immediately from Ohm's law.

$$R = \frac{\Delta V}{I} = \frac{5}{2} = 2.5\ \Omega$$

Now use the given data with the resistivity relation.

$$\rho = \frac{RA}{L} = \frac{(2.5)(8 \times 10^{-5})}{0.3} = 6.7 \times 10^{-4}\ \Omega \cdot m$$

A **resistor** is a type of circuit element with a fixed resistance. Resistors are introduced into circuits to set up specific potential drops between points in the circuit or to protect delicate elements from large currents, among other things. The symbol for a resistor is shown in figure 7.

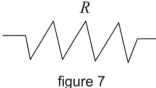

figure 7

When writing the voltage drop across a resistor, you can usually drop the Δ and write simply $V = I R$. While you can always define the resistance of a device for a given voltage drop and current as the ratio $\frac{V}{I}$, this ratio isn't a constant for every type of device. Something as basic as a light bulb will display a variable resistance. This subtlety is not a point of emphasis on the AP test, however, and light bulbs are treated as if they have constant resistance.

Electric Power

Consider a circuit element with a single path for current to flow through it and a potential difference V across it (figure 8). Since charge is a conserved quantity, and since there's only one path in and one path out of the element, the current i is the same coming into and out of the device.

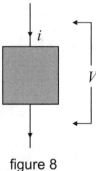

figure 8

As a little bit of charge Δq moves through the device, it loses electrical potential energy, $\Delta U = \Delta q V$, and the device gains this energy. If you divide by the time over which this occurs, you get the rate at which energy is transferred to the device, the power consumed by the device:

$$P = \frac{\Delta U}{\Delta t} = \frac{\Delta q}{\Delta t} V = iV$$

This relation will be true for any device with a single current flowing through it. If the device also obeys Ohm's law with resistance R, you can write

$$P = i(iR) = i^2 R = \frac{V^2}{R}$$

EXAMPLE

A 1,000 W hair dryer is designed to work properly with a 120 V potential difference applied. Find the resistance of the hair dryer and the current established in the connection circuit.

You can use the power relation $P = \dfrac{V^2}{R} \Rightarrow R = \dfrac{(120)^2}{1000} = 14.4 \ \Omega$

Then apply Ohm's law to get the current: $i = \dfrac{V}{R} = \dfrac{120}{14.4} = 8.3$ A

Kirchhoff's Laws

When an assembly of circuit devices is connected to one or more batteries, the current and voltage drops throughout the circuit can be determined theoretically by applying two basic laws called **Kirchhoff's laws** to the circuit. The laws themselves are statements about conservation of charge and the conservative nature of the electric force, phrased in the language of circuits.

I. **Junction Law** (Kirchhoff's first law)—At a junction in a circuit, the sum of the current entering the junction will equal the sum of the current leaving the circuit.

$$\sum_{\text{in}} i = \sum_{\text{out}} i$$

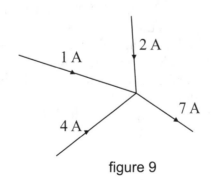

figure 9

Consider the junction of four wires shown in figure 9. Every second, the three wires leading into the junction carry $2 + 1 + 4 = 7$ C of charge. Since charge is conserved, 7 C must leave the junction every second.

II. **Loop Law** (Kirchhoff's second law)—The sum of the potential drops around any closed loop must add to 0.

$$\sum_{\text{loop}} \Delta V = 0$$

Imagine an arbitrary point in a circuit. The potential difference between this point and itself is obviously 0. Since the electric force is conservative, the work done on a test charge must be 0 for any path that begins and ends at this point. And because the potential difference is just the work per charge, the loop law follows.

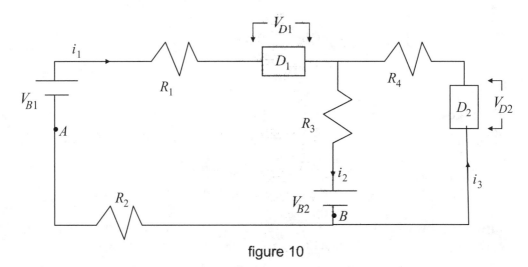

figure 10

Consider the two-loop circuit in figure 10, consisting of two batteries, four resistors, and two other energy-consuming devices. Imagine traversing the left-hand loop clockwise, beginning at point A. First, you go up in potential as the battery is traversed from the negative to the positive terminal. The next three elements, R_1, D_1, and R_3, all have current flowing though them in the same direction that you're following. Since current flows from higher to lower potential, each element will have a negative potential difference across it—that is, you go down in potential as you move through it in this direction. Next, you traverse the second battery from the positive to the negative terminal, implying a negative potential drop. Finally, you traverse R_2 traveling with the current, so once again you have a negative drop. Applying the loop law, you have

$$+V_{B1} - i_1 R_1 - V_{D1} - i_2 R_3 - V_{B2} - i_1 R_2 = 0$$

If you had traversed in the opposite direction, all the signs would have reversed, giving you the same result. If you traverse the right-hand loop clockwise, starting at B, the loop law gives you

$$+V_{B_2} + i_2 R_3 + i_3 R_4 + V_{D_2} = 0$$

Resistors in Series and Parallel

Two circuit elements are in **series** if the two elements will always have equal currents within them, regardless of other changes in the circuit. When several resistors are connected in series, you could replace them with a single resistor so that the overall current drawn from the batteries wouldn't change (figure 11).

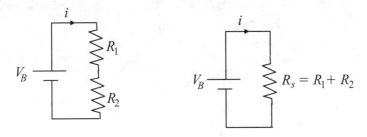

figure 11

This resistor is called the equivalent series resistance, R_s. The value of the resistor is the sum of the individual resistors in series:

$$R_s = R_1 + R_2 + \ldots$$

You can see that adding a resistor in series with another will make it more difficult for charge to move and will decrease the current if the same potential difference is applied. Then, the resistance increases. In simple terms, if you think of $R = \rho \frac{L}{A}$, adding resistors in series is like increasing L, which clearly increases R.

Two circuit elements are said to be in **parallel** if the two elements will always have the same potential difference across them, regardless of other changes in the circuit. When several resistors are in parallel, more paths are available for charge to move through the circuit than when just one resistor is present. This makes it easier for charges to move. The equivalent parallel resistance—the value of the single resistor with which you could replace all the parallel resistors and maintain the same battery currents—will be less than any of the individual resistors (figure 12).

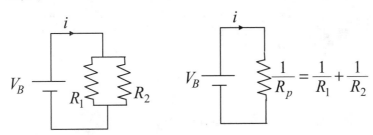

figure 12

The value of this resistor is

$$\frac{1}{R_p} = \frac{1}{R_1} + \frac{1}{R_2} + \ \cdots$$

Notice that for N identical resistors in parallel, the equivalent parallel resistance is $\frac{R}{N}$. In simple terms, if you think of $R = \rho \frac{L}{A}$, adding resistors in parallel is like increasing the cross-sectional area, which decreases the resistance.

EXAMPLE

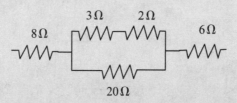

figure 13

Find the equivalent resistance of the resistor combination in figure 13.

Just as you remove parentheses from the inside out in an algebraic expression, you proceed from the inside out in a resistor network. The 2 Ω and the 3 Ω are in series, giving an equivalent value of 5 Ω. This 5 Ω is in parallel with the 20 Ω. Applying the parallel formula, you have

$$\frac{1}{R_p} = \frac{1}{20} + \frac{1}{5} = \frac{1}{4} \Rightarrow R_p = 4 \ \Omega$$

Finally, the 4 Ω, the 8 Ω, and the 6 Ω are all in series, making a total of 18 Ω as the equivalent resistance of the network.

Terminal Voltage

As charges are raised in electric potential within a battery, inevitably losses will occur due to collisions, and some of the theoretical potential energy gain of the charges will be lost to the random thermal motion of the battery molecules. You can model this behavior by thinking of a battery as an ideal voltage source connected in series with a resistor, the so-called **internal resistance** of the battery (figure 14).

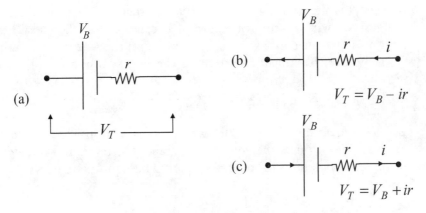

figure 14

Of course, the "resistor" isn't a distinct element that can ever be removed. It's just a way of accounting for the electrical effects of the energy losses within the battery. The **terminal voltage** V_T of the battery is the potential difference between the terminals of the battery, and it will be different from the ideal voltage V_B determined by the chemistry of the battery. The actual value of the terminal voltage will depend on the direction of the current through the battery. In the normal mode of operation, depicted in b, as you proceed from the right to left terminal, there is a voltage drop of $-ir$ through the internal resistance, followed by a voltage rise of V_B through the ideal battery. Then the terminal voltage will be

$$V_T = V_B - ir$$

If the battery is being recharged, the current will flow as in c. Then as you move from right to left, the potential goes up as you pass through the resistor and as you move through the ideal battery. For a recharging battery, you have

$$V_T = V_B + ir$$

Current Division

When electric current enters a junction, Kirchhoff's first law tells you that the sum of the currents entering must equal the sum of the currents leaving. But the specific values of the current entering and leaving a junction are determined by the batteries and resistances in the circuit. Consider the situation shown in figure 15a:

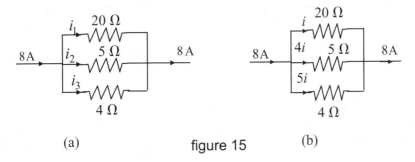

(a)   figure 15   (b)

A current of 8 A enters the junction and divides. (Notice that the resistor values are in simple ratios.) The 20 Ω resistor will get the least current because it has the most resistance. The 5 Ω will get 4 times as much since it has $\frac{1}{4}$ the resistance, and the 4 Ω will get 5 times as much since it has $\frac{1}{5}$ the resistance. Calling the current in the largest resistor i, figure 15b and the junction law give you

$$8 = i + 4i + 5i \Rightarrow i = 0.8 \text{ A}$$

This is the fastest way to determine how currents split at a junction when resistance ratios are simple. An alternative approach uses the equivalent parallel resistance and the fact that parallel resistors all have the same potential drop across them. The equivalent resistance of the three resistors is

$$\frac{1}{R_p} = \frac{1}{20} + \frac{1}{5} + \frac{1}{4} = \frac{1}{2} \Rightarrow R_p = 2 \, \Omega$$

Since the 8 A effectively flows through this resistance, the voltage drop across the network is

$$V = iR_p = 8 \cdot 2 = 16 \text{ V}$$

But this must be the voltage across each resistor, because they are all in parallel. That leads to

$$
\begin{aligned}
16 &= i_1(20) &\Rightarrow \quad i_1 &= 0.8 \text{ A} \\
16 &= i_2(5) &\Rightarrow \quad i_2 &= 3.2 \text{ A} \\
16 &= i_3(4) &\Rightarrow \quad i_3 &= 4 \text{ A}
\end{aligned}
$$

This might be your best approach if the ratios aren't simple.

Simple Circuits

A **simple circuit** is a connection of batteries and resistors that meets two criteria:
1. All batteries are in series.
2. The equivalent resistance of the entire circuit can be obtained by the repeated use of just the series and parallel equivalent resistance formulas.

When batteries are in series, the equivalent battery voltage will be the algebraic sum of the individual voltages of each battery. These criteria imply that a simple circuit can be reduced to a single equivalent voltage source by addition and subtraction, and a single equivalent resistance using the series and parallel formulas. Although a so-called simple circuit need not look simple, the circuits that appear on the AP tests are not overly complex. You'll need to be able to determine the currents established in the circuit, potential drops across elements, terminal voltages, and energy consumption or supply by the elements.

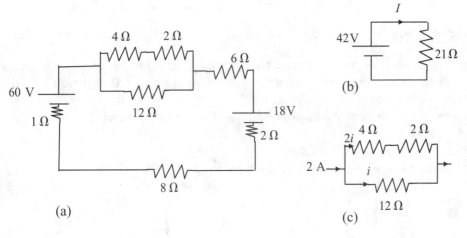

figure 16

EXAMPLE

Figure 16a is a simple circuit. The two batteries with internal resistances of 1 Ω and 2 Ω are in series. Since the batteries are connected to oppose each other, the equivalent battery voltage for the circuit is

$$V_B = 60 - 18 = 42 \text{ V}$$

Notice that the 18 V battery is recharging. The resistors in the network, including the internal resistance, can all be reduced to a single equivalent resistance using the series and parallel rules. The 4 Ω and 2 Ω in series combine to give 6 Ω. This is then in parallel with the 12 Ω, giving you

$$\frac{1}{R_p} = \frac{1}{12} + \frac{1}{6} = \frac{1}{4} \Rightarrow R_p = 4 \text{ } \Omega$$

Finally, you can add this to the 8 Ω, the 6 Ω, and the internal resistances. The total equivalent resistance of the circuit is

$$R_{\text{equiv}} = 4 + 8 + 6 + 3 = 21 \text{ } \Omega$$

Now you've effectively reduced the circuit to what is shown in figure 16b. You can determine the current I in this make-believe circuit from the loop law:

$$42 - I(21) = 0 \Rightarrow I = 2 \text{ A}$$

In the real circuit, this will be the current in the batteries and everything in series with them. Each battery carries 2 A, so you can find the terminal voltages:

$$V_T^{60} = 60 - 2 \cdot 1 = 58 \text{ V}$$

$$V_T^{18} = 18 + 2 \cdot 2 = 22 \text{ V}$$

The 2 A will divide at the junction with the 12 Ω and the 4 Ω resistor. Notice that the top path through this network has a resistance of 6 Ω, so there will be twice as much current along this path as through the 12 Ω resistor. From figure 16c and the junction law, you have

$$2 = i + 2i \Rightarrow i = 0.67 \text{ A}$$

Capacitors in Circuits

When a capacitor is initially connected to a battery, charge will flow for some time until a steady state is established. While the flow is occurring, you have a **transient** situation. You'll need to be able to answer questions about charge stored, voltages difference, and energy stored when one or more capacitors are connected in a circuit, under both steady state and transient conditions.

CAPACITORS IN SERIES AND PARALLEL

The parallel connection of two capacitors is shown in figure 17a.

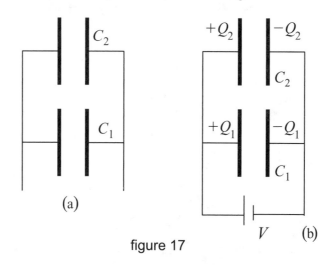

figure 17

When connected to a battery, each capacitor will store a different amount of charge (figure 17b), but each will have the same potential drop across it, since each forms a separate loop with the battery. This connection effectively increases the plate area, and since capacitance is proportional to plate area, $C = \frac{\varepsilon_0 A}{d}$, it should be no surprise that the capacitance has increased. The equivalent parallel capacitance of several capacitors connected in parallel is just the sum of the individual values.

$$C_p = C_1 + C_2 + \ldots$$

When two or more capacitors are connected in series, the equivalent capacitance is less than the smallest value of any of those connected, and the overall capacitance decreases. A battery connected to the free leads in figure 18a

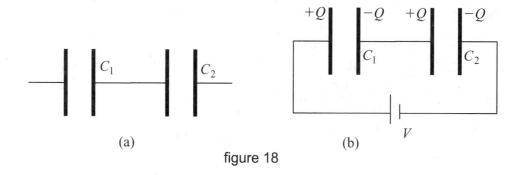

figure 18

will separate charge on the extreme left and right plates shown. The middle two plates are directly connected to each other and will end as an equipotential surface with $+Q$ and $-Q$ drawn to outer plates as shown; there will be no potential drop across the middle region. The potential drop created by the battery is now effectively distributed across the separation of both capacitors, and d has gotten bigger, making for a smaller capacitance. The equivalent capacitance of several capacitors connected in series is determined by

$$\frac{1}{C_s} = \frac{1}{C_1} + \frac{1}{C_2} + \dots$$

Notice that the charge on each series capacitor will be the same, but in general, the voltage drops will be different.

EXAMPLE

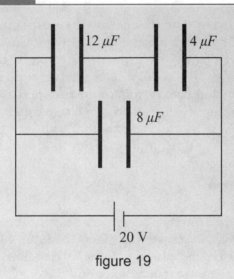

figure 19

Three capacitors are connected to a 20 V battery as shown in figure 19. Determine the charge stored on each and the potential drop across each capacitor.

The 8 μF capacitor is in parallel with the battery, so its voltage is 20 V. From the definition of capacitance, the charge on its plates is

$$Q = CV = (8 \times 10^{-6})(20) = 160 \ \mu\text{C}$$

The series combination of the 12 μF and the 4 μF yields an equivalent capacitance:
$$\frac{1}{C_s} = \frac{1}{12} + \frac{1}{4} = \frac{1}{3} \Rightarrow C_s = 3 \ \mu\text{F}$$

This equivalent capacitance is in parallel with the battery, so the charge it stores is

$$Q = CV = (3 \times 10^{-6})(20) = 60 \ \mu\text{C}$$

This will be the charge on each of the two capacitors in series. Then you can use the definition of capacitance to get voltage drops across the two series capacitors.

$$V_{12} = \frac{Q}{C} = \frac{60}{12} = 5 \text{ V}$$

$$V_4 = \frac{Q}{C} = \frac{60}{4} = 15 \text{ V}$$

Notice that the two voltage drops add up to 20 V, as the loop law for the outer loop would require.

ENERGY AND CAPACITORS

Work must be done by the battery when it separates the charge on two conductors. Imagine the battery with voltage V moving a total charge Q from one plate to another in a parallel plate capacitor. You might suspect that the work this takes could be determined from the relation defining electric potential, $W = QV$. In this case, that assumption isn't quite right because while the capacitor is charging, the full battery voltage doesn't appear across the capacitor; it's only when charge has ceased moving that the capacitor voltage equals the battery voltage. How do you handle this? Because the capacitor voltage starts at 0 and ends at V and is a linear function of Q since $V = \frac{Q}{C}$, the average voltage on the capacitor during the charging process is just $\frac{1}{2}V$. Then the work it takes to charge the capacitor is

$$W = \frac{1}{2}QV$$

This work can be recovered, because you can allow the capacitor to discharge and let the charges move through electrical devices to recover the energy. You can think of energy being stored in the position of the charges on the plates, a form of electrical potential energy. Using this discussion and the definition of capacitance, you can write

$$U_{\text{cap}} = \frac{1}{2}QV = \frac{1}{2}CV^2 = \frac{1}{2}\frac{Q^2}{C}$$

EXAMPLE

Find the total energy stored in the capacitors of figure 19.

You've already computed the charges and voltages of each capacitor, so you could use any of the forms given for U_{cap}. Let's use the voltage squared relation.

$$U_{\text{total}} = U_8 + U_{12} + U_4$$

$$U_{\text{total}} = \frac{1}{2}(8 \times 10^{-6})(20)^2 + \frac{1}{2}(12 \times 10^{-6})(5)^2 + \frac{1}{2}(4 \times 10^{-6})(15)^2$$

$$U_{\text{total}} = 2.2 \text{ mJ}$$

TRANSIENTS

When a network of capacitors and resistors is connected to a battery, the currents that flow will change over time. Eventually a steady state will be reached, characterized by 0 current flowing onto and off any capacitor plates. Let's look at the time dependence of the intermediate currents. Keep in mind, however, that most AP questions involving capacitors charging and discharging will deal with the initial and final state of the circuit. You can answer these questions fairly easily if you remember the two basic properties of a capacitor shown in figure 20.

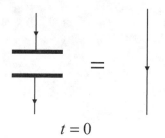
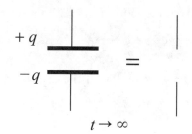

$t = 0$

When capacitor is initially uncharged, it instantaneously provides zero resistance to current, acting like a short circuit.

$t \to \infty$

After a long time, the capacitor will be fully charged; no more charge can flow onto the plates. It behaves as if it had infinite resistance, an open circuit.

figure 20

1. An uncharged capacitor will provide no resistance to charge flowing on or off its plates. Once a little charge has been put on its plates, however, this charge will oppose more charge coming on. Instantaneously, at $t = 0$ when the capacitor is first connected to the circuit, it acts like a short circuit, as if it were just a piece of wire with 0 resistance.

2. Once the capacitor is fully charged, no more current can flow on or off its plates. After a long time, as $t \to \infty$, the capacitor acts like a broken circuit, a wire that has been cut, providing infinite resistance.

To analyze the intermediate times, let's first consider the circuit of figure 21a.

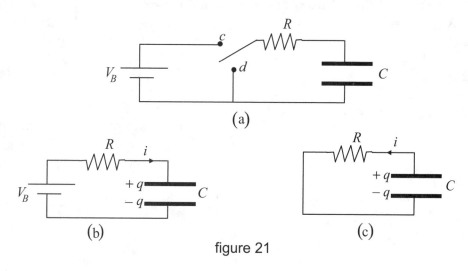

figure 21

When the switch is thrown to c, you have the charging circuit of figure 21b. If you apply the loop law, you have

$$V_B - iR - \frac{q}{C} = 0$$

Notice that at $t = 0$, $q = 0$ and $i = \frac{V_B}{R}$. In other words, initially you can treat the capacitor as a wire segment, a short circuit. As $t \to \infty$, you expect $i \to 0$, and this means $q_{\text{final}} = CV_B$.

Since $i = \frac{dq}{dt}$, this equation can be arranged as

$$\frac{dq}{dt} + \frac{q}{RC} = \frac{V_B}{R}$$

Assuming 0 charge initially on the capacitor, the solution to this differential equation is

$$q(t) = CV_B\left(1 - e^{\frac{-t}{RC}}\right)$$

This equation is plotted in figure 22a.

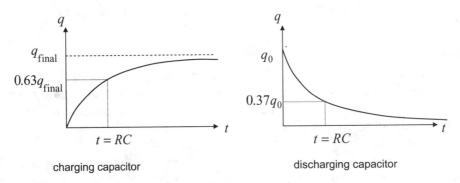

figure 22

Notice the exponential approach to the limiting value CV_B. The quantity RC has the dimensions of time. It's called the **RC time constant** for this circuit, which for obvious reasons is called an **RC circuit**. After a time equal to 1 time constant, the charge has reached 63 percent of its final value, since $(1 - e^{-1}) = 0.63$. In another time constant, the charge will increase to 63 percent of what remains. After N time constants, the difference between the charge on the capacitor and the limiting value is $(0.37)^N$. In 5 time constants, the capacitor is within 1 percent of being fully charged.

After charging the capacitor, you can throw the switch to d, discharging the capacitor as shown in figure 21c. Since the battery has been removed, the differential equation becomes

$$\frac{dq}{dt} + \frac{q}{RC} = 0$$

Assuming q_0 is initially on the capacitor, this differential equation solves to

$$q(t) = q_0 e^{\frac{-t}{RC}}$$

This exponential decay is plotted in figure 22b. After 1 time constant, the charge on each plate has decreased to 37 percent of its initial value, since $e^{-1} = 0.37$.

EXAMPLE

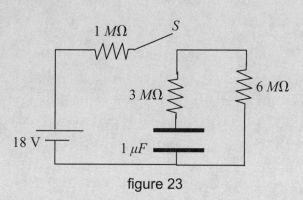

figure 23

Figure 23 shows an RC circuit. With the capacitor initially uncharged, the switch S is thrown down, connecting the battery to the rest of the circuit.

(a) At $t = 0$, when the switch makes contact, find the current i_3 in the 3 $M\Omega$ resistor, the current i_6 in the 6 $M\Omega$ resistor, and the current i_1 in the 1 $M\Omega$ resistor.

(b) Find these currents after a long time.

After a long time, the switch is opened.

(c) Find i_6 just after the switch is opened.

(d) Find the charge on the capacitor 18 seconds after the switch is opened.

(e) How much energy is consumed by the 6 $M\Omega$ resistor during the discharging process?

(a) When S is first closed, the capacitor behaves like a wire segment. Then the 3 $M\Omega$ and the 6 $M\Omega$ are in parallel with an equivalent resistance of

$$\frac{1}{R_p} = \frac{1}{6} + \frac{1}{3} = \frac{1}{2} \Rightarrow R_p = 2 \ M\Omega$$

Since this resistance is in series with the 1 $M\Omega$, the equivalent resistance of the circuit at $t = 0$ is 3 $M\Omega$. An 18 V battery will then supply

$$i = \frac{V}{R_{eq}} = \frac{18}{3 \times 10^6} = 6 \ \mu A$$

All of it will flow through the 1 $M\Omega$, and it will split into a 2-to-1 ratio at the junction, due to the resistance ratios. At $t = 0$:

$$i_1 = 6 \ \mu A \qquad i_3 = 4 \ \mu A \qquad i_6 = 2 \ \mu A$$

(b) After a long time, i_3 will be 0 and $i_1 = i_6$. Their values can be determined by applying the loop law around the outer loop.

$$+18 - i_1(1 \times 10^6) - i_1(6 \times 10^6) = 0 \Rightarrow i_1 = 2.57 \ \mu A$$

(c) When the switch is reopened, charge will flow off the capacitor. Since it was in parallel with the 6 $M\Omega$ resistor just before S is opened, its initial potential difference is

$$V_0 = i_6 R_{6M\Omega} = (2.57 \times 10^{-6})(6 \times 10^6) = 15.4 \ V$$

You can now apply the loop law to the discharging loop to find $i_3 = i_6$.

$$15.4 - i_3(3 \times 10^6) - i_3(6 \times 10^6) = 0 \Rightarrow i_3 = 1.71 \ \mu A$$

(d) The discharge circuit consists of 9 $M\Omega$ in series with 1 μF, so the time constant is $RC = 9$ s. The initial charge on the capacitor before discharging begins will be

$$q_0 = CV_0 = (1 \times 10^{-6})(15.4) = 15.4 \ \mu C$$

The discharging equation then gives you

$$q(18) = q_0 e^{\frac{-t}{RC}} = 15.4 e^{\frac{-18}{9}} = 2.1 \ \mu C$$

(e) The energy stored in the capacitor just before discharging starts is

$$U = \frac{1}{2} CV_0^2 = \frac{1}{2}(1 \times 10^{-6})(15.4)^2 = 119 \ \mu J$$

This energy will be consumed by each resistor at a rate $P = i^2 R$. Since they will have the same current, the consumption rate will depend on the resistor ratio, and since they consume the energy over the same time period, it follows that the 6 $M\Omega$ resistor will consume $\frac{6}{9}$ of the energy available.

$$E_{6M\Omega} = \frac{6}{7}(119) = 102 \ \mu J$$

KEY FORMULAS

Electric Current	$i = \dfrac{dq}{dt}$
Current Density	$j = \dfrac{i}{A}$
Resistor Voltage Drop	$V = iR$
Resistivity	$R = \rho\dfrac{L}{A}$
Electric Power	$P = iV$
Resistance Power	$P = i^2R = \dfrac{V^2}{R}$
Junction Law	$\displaystyle\sum_{\text{in}} i = \sum_{\text{out}} i$
Loop Law	$\displaystyle\sum_{\text{loop}} \Delta V = 0$
Series Resistors	$R_s = R_1 + R_2 + \ldots$
Parallel Resistors	$\dfrac{1}{R_p} = \dfrac{1}{R_1} + \dfrac{1}{R_2} + \ldots$
Terminal Voltage	$V_T = V_B \pm ir$
Capacitors in Series	$\dfrac{1}{C_s} = \dfrac{1}{C_1} + \dfrac{1}{C_2} + \ldots$
Capacitors in Parallel	$C_p = C_1 + C_2 + \ldots$
Energy in Capacitor	$U = \dfrac{1}{2}\dfrac{Q^2}{C} = \dfrac{1}{2}CV^2 = \dfrac{1}{2}QV$
Charging Capacitor	$q(t) = CV_B\left(1 - e^{\frac{-t}{RC}}\right)$
Discharging Capacitor	$q(t) = q_0 e^{-\frac{t}{RC}}$

PRACTICE EXERCISES

SECTION I MULTIPLE CHOICE

1. A current of 3.2 A flows in a segment of copper wire. The number of electrons crossing the cross-sectional area of the wire every second is most nearly

   (A) 3.2   (B) 2×10^{19} (C) 2×10^{-19} (D) 3.2×10^{19} (E) 3.2×10^{-19}

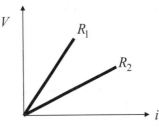

figure 24

2. Resistors R_1 and R_2 have voltage vs. current graphs as shown in the figure. The graph that best represents the voltage vs. current graphs for the equivalent series and parallel resistances R_s and R_p of the two is

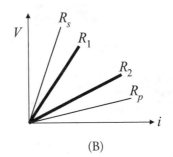

(A)

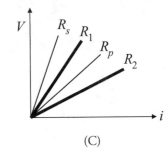

(C)

(B)

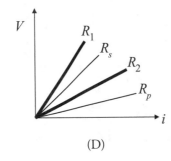

(D)

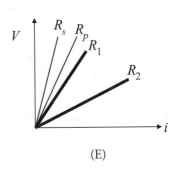

(E)

figure 25

3. A cylindrical length L of conducting material with cross-sectional area A has a resistivity ρ. Another material with twice the resistivity is to be drawn to a length $2L$ to form a resistor with the same resistance as the original. Its cross-sectional area must be

   (A) A (B) $2A$ (C) $3A$ (D) $4A$ (E) $\frac{1}{4}A$

Questions 4 and 5

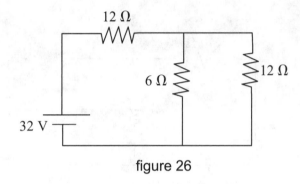

figure 26

4. The voltage drop across the 6 Ω resistor is most nearly

   (A) 16 V   (B) 10.7 V   (C) 8 V   (D) 32 V   (E) 24 V

5. The electrical energy converted to thermal energy in the resistors in 10 seconds is

   (A) 240 J   (B) 24 J   (C) 64 J   (D) 1,000 J   (E) 640 J

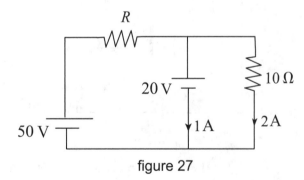

figure 27

6. The circuit shown in the figure carries 1 A and 2 A in two branches as shown. The value of R is most nearly

   (A) 10 Ω (B) 20 Ω (C) 30 Ω (D) 40 Ω (E) 50 Ω

7. Which of the following statements is true?
   I. The terminal voltage of a battery depends on the resistance connected to the terminals.
   II. The terminal voltage of a battery is always less than the ideal voltage of the battery.
   III. The terminal voltage of a battery is always greater than the ideal voltage of the battery.

   (A) none of the above   (B) I only   (C) II only   (D) III only   (E) I and II only

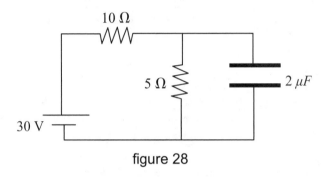

figure 28

8. The circuit shown in the figure has been connected for a long time. The charge on one of the capacitor plates is
   (A) 60 μC   (B) 20 μC   (C) 2 μC   (D) 40 μC   (E) 30 μC

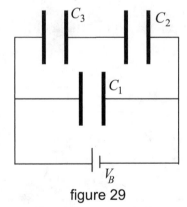

figure 29

9. Which of the following is true for the connection shown in the figure?
   I. The magnitude of the charge on one plate of C_2 is the same as that on one plate of C_3.
   II. The potential drop across C_1 will equal the battery voltage.
   III. The magnitudes of the potential drops across C_2 and C_3 will add up to the drop across C_1.

   (A) I only   (B) II only   (C) III only   (D) I and III only   (E) I, II, and III

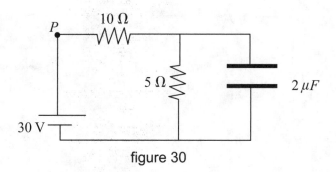

figure 30

10. The circuit shown in the figure had been connected for a long time when the connection at point P failed. The charge remaining on one of the capacitor plates 10 μs after the failure was most nearly

(A) 5 μC   (B) 7 μC   (C) 10 μC   (D) 15 μC   (E) 20 μC

CHAPTER 11

PRACTICE EXERCISES

SECTION II FREE RESPONSE

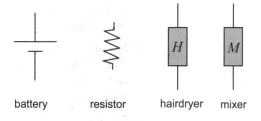

figure 31

1. You are given a 120 V battery; a hairdryer designed to work properly at 120 V, which is rated at 1,200 W; and a mixer designed to work properly at 60 V, where it's rated at 120 W. You also happen to have a large supply of 60 Ω resistors.
   (a) Determine the resistance of the hairdryer and the mixer at their rated voltages.
   (b) What current is established in the mixer when it's working properly?
   (c) Using the symbols shown in the figure, draw the connections needed to make both devices work simultaneously.
   (d) What power must the battery supply to run your circuit?

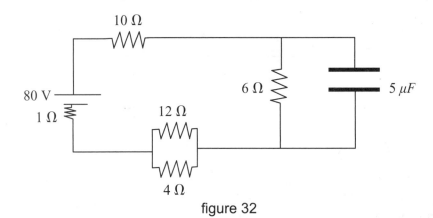

figure 32

2. The circuit in the figure has been connected for a long time. The battery has an internal resistance of 1 Ω.
   (a) Determine the terminal voltage of the battery.
   (b) Determine the current in the 4 Ω resistor.
   (c) What is the charge stored on one of the capacitor plates?
   (d) How long will it take for the 10 Ω resistor to consume as much energy from the circuit as is stored in the capacitor?

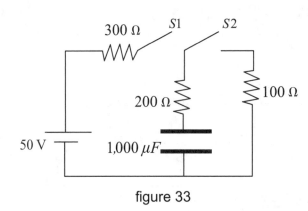

figure 33

3. The circuit in figure 33 has two switches, S1 and S2, that are initially open. At $t = 0$, S1 is closed and the capacitor begins to charge.
   (a) Determine the current in the 200 Ω resistor just after S1 is closed.
   (b) When charge has stopped moving, how much energy is stored in the capacitor?
   (c) How much electrical energy does the battery supply to the circuit in the charging process?

   After a long time, S1 is opened and then S2 is closed.
   (d) What constitutes a "long time" in the charging process? Explain.
   (e) What will be the potential difference across the capacitor 0.9 s after S2 is closed?

Answers and Explanations

MULTIPLE CHOICE

1. The answer is C. Each electron carries a charge of 1.6×10^{-19} C. The definition of current equation gives

$$i = \frac{\Delta q}{\Delta t} \Rightarrow 3.2 = \frac{N(1.6 \times 10^{-19})}{1} \qquad\qquad \text{So } N = 2 \times 10^{19}$$

2. The answer is B. The series resistance is the sum of the two resistors, so the slope of V vs. I must be greater than either individual graph. The parallel resistance is less than the smallest resistance, in this case R_2, so the V vs. I graph must have a slope smaller than either individual graph.

3. The answer is D. The original resistance is $\rho\frac{L}{A}$. The second resistance will be $\rho'\frac{L'}{A'} = (2\rho)\frac{2L}{A'}$. Since the two resistances must be equal, $A' = 4A$

4. The answer is C. The equivalent resistance of the circuit is 16 Ω since the two parallel resistors give 4 Ω, so 2 A is drawn from the battery. All of this goes through the 12 Ω resistor, so using the loop law for the left loop gives you
$$+ 32 - (2)(12) - V_{6\Omega} = 0 \Rightarrow V_{6\Omega} = 8 \text{ V}$$

5. The answer is E. The energy supplied by the battery will equal the energy consumed by the resistors. Since the battery has 2 A established in it, the power supplied by the battery is $P = iV_B = (2)(32) = 64$W. In 10 s, 640 J is supplied.

6. The answer is A. The junction law tells you that 3 A is present in R. Applying the loop law to the left loop, you have $50 - 3R - 20 = 0$, so $R = 10$ Ω.

7. The answer is B. $V_T = V_B \pm ir$, so the terminal voltage can be either greater than or less than the ideal voltage, depending on whether the battery is being recharged or is supplying energy to the circuit. This eliminates II and III. Since the current i depends on what is connected to the terminals, I is true.

8. The answer is B. After a long time, there will be no current in the capacitor branch, so the left loop has a single current established in it. Applying the loop law here gives you $30 - 10i - 5i = 0$, so $i = 2$ A. The capacitor is in parallel with the 5 Ω resistor, so its potential difference is $V_{cap} = V_{5\Omega} = (2)(5) = 10$ V. From the definition of capacitance, you have $Q = CV_{cap} = (2 \times 10^{-6})(10) = 20 \ \mu$C.

9. The answer is E. I is true because series connected capacitors will have the same magnitude of charge on each plate; you can think of the battery as separating the charge of the extreme left and right plates. The inner plates will redistribute charge to create inner equipotential surfaces, which involves separating the same magnitude of charge here as well. The loop law tells you that II and III are true.

10. The answer is B. After a long time, 2 A is established in the 5 Ω resistor, as you can see by applying the loop law to the inner loop. The 10 V potential drop across the 5 Ω resistor will also appear across the capacitor since they are in parallel. This means that $Q = CV_{cap} = 20 \ \mu C$ lies on a capacitor plate. The discharging circuit has a time constant of $RC = (5)(2 \times 10^{-6}) = 10 \ \mu s$, which is the time proposed in the question. For a discharging capacitor, after 1 time constant the charge is reduced to 37 percent of the initial value, which corresponds to 7.4 μC.

FREE RESPONSE

1. (a) You can use the power equation $P = \dfrac{V^2}{R}$ for each device, so

$$1{,}200 = \dfrac{(120)^2}{R_H} \qquad R_H = 12 \ \Omega \qquad 120 = \dfrac{(60)^2}{R_M} \qquad R_M = 30 \ \Omega$$

   (b) Use Ohm's law for the mixer.
   $V = iR$
   $60 = i(30) \Rightarrow i = 2$ A

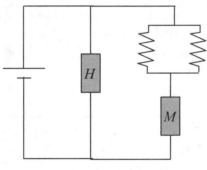

figure 34

   (c) The hairdryer will be connected in parallel with the battery to get the needed 120 V potential difference. Since the mixer requires only 60 V, you must insert a resistor in series with it to lower the voltage drop. The resistor must have a voltage drop of 60 V as well so that the two add up to 120 V by the loop law. Since the current in the mixer is 2 A, Ohm's law says that the resistor must have a value $R = \dfrac{60}{2} = 30 \ \Omega$. Two parallel 60 Ω resistors will do the job.

(d) The current in the hairdryer will be $i' = \frac{120}{12} = 10$ A. The junction law tells you that the total current established in the battery will then be 12 A, because there is 2 A in the mixer branch. The power supplied by the battery is

$$P = IV = (12)(120) = 1{,}440 \text{ W}$$

2. (a) After a long time, the capacitor will be fully charged. It could then be removed without changing anything in the battery-resistance part of the circuit, so you can analyze the latter as if the capacitor weren't present. The equivalent resistance of the circuit is 20 Ω since the two parallel resistors add to 3 Ω and the rest, including the internal resistance, are in series. The current established in the battery will be $i = \frac{80}{20} = 4$ A. The terminal voltage will be $V_T = V_B - ir = 80 - (4)(1) = 76$ V.

   (b) The 4 A will divide at the junction of the 12 Ω and the 4 Ω resistors. If you assume a current x is established in the 12 Ω, then $3x$ will be in the 4 Ω. The junction law then says $x + 3x = 4$. Then, $x = 1$ A, and the 4 Ω resistor will carry 3 A.

   (c) The capacitor is in parallel with the 6 Ω resistor, so it will have the same potential difference across it. $V_{cap} = V_{6\Omega} = (4)(6) = 24$ V. From the definition of capacitance, you have $Q = CV_{cap} = (5 \times 10^{-6})(24) = 120 \ \mu\text{C}$.

   (d) The energy stored in the capacitor is

   $$U = \frac{1}{2}CV_{cap}^2 = \frac{1}{2}(5 \times 10^{-6})(24)^2 = 1{,}440 \ \mu\text{J}$$

   The power dissipated in the 10 Ω resistor is

   $$P = i^2R = 4^2(10) = 160 \text{ W}$$

   Since watts are J/s, the time Δt must satisfy

   $$P\Delta t = U$$

   $$\Delta t = \frac{1{,}440 \times 10^{-6}}{160} = 9 \ \mu\text{s}$$

3. (a) The capacitor acts like a short circuit at $t = 0$, so the battery "sees" a resistance of 500 Ω, and the current will be $i = \frac{50}{500} = 0.1$ A.

   (b) The capacitor will develop a 50 V potential difference when it's fully charged, so the energy stored will be

   $$U = \frac{1}{2}CV^2 = \frac{1}{2}(10^{-3})(50)^2 = 1.25 \text{ J}$$

(c) The instantaneous power supplied by the battery is $P = iV = 50i$. Since the current is changing, you must integrate from 0 to infinity (long time) to find the total energy supplied by the battery. You can find the current by differentiating the formula for the charge on a charging capacitor.

$$i = \frac{dq}{dt} = \frac{d}{dt}\left[CV_B\left(1 - e^{-\frac{t}{RC}}\right)\right] = \frac{V_B}{R}e^{-\frac{t}{RC}} = 0.1e^{-\frac{t}{0.5}}$$

Notice that $RC = (500)(10^{-3}) = 0.5$ s. Then you have

$$E_{supplied} = \int_0^\infty P dt = \int_0^\infty (50)(0.1e^{-2t})dt$$

$$E_{supplied} = 2.5 \text{ J}$$

(d) The time constant of the charging circuit is 0.5 s. Since the difference between the charge on the capacitor and the final value decreases by 63 percent after each time constant, certainly 10 time constants will be a long time, so 5 s is a "long time."

(e) When $S1$ is opened followed by $S2$ being closed, the capacitor will discharge, reducing the voltage. From the discharging capacitor equation, you will have

$$V(t) = \frac{q(t)}{C} = \frac{q_0}{C}e^{-\frac{t}{RC}} = V_0e^{-\frac{t}{RC}}$$

In this case, V_0 will be 50 V because this is the voltage across the capacitor just before the switches were reset. The time constant will now be $RC = (300)(10^{-3}) = 0.3$ s, since the resistance in the discharging circuit is 300 Ω. Then, since 0.9 s is 3 time constants, you have

$$V(0.9) = 50e^{-3} = 2.5 \text{ V}$$

12

Magnetostatics

Magnetic effects are associated with moving charges, so statics and magnetism may not seem like a natural pair. Magnetostatics, however, deals with situations where the magnetic field present doesn't change in time. In particular, this chapter will look at the effects of a magnetic field on moving charges and the creation of the magnetic field by electric currents. The next chapter will discuss magnetic fields that change over time.

Magnetic Field and Force

A **magnetic field** $\vec{B}$ can be created in a region of space in a number of ways, which you'll investigate in a later section. For now, let's assume that a field is present. Just as with an electric field, a magnetic field can be described by **magnetic field lines**. These lines give a concrete though qualitative picture of the field in a region. The magnetic field at a point will be tangential to the local field line (figure 1).

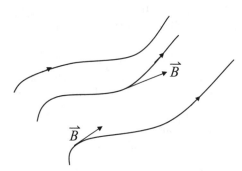

Magnetic field is tangential to the field lines.

figure 1

The field will be strongest where the field lines are most dense. The effects of the field on an object are summarized in the force law:

$$\vec{F} = q\vec{v} \times \vec{B}$$

Here q is the charge of the object, $\vec{v}$ is the object's velocity, and $\vec{B}$ is the local magnetic field (figure 2).

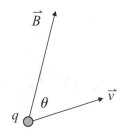

figure 2

The SI units for magnetic field are $\dfrac{N}{C \cdot \frac{m}{s}}$, called a **tesla** (T).

Let's discuss the implications of the force law:
1. To experience a magnetic force, an object must carry electric charge and the object must be moving.
2. For a fixed speed, the magnitude of the force, $F = qvB \sin\theta$, depends on the direction of the particle's velocity vector with respect to the field. If the object moves along a field line, the force is 0. The maximum force for a fixed speed occurs when the charge moves perpendicular to the field. Conceptually, the force exerted on the charge depends on the efficiency with which it cuts across the field lines.
3. The force, velocity, and field are related through a vector cross product. This means that the force will always be perpendicular to both the velocity and the field. There are two directions that satisfy this condition, and the right-hand rule tells you which of these is correct.
4. The instantaneous power delivered to an object by a force is $P_F = \vec{F} \cdot \vec{v}$. Since the magnetic force is always perpendicular to the velocity, $\vec{F} \cdot \vec{v} = 0$, it cannot change its energy. The magnetic force cannot do work on a moving charged particle.

Motion in a Uniform Field

When a charge enters a region where the magnetic field is uniform spatially, three basic types of motion paths are possible, depending on the relative directions of $\vec{v}$ and $\vec{B}$.
1. $\sin\theta = 0$: The particle is moving parallel or antiparallel to the field. This means the force is 0, so there's no acceleration, and the motion path will be a straight line followed with a constant speed.

2. $\sin\theta = 1$: The particle is moving perpendicular to the field. The force will be its maximum value for a given speed, $F = qvB$. You can see from figure 3 that the force keeps changing direction because the velocity changes direction.

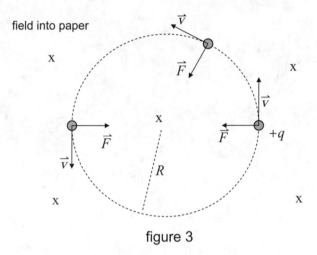

figure 3

There's no force component to move the charge out of the plane it's in, and since the magnetic force does no work, the charge will maintain the same speed. The resulting motion type is uniform circular motion, with the field lines cutting directly through the plane of the circle. Since the magnetic force is supplying the centripetal force, you have

$$qvB = m\frac{v^2}{R} \quad \Rightarrow \quad R = \frac{mv}{qB}$$

3. $\sin\theta \neq 0, 1$: The particle is moving neither parallel nor perpendicular to the field. To see how this works, let's break the velocity vector into components parallel to the field and perpendicular to the field: $v_\perp$, v_{11} (figure 4).

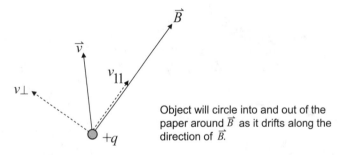

Object will circle into and out of the paper around $\vec{B}$ as it drifts along the direction of $\vec{B}$.

figure 4

If only v_{11} were present, you would have case 1, with the particle drifting uniformly down the field lines. If only $v_\perp$ were present, you would have case 2, with the particle circling around the field lines. With both present, you have the superposition of these two motions. The motion path is a helix with its axis determined by the direction of the field.

EXAMPLE

$B = 0.1$ T   out of paper

0	0	0	0
0	0 $\vec{v}$	0	0
0	0	0	0

(a)

$\vec{v}$

$\vec{F}$

R

(b)

figure 5

An electron is moving as shown in figure 5a with a speed of 2×10^5 m/s in a uniform field of 0.1 T.

(a) Find the magnitude of the magnetic force exerted on the electron.
(b) Sketch the circular motion path and find its radius.
(c) How long will it take for the electron to complete one revolution?

(a) The magnitude of the force follows from the basic force law with $\sin\theta = 1$:

$$F = qvB = (1.6 \times 10^{-19})(2 \times 10^5)(0.1) = 3.2 \times 10^{-15} \text{ N}$$

(b) The right-hand rule for $\vec{v} \times \vec{B}$ results in a direction to the right and up slightly in the plane of the paper, but since the electron is negative, the force is opposite this. The electron circles in a counterclockwise manner, as shown in figure 5b. The radius is

$$R = \frac{mv}{qB} = \frac{(9 \times 10^{-31})(2 \times 10^6)}{(1.6 \times 10^{-19})(0.1)} = 1.13 \times 10^{-4} \text{ m}$$

(c) In general, such a circulating charge will travel one circumference at the same speed, so

$$2\pi R = vT$$
$$2\pi \frac{mv}{qB} = vT \qquad \Rightarrow T = \frac{2\pi m}{qB}$$

This means that the period is independent of the speed of the charge; fast ones move in big circles, slow ones in small circles, but they all take the same time to circulate once. For your case:

$$T = \frac{2\pi(9 \times 10^{-31})}{(1.6 \times 10^{-19})(0.1)} = 3.53 \times 10^{-10} \text{ s}$$

Magnetic Force on a Current-Carrying Wire

When a wire carrying current is placed in a magnetic field, each of the moving charges will feel a force. Since the thermal motion is random, it's only the drift speed that leads to an overall net force on the wire. While these speeds are very small, the large numbers of charges moving can lead to significant forces. Consider a straight wire segment (figure 6) of length Δl containing N charges, each with charge q in a uniform field $\vec{B}$.

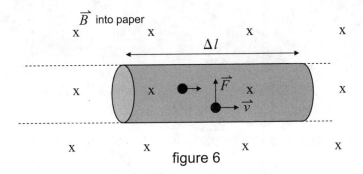

figure 6

Let's assume the charges are moving at right angles to the field with a speed v. The total force on the wire segment will be

$$F = N(qvB)$$

Since all N charges move through the segment in the time $\Delta t = \frac{\Delta l}{v}$ that it takes to traverse the segment, the current can be written as

$$i = \frac{\Delta q}{\Delta t} = \frac{Nq}{\frac{\Delta l}{v}} = \frac{Nqv}{\Delta l}$$

Substituting into the force equation gives you $F = i\Delta lB$.
Should the direction of current be angled with respect to the field, you'll have

$$F = i\Delta lB \sin\theta$$

where θ is the angle between the current direction and the field. You can determine the direction of the force by applying the right-hand rule to the moving charges, which are assumed to be positive since you are assuming conventional current. In vector notation, you can write the force on a current segment in a uniform field as

$$\vec{F} = i\Delta\vec{l} \times \vec{B}$$

When the wire segment isn't straight or when the field varies spatially, you must consider the effect on an infinitesimal segment of wire as shown in figure 7.

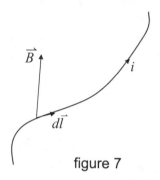

figure 7

The force exerted on this segment is infinitesimal as well.

$$d\vec{F} = i\,d\vec{l} \times \vec{B}$$

To find the total force on the wire, you would have to integrate over the length of the wire.

EXAMPLE

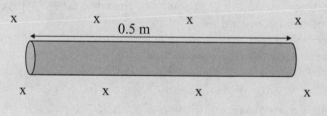

figure 8

A straight segment of wire 50 cm long with a mass of 30 g is positioned horizontally in a uniform magnetic field of 0.025 T so that the current moves perpendicular to the field, depicted into the paper in figure 8. What current magnitude and direction must be established in the wire so that the magnetic force just counterbalances the weight of the wire?

Since the weight acts down, the magnetic force must act up. The right-hand rule tells you that the current is directed to the right. Because $\sin\theta = 1$, you have for equilibrium:

$$i\Delta l B = mg \quad \Rightarrow i = \frac{mg}{\Delta l B} = \frac{(0.030)(10)}{(0.5)(0.025)} = 24 \text{ A}$$

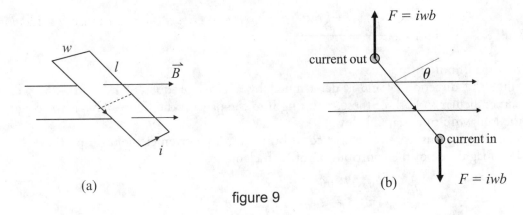

(a)

(b)

figure 9

Consider a rectangular loop of wire of dimensions l and w, carrying current i as shown in figure 9a. The side view in (b) shows that the two widths experience equal but opposite forces that tend to cause the loop to rotate. This effect is the basis of the electric motor. The net torque about the central axis of the loop, shown as the dotted line in (a), will be

$$net\ \tau = 2(iwB\sin\theta)\frac{l}{2} = iAB\sin\theta \qquad\qquad A = \text{area of loop}$$

Law of Biot-Savart

Electric fields are created by charges, and charges placed in an electric field will experience a force. An analogous statement is true for magnetic fields: Moving charges can experience a magnetic force, and moving charges create magnetic fields. Since electric currents in wires are a result of the organized motion of charges within the wires, it follows that electric currents will create magnetic fields in the region around them. The law of **Biot-Savart** describes the contribution made to the magnetic field by an element of the wire $\vec{dl}$ carrying current i. Figure 10 displays the geometry and notation. The direction of $\vec{dl}$ is parallel to the current.

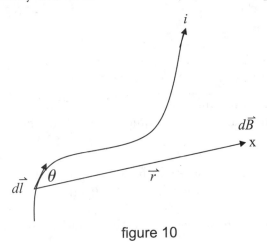

figure 10

The law is
$$d\vec{B} = \frac{\mu_0}{4\pi} \frac{id\vec{l} \times \hat{r}}{r^2}$$

Here are some important points:
1. Since the direction of $d\vec{B}$ is determined by a cross product of $d\vec{l}$ and $\hat{r}$, it will be perpendicular to both of these, pointing into the page in the figure. This is the origin of the long wire rule, stated below.
2. The law is an inverse square law; contributions from a given element drop off as $\frac{1}{r^2}$.
3. The magnitude of the contribution of each element is

$$dB = \frac{\mu_0}{4\pi} \frac{idl \sin\theta}{r^2}$$

The largest contribution of an element at a given distance comes at points perpendicular to $\vec{r}$. Points parallel to $\vec{r}$, along the line of the current, get 0 contribution.

An important special case is the field created by a long wire. Figure 11 shows the direction of the field in the region around the wire.

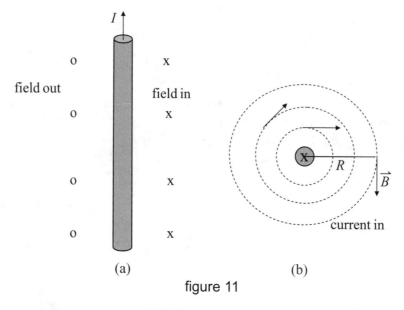

figure 11

The field lines created by such a current form concentric circles centered on the wire. Another right-hand rule, the long wire rule, can be used to quickly determine the field direction around a long wire.

Long wire rule: Place the thumb of your right hand along the wire in the direction of the current. Your fingers will wrap around the wire in the direction of the field line circulation.

Of course, the field itself is tangential to the field lines. You should try out the rule on figure 11, where the correct field directions are shown.

EXAMPLE

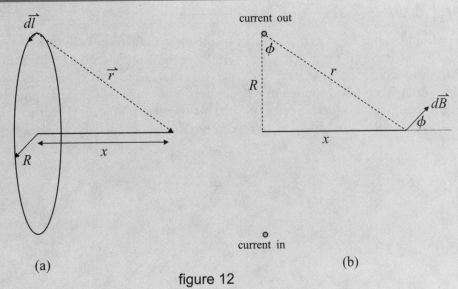

(a)

figure 12

(b)

Find the magnetic field magnitude and direction along the axis of a circular ring of radius R carrying current i as shown in figure 12a.

Notice that an arbitrary element $\vec{dl}$ is perpendicular to the $\vec{r}$ that locates the point where you want to calculate the field, so $\sin\theta = 1$ in the formula. Figure 12b shows the geometry from a side angle of the loop. The magnitude of contribution of each element will be

$$dB = \frac{\mu_0}{4\pi} \frac{idl}{r^2}$$

Symmetry tells you that only the component of each contribution along the x-axis will survive, since contributions from opposite sides of the loop will cancel out any components perpendicular to the axis. This means that you only need to sum up the effective contribution:

$$dB_{\text{eff}} = \frac{\mu_0}{4\pi} \frac{idl}{r^2} \cos\phi$$

Notice that each contribution points in the same direction, so you simply add them up. Because i, r, and φ are constant over the loop, the integration is just a sum of the dl's, giving the circumference of the loop.

$$B = \frac{\mu_0}{4\pi} \frac{i(2\pi R)}{r^2} \cos\phi = \frac{\mu_0}{4\pi} \frac{i(2\pi R)}{R^2 + x^2} \left(\frac{R}{(R^2 + x^2)^{\frac{1}{2}}} \right)$$

$$B = \frac{\mu_0 i}{2} \frac{R^2}{(R^2 + x^2)^{\frac{3}{2}}}$$

Ampere's Law

You'll recall that Gauss's law relates the flux of the electric field through a closed surface to the charges contained within the surface. For certain charge configurations with a high degree of symmetry, you could use the law to solve for the electric field created by the charge configuration. **Ampere's law** applied to magnetostatics is in many ways analogous to this. A line integral involving the magnetic field is related to the electric currents within the integration path. For certain symmetric situations, you can use the law to solve for the magnetic field.

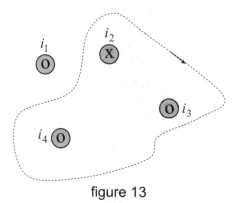

figure 13

Consider a number of electric currents running into or out of the page as depicted in figure 13. These currents create a complex field $\vec{B}$ in the surrounding region. You could compute the line integral of $\vec{B}$ around a closed path like the one shown in dotted lines in the picture. This type of path is called an **Amperean path**. Ampere's law states:

$$\oint_{\substack{\text{closed} \\ \text{path}}} \vec{B} \cdot d\vec{l} = \mu_0 i_{\text{enclosed}} \qquad \mu_0 = 1.26 \times 10^{-6} \frac{T \cdot m}{A}$$

μ_0 is called the permeability constant. Notice that i_2, i_3, and i_4 cut through the path shown, but i_1 does not. Only the former will contribute to i_{enclosed}. Since currents may run in different directions, you need a sign convention for the path.

For a chosen path of integration, curl the fingers of your right hand to match the circulation of the path. Your thumb direction will define the positive current direction.

In the figure, i_2 is positive, while i_3 and i_4 are negative. For the example, the law would give

$$\oint_{\substack{\text{closed} \\ \text{path}}} \vec{B} \cdot d\vec{l} = \mu_0(i_2 - i_3 - i_4)$$

You could choose any number of paths. The value of the integral will depend only on the currents that are enclosed by the path. Note the similarities to Gauss's law, but also notice that Gauss's law deals with an area integral (flux), while Ampere's law deals with a line integral.

As you'll see in cases where there's a high degree of symmetry, a suitably chosen Amperean path will allow you to factor B out of the integral and solve for it in terms of the currents involved. Symbolically, this takes the form

$$\oint_{\substack{\text{closed} \\ \text{path}}} \vec{B} \cdot d\vec{l} = \oint_{\text{cp}} Bdl = B \oint_{\text{cp}} dl = BL = \mu_0 i_{\text{enclosed}}$$

$$B = \frac{\mu_0 i_{\text{enclosed}}}{L}$$

Here, L is a length associated with the integration path, and i_{enclosed} is the current cutting through the path as already discussed.

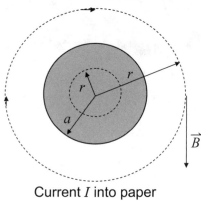

Current I into paper

figure 14

As a first example, consider a long wire as shown in figure 14, carrying a current I into the paper. Assume the current is distributed uniformly over the cross-sectional area of the wire—the current density $\vec{j}$ is uniform. The cylindrical symmetry indicates that circular Amperean paths centered on the wire will work. These are shown as dotted lines in the figure. Along these paths, $\vec{B} \cdot d\vec{l} = Bdl$ since the two vectors are parallel. Along any one such path, the magnitude of B will remain constant because the distance from the center of the wire is constant. Then you have

$$\oint_{\text{circle}} \vec{B} \cdot d\vec{l} = \oint_{\text{circle}} Bdl = B \oint_{\text{circle}} dl = B(2\pi r) = \mu_0 i_{\text{enclosed}}$$

For $r > a$, the path encloses all the current, so you have

$$B = \frac{\mu_0 I}{2\pi r} \qquad\qquad r > a$$

For $r < a$, the path encloses a current determined by the ratio of the enclosed area to the total cross-sectional area.

$$B(2\pi r) = \mu_0 I \left(\frac{\pi r^2}{\pi a^2} \right)$$

$$B = \frac{\mu_0 I}{2\pi a^2} r \qquad\qquad r < a$$

A graph of this field is shown in figure 15.

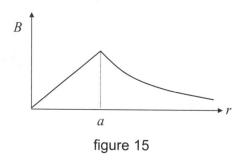

figure 15

EXAMPLE

figure 16

The two wires in figure 16, separated by 0.5 m, carry 8 A and 4 A as shown. Find the magnitude and direction of the magnetic field between the wires, 0.1 m from the 4 A current.

Using the long wire rule, you can see that between the wires, the 4 A current creates a field out of the paper, while the 8 A current creates a field into the paper. The net field magnitude will then be the difference of the two individual magnitudes. You can use the formula for the field outside a long wire to find the magnitudes of each:

$$B_4 = \frac{\mu_0 I}{2\pi R} = 2 \times 10^{-7} \frac{4}{0.1} = 8 \ \mu T \qquad \frac{\mu_0}{2\pi} = 2 \times 10^{-7} \frac{T \cdot m}{A}$$

$$B_8 = 2 \times 10^{-7} \frac{8}{0.4} = 4 \ \mu T$$

Since the 4 A field is larger, the net field is out of the paper, and the magnitude is $8 \ \mu T - 4 \ \mu T = 4 \ \mu T$.

Another important current distribution is a **solenoid**, which consists of a single length of wire wrapped into many consecutive loops—for example, wire wrapped tightly around a cardboard tube. If there are N loops wound along a length L, the number of loops per unit length is $n = \frac{N}{L}$. A cross section of a short length of such a device is shown in figure 17a.

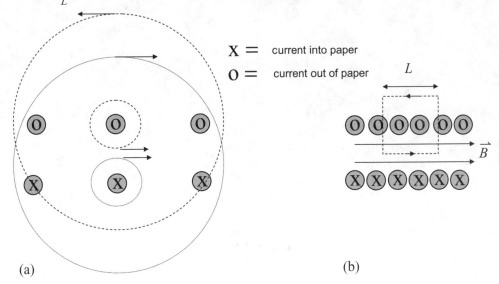

(a)

$X =$ current into paper

$O =$ current out of paper

(b)

Outside solenoid core, field contributions tend to cancel.
Inside the core, they add.

figure 17

As the current winds around, it will go into and out of the paper as shown. The figure shows the field lines created by the little segments of wire in the middle of the diagram. Notice that the fields of the upper and lower segments are parallel on the inside of the solenoid, while outside the solenoid the two segments produce fields that oppose each other. In the idealized case of an infinitely long solenoid, the outside field is 0 and the inside field is parallel to the solenoid axis.

You can use Ampere's law to find the field inside. For an ideal solenoid with n loops per unit length carrying current i, draw an Amperean path as shown in b. The only contribution comes from the length inside the solenoid where $\vec{B}$ and $\vec{dl}$ are parallel. Along this path, the magnitude of $\vec{B}$ will remain constant, so you have

$$\oint_{\substack{\text{closed} \\ \text{path}}} \vec{B} \cdot \vec{dl} = \int_{\text{path}} B dl = B \int_{\text{path}} dl = BL = \mu_0 i_{\text{enclosed}}$$

Each loop of wire cutting through the path will contribute to the current enclosed. Since there are $N = nL$ loops cutting through, you have

$$BL = \mu_0 i_{\text{enclosed}} = \mu_0 nLi$$

$$B = \mu_0 ni$$

Notice that the field is uniform inside the solenoid.

Force Between Long Current-Carrying Wires

Consider figure 18, depicting two parallel wires separated by a distance d, carrying currents I_1 and I_2 in the same direction.

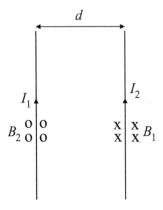

figure 18

Each current creates a field around it, and this field will affect the other current. In the diagram, B_1, created by I_1, will affect the wire carrying I_2. A similar statement can be made for the field B_2 created by I_2. A segment of length Δl of the wire carrying I_1 will experience a force

$$F = I_1 \Delta l B_2 = I_1 \Delta l \left(\frac{\mu_0}{2\pi} \frac{I_2}{d} \right)$$

$$F = \Delta l \left(\frac{\mu_0}{2\pi} \frac{I_1 I_2}{d} \right)$$

The right-hand rule tells you this force is directed to the left: Parallel currents attract. You would have seen a similar result if you had looked at the force exerted on a segment of the wire carrying I_2; the same magnitude of force would be present but acting to the right. Of course, this is consistent with the law of action-reaction. Convince yourself using the right-hand rules that antiparallel currents repel each other. Notice that the force is proportional to the product of the currents and inversely proportional to the distance between them.

KEY FORMULAS

Magnetic Force on a Charge	$\vec{F} = q\vec{v} \times \vec{B}$
Radius of Circular Orbit	$R = \dfrac{mv}{qB}$
Magnetic Force on a Current Element	$d\vec{F} = id\vec{l} \times \vec{B}$
Torque on a Current Loop	$net\tau = iAB \sin\theta$
Law of Biot-Savart	$d\vec{B} = \dfrac{\mu_0 i}{4\pi} \dfrac{d\vec{l} \times \hat{r}}{r^2}$
Ampere's Law	$\displaystyle\oint_{\substack{closed \\ loop}} \vec{B} \cdot d\vec{l} = \mu_0 i_{enclosed}$
Field Outside a Long Wire	$B = \dfrac{\mu_0}{2\pi} \dfrac{I}{R}$
Field Within a Solenoid	$B = \mu_0 ni$
Force Between Parallel Currents	$F = \dfrac{\mu_0}{2\pi} \dfrac{I_1 I_2}{d}$

PRACTICE EXERCISES

SECTION I MULTIPLE CHOICE

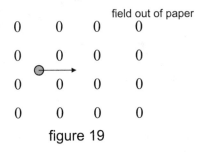

figure 19

1. An electron is moving to the right in a region where a uniform magnetic field is directed out of the paper. The direction of the force on the electron will be

   (A) up   (B) down   (C) left   (D) right   (E) into paper

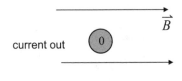

figure 20

2. A wire carries electric current out of the paper as shown in the figure. With a magnetic field directed to the right, the force on the wire will be directed

   (A) up   (B) down   (C) left   (D) right   (E) into paper

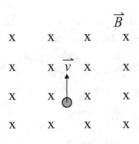

figure 21

3. A positive charge q is moving with velocity $\vec{v}$ perpendicular to a magnetic field $\vec{B}$ shown into the paper in the figure. The magnitude and direction of the electric field that will allow the charge to pass undeflected are

	Magnitude	Direction
(A)	qvB	left
(B)	$\frac{B}{v}$	left
(C)	Bv	right
(D)	Bv	left
(E)	Bv	out of paper

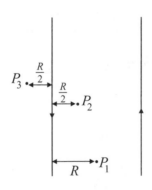

figure 22

4. Two long parallel wires carry equal currents in opposite directions. A proton moving at a speed of 2×10^5 m/s would experience the maximum force

(A) at P_1 moving left   (B) at P_2 moving left   (C) at P_3 moving left
     (D) at P_2 moving into paper   (E) at P_1 moving into paper

5. An electron moving with a speed of 2×10^6 m/s perpendicular to a uniform magnetic field of 10^{-3} T will execute one revolution of a circular path in a time most nearly

(A) 1 s   (B) 10^{-6} s   (C) 10^{-8} s   (D) 10^{-10} s   (E) 10^{-15} s

6. Two long parallel wires separated by a distance D carry currents I_1 and I_2. To increase the force exerted by each wire on the other by a factor of 2, you could
   I. double each current and double the separation
   II. double one current only and keep the separation the same
   III. keep the currents the same and halve the separation

   (A) I and II only   (B) I and III only   (C) II and III only
        (D) I, II, and III   (E) II only

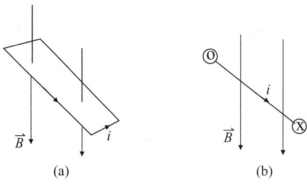

(a)   (b)

figure 23

7. A rectangular loop carrying current i is positioned in a uniform magnetic field as shown in the figure. Referring to (b) where the loop is shown from the side, the loop will

   (A) move down as a unit   (B) move up as a unit   (C) remain stationary
        (D) rotate clockwise   (E) rotate counterclockwise

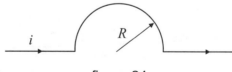

figure 24

8. An otherwise straight wire has one section bent into a semicircle as shown in the figure. The magnetic field at the center of the semicircle is

   (A) $\dfrac{\mu_0 i}{2\pi R}$ (B) $\dfrac{\mu_0 i}{2R}$ (C) $\dfrac{\mu_0 i}{\pi R^2}$ (D) $\dfrac{\mu_0 i}{4R}$ (E) 0

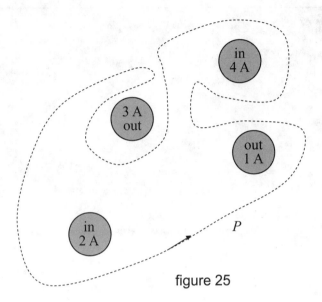

figure 25

9. The figure shows 4 currents and a path P around which a line integral of the magnetic field is to be computed. The arrow indicates the direction of integration. The value of $\oint_P \vec{B} \cdot d\vec{l}$ is

(A) $2\mu_0$ (B) $7\mu_0$ (C) $-7\mu_0$ (D) $5\mu_0$ (E) $-5\mu_0$

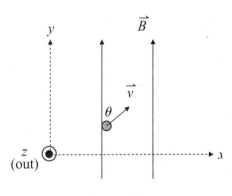

figure 26

10. A positive charge currently has a velocity in the x-y plane, making an angle θ with respect to a uniform magnetic field directed along the $+y$-axis. The subsequent motion of the charge could best be described as

(A) circular motion in the x-y plane
(B) uniform motion
(C) circular motion in the x-z plane
(D) helical motion with axis parallel to the z-axis
(E) helical motion with axis parallel to the y-axis

PRACTICE EXERCISES

SECTION II FREE RESPONSE

$$
\begin{array}{cccc}
\text{X} & \text{X} & \text{X} \ \vec{B} & \text{X} \\
\text{X} & \text{X} & \text{X} & \text{X} \\
\text{X} & \text{X} & \text{X} & \text{X} \\
\text{X} & \text{X} & \text{X} & \text{X} \\
\hline
\text{X} & \text{X} & \text{X} & \text{X} \\
\text{X} & \text{X} & \text{X} & \text{X} \\
\end{array}
$$

selector

V_g ↕

S

figure 27

1. A mass spectrometer design has the following components: Positive ions of charge q and mass m are formed at a source S and accelerated through a potential difference V_g. The ions pass through a grid and into a velocity selector where there exists a magnetic field $\vec{B}$ as shown in the figure and an electric field. When the charges leave the selector, they enter a region where the same magnetic field is present, but there is no electric field. Respond to the following in terms of q, m, V_g, and B.
   (a) Determine the speed v_0 of the charges as they pass through the grid if they were initially at rest as they left the source.
   (b) Sketch the path of the charges after they leave the selector.
   (c) Determine the radius of the path.
   (d) Charges leaving the source may have nonzero speeds. What electric field, magnitude and direction, must exist in the selector to insure that only the charges with v_0 leaving the grid will pass undeflected through the selector?

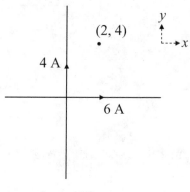

figure 28

2. Two wires carrying currents of 4 A and 6 A, respectively, are oriented perpendicular to each other and cross without electrical connection at the origin.
   (a) Determine the magnetic field magnitude and direction at the point (2, 4).
   (b) An electron passes through this point, moving with a speed of 3×10^5 m/s toward the 4 A wire ($-x$ direction). Find the magnitude and direction of the force on the electron.

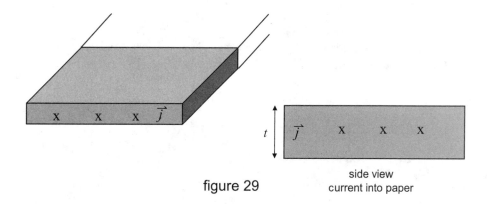

figure 29

3. A conducting sheet of thickness t and infinite in the other dimensions carries a uniform current density $\vec{j}$ directed into the page in the figure.
   (a) Draw the Amperean path that would allow you to determine the magnetic field outside the conductor.
   (b) Using Ampere's law, find the field outside the conductor.
   (c) Draw the Amperean path that would allow you to determine the magnetic field inside the conductor.
   (d) Using Ampere's law, find the field inside the conductor.

Answers and Explanations

MULTIPLE CHOICE

1. The answer is A. The right-hand rule for $\vec{v} \times \vec{B}$ gives a direction down, but since the electron is negative, the force is up.

2. The answer is A. The drift velocity of the charges is out of the page, so $\vec{v} \times \vec{B}$ is up. Since current is assumed to be the flow of positive charge, this is the answer.

3. The answer is C. The magnetic force is qvB directed to the left, so the electric force must equal this and point to the right. Since the charge is positive, this is the field direction as well. For the magnitude, you have

$$qvB = qE \qquad\qquad \Rightarrow E = Bv$$

4. The answer is B. The field created by either wire is directed into or out of the paper at any of the points, so D and E would yield 0 force. The fields created by each current are directed out of the paper for regions between the wires, so they reinforce each other in this region. At P_3, the two contributions oppose each other, and the point is also farther away from the right-hand current. This means that only A or B could be correct. The stronger total field occurs at P_2, as you can see:

$$B_2 = \frac{\mu_0 i}{2\pi}\left(\frac{1}{\frac{R}{2}} + \frac{1}{\frac{3R}{2}} \right) = \frac{\mu_0 i}{2\pi}\frac{8}{3R}$$

$$B_1 = \frac{\mu_0 i}{2\pi}\left(\frac{1}{R} + \frac{1}{R} \right) = \frac{\mu_0 i}{2\pi}\frac{2}{R}$$

5. The answer is C. The equation is $T = \dfrac{2\pi m}{qB} \cong \dfrac{2\pi(10^{-30})}{(10^{-19})(10^{-3})} \cong 10^{-8}$ s. The exact answer is 3.5×10^{-8} s.

6. The answer is D. The force on either wire is given by

$$F = \frac{\mu_0}{2\pi}\frac{I_1 I_2}{d}L$$

where L is the length of a wire. Doubling each current and doubling the separation causes F to change by a factor $\frac{(2)(2)}{2} = 2$, so the force doubles. Similar reasoning for the other choices shows that all three will double the force.

7. The answer is D. Referring to figure 23b, the right-hand rule tells you that the force on the segment carrying current out of the page is to the right, while the force on the segment carrying current into the page will be to the left. These two forces produce a torque that tends to cause clockwise rotation.

8. The answer is D. Applying the law of Biot-Savart to two straight segments indicates that they contribute 0 field at the center of the semicircle since the current is directed at this point, making $\theta = 0$ in the law. You can think of the curved segment as many little segments all the same distance from the center and perpendicular to the line connecting to the center, so $\theta = 90°$. Each segment produces a field into the paper, so they just add up:

$$dB = \frac{\mu_0 i}{4\pi R^2} dl \qquad \Rightarrow B = \frac{\mu_0 i}{4\pi R^2}(\pi R) = \frac{\mu_0 i}{4R}$$

9. The answer is E. The integration direction makes currents out of the page positive in Ampere's law, so $\oint_P \vec{B} \cdot d\vec{l} = \mu_0(1-2-4) = -5\mu_0$.

10. The answer is E. Since the velocity has components both parallel and perpendicular to the field, it will drift down the field lines as it circles them. This is a helix with axis along the field, the y-axis.

FREE RESPONSE

1. (a) The kinetic energy gained as the charges move to the grid will equal the potential energy lost.

   $$\frac{1}{2}mv_0^2 = qV_g \qquad \Rightarrow v_0 = \sqrt{\frac{2qV_g}{m}}$$

   (b) The charges will execute a semicircle as they leave the selector, bending in a counterclockwise sense.

   (c) Using the centripetal force relation (Newton's second law), you have

   $$qvB = m\frac{v^2}{r} \qquad \Rightarrow R = \frac{mv}{qB}$$

   (d) As the charges move through the selector, the magnetic force qvB pushes them to the left. If you want the charges moving with speed v_0 to be undeflected, you must introduce an electric field directed to the right with magnitude satisfying

   $$qv_0B = qE \qquad \Rightarrow E = v_0B$$

2. (a) Use superposition. Find the field due to each wire, using the long wire formula. For the 4 A current,
$$B = (2 \times 10^{-7})\frac{4}{2} = 4 \times 10^{-7} \text{ T directed into paper}$$
For the 6 A current,
$$B = (2 \times 10^{-7})\frac{6}{4} = 3 \times 10^{-7} \text{ T directed out of paper}$$
The net field is then $B_{net} = 1 \times 10^{-7}$ T directed into the paper.

(b) The electron is moving at right angles to the field, so the magnitude of the force is
$$F = qvB = (1.6 \times 10^{-19})(3 \times 10^5)(1 \times 10^{-7}) = 4.8 \times 10^{-21} \text{ N}$$
Since $\vec{v} \times \vec{B}$ is directed down, the negative electron is force up in the $+y$ direction.

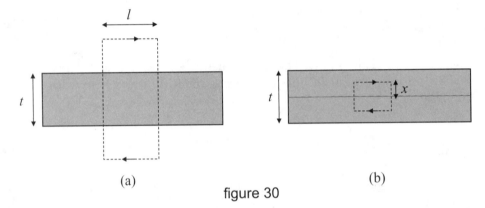

(a)   (b)

figure 30

3. (a) Symmetry tells you that the field must point to the right above the sheet and to the left below the sheet. If you make a path as shown in a, extending equal amounts from the center of the sheet, the field will have the same magnitude along each horizontal segment. There will be no contributions from the vertical segments since $\vec{B} \cdot \vec{dl} = 0$ here.

(b) The current enclosed by the path is $i_{enclosed} = jlt$, so
$$\oint_{path} \vec{B} \cdot \vec{dl} = \mu_0 i_{enclosed}$$
$$2Bl = \mu_0(jlt)$$
$$B = \frac{1}{2}\mu_0 jt$$

(c) The arguments in part a can be applied to the path shown in b.

(d) The current enclosed is now $i_{enclosed} = jl(2x)$, so
$$\oint_{path} \vec{B} \cdot \vec{dl} = \mu_0 i_{enclosed}$$
$$2Bl = \mu_0 jl(2x)$$
$$B = \mu_0 jx$$

CHAPTER 13

Electromagnetic Induction

You've seen in previous chapters that electric and magnetic fields are intimately related to electric charges. Charges create the fields, and charges experience forces within the fields. In this chapter, you'll find out how electric and magnetic fields are intimately related to each other as well, and how changing one of them can create the other. Of particular importance is the creation of "induced" voltages and currents in electric circuits. You'll also learn to quantitatively describe the electric field created even when a circuit isn't present, and you'll learn about self-inductance and applications to inductive circuits.

Motional Induced Voltages

Consider a conducting rod of length L moving with speed v through a uniform magnetic field $\vec{B}$ such that the length cuts directly across the field lines (figure 1). The mobile electrons in the conductor will each experience a force $F = qvB$ directed down in the diagram.

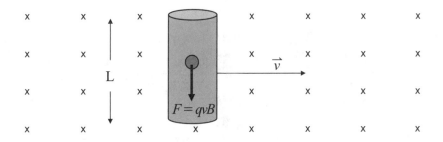

figure 1

Because the electrons in the conductor aren't really free but are constrained to remain in the conductor (recall that a free electron moving this way would move in a circle), a fairly complex process is occurring within the conductor, but the net result is that electrons are forced down the rod, leading to a polarization or separation of charge within the rod. This polarization creates an electric field within the rod. Equilibrium will be quickly established, with the magnetic force down being balanced by the electric force up (figure 2):

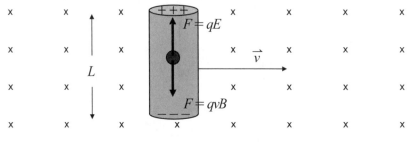

figure 2

$$qE = qvB \Rightarrow E = Bv$$

The two ends of the rod will have a potential difference between them:

$$V_{\text{in}} = EL = BLv$$

The motion of the rod though the magnetic field has created a voltage difference across the rod, an **induced voltage**. If this rod is now connected to a circuit properly, the voltage can be used to create an electric current, and you'll have an electric generator, a device that converts mechanical energy to electrical energy. A simple system that does this is the so-called "rail system," shown in figure 3. Many AP questions are framed in the context of this system, so be sure you understand it well.

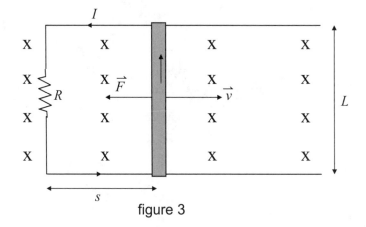

figure 3

Notice that the additional rails (assumed to have negligible resistance) and resistor provide a return path for separated charge so a current will flow around the loop as pictured. Since the resistor is connected directly across the moving rail, you have

$$I = \frac{V_{\text{in}}}{R} = \frac{BLv}{R}$$

This is the induced current. Now you can see an interesting effect: The induced current will behave like any current in a magnetic field and feel a force $F = ILB$. The induced current, itself a product of the magnetic field (and the motion of the rod), will interact back with the field that helped create it in the first place. Using the right-hand rule, you can see that the force on the rail will be to the left, opposite to the direction the rail is moving. Notice that it was motion *to the right* that created the current, and the induced current flowed counterclockwise, creating a force *to the left* on the moving rail. In this case, the induced current flowed in such a way that it created a force that opposed the motion of the rail. This will be true in general and is summarized in **Lenz's law**:

The induced current in any system will always flow in such a way as to oppose the change that caused it.

Lenz's law is consistent with the conservation of energy principle, as you'll see in this example. If the force on the rail was to the right, this would cause the rail to move faster, creating a larger current and an even bigger force. The tiniest push on the rail would then lead to very large currents and rail speeds, obviously violating the energy conservation principle.

Suppose some agent (for example, a person or a machine) pulls on the rail to keep it from slowing down. Then the agent must supply energy at the rate (power):

$$P_{agent} = F_{agent}v = (ILB)v = \left(\frac{BLv}{R}\right)LBv = \frac{B^2L^2v^2}{R}$$

On the other hand, as the current flows in the circuit, thermal energy will appear in the resistor at the rate:

$$P_R = I^2R = \left(\frac{BLv}{R}\right)^2 R = \frac{B^2L^2v^2}{R}$$

You can see that $P_{agent} = P_R$. You cannot get out any more electrical energy than you put in mechanically.

Magnetic Flux

Motional induced voltages are fairly easy to understand because you can think in terms of forces to derive the induced voltage. Induced voltages occur in many situations, and identifying forces would be very difficult in all cases. A more general approach involves introducing the concept of **magnetic flux**, Φ. The flux of the magnetic field through an area is defined similarly to that of the electric field.

$$\Phi_B = \oint_{area} \vec{B} \cdot d\vec{A}$$

From a conceptual point of view, the magnetic flux measures how much of the field cuts through an area (figure 4).

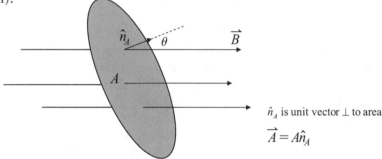

$\hat{n}_A$ is unit vector $\perp$ to area

$\vec{A} = A\hat{n}_A$

figure 4

For example, if a uniform field cuts through a planar area A you have:

$$\Phi_B = \vec{B} \cdot \vec{A} = BA\cos\theta$$

The units of Φ_B are $T \cdot m^2$, also called a **weber**. Here θ is the angle between the field and a line perpendicular to the area plane. Even if both the field and the area are large, Φ_B could be small if the angle is close to $90°$ and not much of the field cuts through the area.

In your applications of Gauss's law, you found the flux through a closed surface. For the current applications of magnetic flux, the surface will be open, with no "inside" or "outside."

EXAMPLE

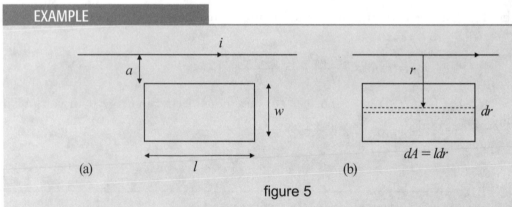

$dA = ldr$

(a) l (b)

figure 5

A rectangular loop of dimensions w and l is a distance a from a long wire carrying current i (figure 5a). Find the flux through the loop.

The long wire right-hand rule tells you that the field is into the paper. The field isn't uniform, however, falling off as $\frac{1}{r}$. You must integrate through the loop, finding the elemental contributions and summing them up. Figure 5b shows an element of thickness dr. The field along this element is uniform, since r is fixed, so

$$d\Phi_B = B(r)dA = \frac{\mu_0 i}{2\pi r}ldr \quad (\vec{B} \text{ and } d\vec{A} \text{ are parallel})$$

Since r varies from a to $a + w$, you have

$$\Phi_B = \int_a^{a+w} \frac{\mu_0 i}{2\pi r}ldr = \frac{\mu_0 il}{2\pi}\ln\frac{a+w}{a}$$

Faraday's Law

So what does flux have to do with induced voltages? Let's re-examine the rail system, focusing on the flux through the current loop. In figure 3, the flux through the loop is given by

$$\Phi_B = BLs$$

In a small time Δt the flux will change, in this case increasing because the area is increasing. Let's calculate the rate at which the flux changes:

$$\frac{\Delta \Phi_B}{\Delta t} = BL\frac{\Delta s}{\Delta t}$$

In the limit where Δt is infinitesimal you have

$$\frac{d\Phi_B}{dt} = BLv = V_{in}$$

You can see that the rate at which the flux changes is just the induced voltage. While it was derived for the special case of the rail system, the validity of this statement is much broader and is known as **Faraday's law**. When the magnetic flux through a loop changes, a voltage will be induced. For a single loop, you have

$$V_{in} = -\frac{d\Phi_B}{dt}$$

The minus sign is the mathematical way of accounting for Lenz's law: The current created by the induced voltage will flow to oppose the change that caused it. If you're only concerned with the size of the induced voltage, you can dispense with the minus sign, but be prepared to identify induced current direction.

If there are N loops wound in the same direction, each loop will have the preceding voltage induced, so that

$$V_{in} = -N\frac{d\Phi_B}{dt}$$

You can then find the induced current in the circuit if the overall resistance is known.

EXAMPLE

In the example developed previously and shown in figure 5, let's suppose that the long wire carried a time-dependent current, $i(t) = 3t + 1$. Let's also assume that the loop is fixed in the position shown. Determine the induced voltage in the loop.

You've calculated the flux through the loop already. Now substitute the form for i into your result.

$$\Phi_B = \frac{\mu_0 i l}{2\pi} \ln \frac{a + w}{a} = \frac{\mu_0 (3t + 1) l}{2\pi} \ln \frac{a + w}{a}$$

From Faraday's law, you have

$$V_{\text{in}} = \frac{d\Phi_B}{dt} = -\frac{3\mu_0 l}{2\pi} \ln \frac{a + w}{a}$$

Lenz's Law and Flux

A common question on the AP test involves determining the direction of the induced current. The easiest way to do this is to apply Lenz's law while thinking about the *magnetic field created by the induced current*, and what this will do to the overall flux through the loop. Since the induced current will always flow in such a way as to oppose the change that caused it, the induced current will create its own field that will try to keep the flux from changing. To determine the direction of the field created by a current loop at points inside the circumference of the loop, you can use a variation of the long wire right-hand rule:

Loop right-hand rule: Curl the fingers of the right hand around the loop in the direction of the current flow. The thumb will point in the direction of the magnetic field within the loop created by this current.

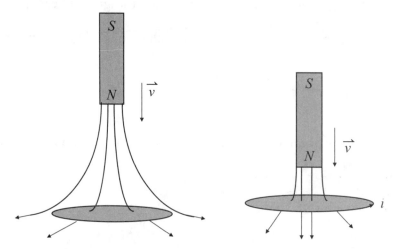

As flux into the loop increases, a current flows, creating its own field that opposes the original change in flux.

figure 6

In figure 6, the flux through the loop increased as the magnet fell. The induced current will create an upward field to oppose the change. In terms of the loop right-hand rule, to get your thumb to point up, the current must flow as shown in the figure.

Induced Electric Fields

From the definition of electric potential, you have seen that

$$\Delta V = \int_a^b \vec{E} \cdot d\vec{l}$$

In situations where there are no time-dependent fields, ΔV would be 0 if a and b were the same point. Since the electric force is conservative, it takes no work to move a charge around a closed loop. But this isn't the case if time-dependent magnetic fields are present. When a magnetic field changes in time, it creates an electric field. The line integral of this field around a loop won't be 0. In fact, it will equal the induced voltage in the loop. Even if there's no physical conducting loop present, you can still relate the changing flux through a fictitious loop to the line integral of the electric field around the loop. You can generalize Faraday's law to relate the changing magnetic flux and the electric field created by this change:

$$V_{in} = -\frac{d\Phi_B}{dt}$$

$$\oint_{\text{loop}} \vec{E} \cdot d\vec{l} = -\frac{d}{dt} \oint_{\text{area}} \vec{B} \cdot d\vec{A}$$

It's important to understand the relationship between the two integrals. The *loop* refers to the closed curve bounding the area as shown in figure 7.

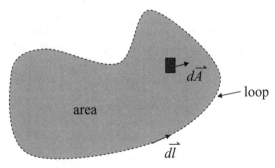

figure 7

The direction of the area element $d\vec{A}$ is determined by a right-hand rule similar to the loop right-hand rule: Curl the fingers of the right hand in the direction of the integration path, and $d\vec{A}$ will point in the direction of the thumb.

Although this equation relates the integrals of the two fields, with enough symmetry you can obtain a relation between the fields themselves. Suppose the magnetic field is uniform over a region that's cylindrically symmetric. A good example is the magnetic field inside a long solenoid, which is constant inside the solenoid and 0 elsewhere. If the magnetic field changes as time develops, an electric field will be created. You can determine the magnitude and direction of this electric field by applying Faraday's law in the integral form shown earlier. In figure 8, the shaded region contains a uniform field that's directed into the paper.

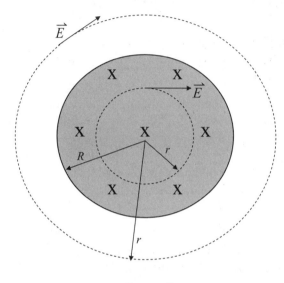

figure 8

If the field strength decreases, an electric field will be created as shown in the figure. You can determine the direction of the field by imagining a loop centered on the magnetic field axis and then using Lenz's law to determine the direction a current would flow if the loop were a real conductor. The induced electric field will point in the same direction as the current flow. At a given distance from the center of symmetry, the induced electric field magnitude will be constant and will factor out of the integral. So for $r < R$, you have

$$\oint_{\text{loop}} \vec{E} \cdot \vec{dl} = -\frac{d}{dt} \oint_{\text{area}} \vec{B} \cdot d\vec{A}$$

$$\Rightarrow E = -\frac{dB}{dt}\frac{r}{2}$$

$$E(2\pi r) = -\frac{dB}{dt}(\pi r^2)$$

For $r > R$, there's no magnetic field, but an electric field is still created in this region because the changing field within the shaded region causes the flux through the larger area to change.

$$E(2\pi r) = -\frac{dB}{dt}(\pi R^2) \qquad \Rightarrow E = -\frac{dB}{dt}\frac{R^2}{2r}$$

Self-Induction and Inductance

Consider an ideal solenoid of length l, cross-sectional area A, and n turns per unit length, so that the total number of loops is $N = nl$. You saw in the last chapter that when a current is eventually established in the device, there will be a uniform field within the solenoid given by $B = \mu_0 ni$. This field actually cuts through the loops of the solenoid and creates a magnetic flux:

$$\Phi_B = NBA = (nl)(\mu_0 ni)A = (\mu_0 n^2 lA)i$$

Should the current change, there will be a change in the flux and a voltage will be induced. Because it's the changing field of the solenoid itself that induces the voltage, this process is called **self-induction**. Notice that the flux is proportional to the current:

$$\Phi_B = (\mu_0 n^2 lA)i = Li \qquad L = \mu_0 n^2 lA$$

The proportionality constant L is called the **self-inductance** of the coil. Notice that it depends solely on geometrical factors l, A, and n. The SI units of self-inductance are $\frac{V \cdot s}{A}$, called a **henry** (H). From Faraday's law, you then have

$$V_{in} = -L\frac{di}{dt}$$

For more complicated devices, you can use this equation to define and measure self-inductance. Simply measure the induced voltage when the current is changed in a controlled way. Then,

$$L = -\frac{V_{in}}{\left(\frac{di}{dt}\right)}$$

RL Circuits

Inductors can be placed in electric circuits and are designated with the symbol shown in figure 9.

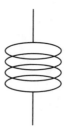

figure 9

Consider the circuit shown in figure 10, which has a resistor and an inductor in series. Such circuits are called **RL circuits**.

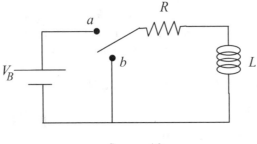

figure 10

Your approach to these circuits should be similar to your approach to RC circuits: You can answer most of the important questions by understanding how the inductor behaves in the limits $t = 0$ and $t \to \infty$. At $t = 0$, you throw the switch to a. Initially there's 0 current in the inductor, and the inductor will resist any change in this condition, so when the switch is first closed, $i = 0$.

The inductor initially behaves as an open circuit. As time develops, current will begin to be established in the inductor. Eventually a steady state will be established in which the current reaches a constant maximum value. Since the inductor itself is usually considered to have 0 electrical resistance, the steady state current value depends on the series resistance R, so that as $t \to \infty$, $i \to \frac{V_{in}}{R}$. The inductor behaves in this limit like a piece of zero-resistance wire.

Notice that these limiting conditions are just the opposite to those of a capacitor in an RC circuit. If you wait a long time so that the steady state has been reached, and then throw the switch to b, the inductor initially will resist any change and maintain the current that was established before the switch was thrown. Eventually the current will die off, and as $t \to \infty$, $i \to 0$. The key to understanding the qualitative behavior of inductors in circuits is to remember that they try to maintain the flow of charge that exists within them. Any change is opposed by an induced voltage, which creates an induced current that flows in a way that tries to maintain the current as it was.

To determine the behavior of the circuit for in-between times, you can apply the loop law. When the switch is at a, you have

$$+V_B - iR - L\frac{di}{dt} = 0 \qquad \Rightarrow \frac{di}{dt} + \frac{R}{L}i = \frac{V_B}{L}$$

If the switch was closed at $t = 0$, the solution to this differential equation is

$$i(t) = \frac{V_B}{R}\left(1 - e^{-\frac{R}{L}t}\right)$$

Notice that the behavior of the current in an RL circuit is analogous to the behavior of the charge in an RC circuit. The graph of its behavior is shown in figure 11a. The **inductive time constant** in this circuit is $\tau = \frac{L}{R}$. In 1 time constant, the current increases to 63 percent of the steady state value.

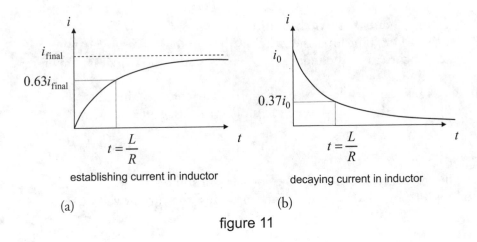

establishing current in inductor

(a)

decaying current in inductor

(b)

figure 11

When the switch is thrown to b, the loop law gives you

$$-iR - L\frac{di}{dt} = 0 \quad \Rightarrow \quad \frac{di}{dt} + \frac{R}{L}i = 0$$

If you assume that the current was i_0 just before the switch was thrown, the solution to this differential equation is

$$i(t) = i_0 e^{-\frac{R}{L}t}$$

Figure 11b displays the graph of this function. In 1 time constant, the current decays to 37 percent of its initial value.

EXAMPLE

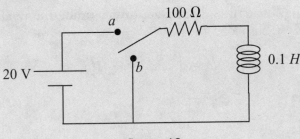

figure 12

Consider the circuit shown in figure 12. The switch is thrown to a at $t = 0$. After a long time, the switch is thrown to b.
   (a) Find the value of the current in the inductor
      (i) when the switch is first thrown to a
      (ii) after a long time but before the switch is thrown to b

(iii) just after the switch is thrown to *b*
(iv) a long time after the switch is thrown to *b*
(b) Find the current in the inductor 2×10^{-3} s after the switch is thrown to *b*.

(a) Since the inductor resists a change in the current, just after the switch is thrown to *a*, $i = 0$. After a long time, the inductor is just a piece of wire,

$$\text{so } i = \frac{V_B}{R} = \frac{20}{100} = 0.2 \text{ A.}$$

Just after the switch is thrown to b, the current will still be 0.2 A, since the inductor opposes any change. A long time after this, the current will be 0.
(b) The time constant of the circuit is

$$\tau = \frac{L}{R} = \frac{0.1}{100} = 10^{-3} \, s$$

The current after 2 time constants, 2×10^{-3} s, will be

$$i = i_0 e^{-\frac{R}{L}t} = 0.2e^{-2} = 0.027 \text{ A}$$

Energy and Inductors

When an inductor is connected to a battery, the inductor resists the establishment of current. The battery must do work to eventually establish the steady state current. At any instant, the rate at which energy is transferred to the inductor is

$$P_L = iV_{\text{in}} = iL\frac{di}{dt}$$

You can rearrange this equation and integrate to determine the total energy absorbed by the inductor as current is established:

$$U_L = \int_0^t P_L dt = \int_0^i Li' di' = \frac{1}{2}Li^2$$

EXAMPLE

How much energy is stored in the inductor of the previous example when the steady state has been reached after the switch was thrown to *a*?

The steady state current was 0.2 A, so you have

$$U_L = \frac{1}{2}Li^2 = \frac{1}{2}(0.1)(0.2)^2 = 2 \times 10^{-3}\,\text{J}$$

This energy is associated with establishing the magnetic field of the inductor. If you look at the specific case of a solenoid, you can relate the energy directly to the magnetic field. Recall that for a solenoid you have

$$L = \mu_0 n^2 l A \qquad\qquad B = \mu_0 n i$$

Substituting into the energy equation gives you

$$U_L = \frac{1}{2}Li^2 = \frac{1}{2}(\mu_0 n^2 l A)\left(\frac{B}{\mu_0 n}\right)^2 = \frac{B^2}{2\mu_0}(Al)$$

Since *Al* is the volume inside the solenoid where the field is contained, if you divide by this, you obtain the energy density associated with a magnetic field:

$$u_B = \frac{U_L}{Al} = \frac{B^2}{2\mu_0}$$

It's important that you go back over the steps leading to the formulas for energy in a capacitor and electric energy density and note how similar they are.

LC Circuits

Consider the circuit shown in figure 13. With the switch thrown to *a*, the capacitor will charge. When it's fully charged, you throw the switch to *b*.

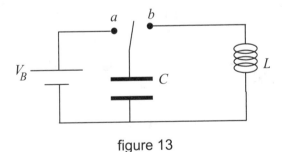

figure 13

The capacitor will begin to discharge, and the energy that was in the electric field in the capacitor will be transferred to energy stored in the magnetic field of the inductor. The inductor resists change, however, so once all the energy has left the capacitor and the maximum current is flowing through the inductor, the current will begin to deposit charge of the opposite polarity on the capacitor. The energy will begin to reappear in the electric field, and the capacitor will recharge with a reverse polarity on its plates. After that, the process repeats, bringing the capacitor back to its initial state. Now, you have an oscillation. This combination of an inductor and capacitor is called an **LC circuit**. The mathematical description follows from applying the loop law to the oscillating circuit:

$$\frac{q}{C} + L\frac{di}{dt} = 0$$

Since $i = \frac{dq}{dt}$, you can write this as

$$\frac{d^2q}{dt^2} + \frac{q}{LC} = 0$$

From your work on oscillators in mechanics, you should recognize this as a harmonic oscillator with period

$$T = 2\pi\sqrt{LC}$$

You won't have to do quantitative work with such circuits on the AP test, but you may have to answer questions referring to their qualitative behavior and know the period and frequency of oscillation.

Maxwell's Equations

Let's summarize the basic laws of electromagnetism, with some comments on their interpretation.

$$\oint_{\substack{\text{closed} \\ \text{surface}}} \vec{E} \cdot d\vec{A} = \frac{Q_{\text{in}}}{\varepsilon_0}$$

Gauss's law relates the charge inside a closed surface to the flux of the electric field through the surface.

$$\oint_{\substack{\text{closed} \\ \text{loop}}} \vec{B} \cdot d\vec{l} = \mu_0 i_{\text{enclosed}}$$

Ampere's law relates the line integral of the magnetic field around a closed loop to the current enclosed within the loop.

$$\oint_{\substack{\text{closed} \\ \text{loop}}} \vec{E} \cdot d\vec{l} = -\frac{d}{dt} \oint_{\text{area}} \vec{B} \cdot d\vec{A}$$

Faraday's law relates the line integral of the electric field around a closed loop to the rate of change of magnetic flux through the area enclosed by the loop.

It's an experimental fact that point sources of magnetism, so-called magnetic monopoles, don't exist. Any closed surface that encloses a north magnetic pole must also enclose a south magnetic pole. That means you can write a flux equation for the magnetic field analogous to Gauss's law:

$$\oint_{\substack{closed \\ surface}} \vec{B} \cdot d\vec{A} = 0$$

There's been speculation in the past that magnetic monopoles do exist. It's interesting to consider how their presence would affect these four equations. Not only would you have to account for the magnetic charge in a Gauss's law type of equation, but you would also have to account for the flow of this charge in an Ampere's law type of equation. Calling Q^e, Q^m, i^e, and i^m the respective electric and magnetic charges and currents, you would have

$$\oint_{\substack{closed \\ surface}} \vec{E} \cdot d\vec{A} = \frac{Q^e_{in}}{\varepsilon_0} \qquad \oint_{\substack{closed \\ loop}} \vec{E} \cdot d\vec{l} = \frac{i^m_{enclosed}}{\varepsilon_0} - \frac{d}{dt} \oint_{area} \vec{B} \cdot d\vec{A}$$

$$\oint_{\substack{closed \\ surface}} \vec{B} \cdot d\vec{A} = \mu_0 Q^m_{in} \qquad \oint_{\substack{closed \\ loop}} \vec{B} \cdot d\vec{l} = \mu_0 i^e_{enclosed}$$

With the addition of magnetic charges and currents, there's almost total symmetry in the form of these equations. The only lack of symmetry is in the last one, where a corresponding term relating the rate of change of *electric flux* would have to be added. This would be an analogous effect to Faraday's law. In fact, this effect is real and was first proposed by Maxwell. It leads to the equation

$$\oint_{\substack{closed \\ loop}} \vec{B} \cdot d\vec{l} = \mu_0 i^e_{enclosed} + \mu_0 \varepsilon_0 \frac{d}{dt} \oint_{area} \vec{E} \cdot d\vec{A}$$

Qualitatively, you can say that this equation shows that magnetic fields are created by both electric currents and changing electric fields. While you "derived" this result from symmetry considerations, the equation keeps this form even in the real world, where apparently magnetic charges and currents don't exist. The four Maxwell equations of electrodynamics, then, are

$$\oint_{\substack{closed \\ surface}} \vec{E} \cdot d\vec{A} = \frac{Q_{in}}{\varepsilon_0} \text{ (Gauss)} \qquad \oint_{\substack{closed \\ loop}} \vec{E} \cdot d\vec{l} = -\frac{d}{dt} \oint_{area} \vec{B} \cdot d\vec{A} \text{ (Faraday)}$$

$$\oint_{\substack{closed \\ surface}} \vec{B} \cdot d\vec{A} = 0 \qquad \oint_{\substack{closed \\ loop}} \vec{B} \cdot d\vec{l} = \mu_0 i_{enclosed} + \mu_0 \varepsilon_0 \frac{d}{dt} \oint_{area} \vec{E} \cdot d\vec{A} \text{ (Ampere)}$$

You've done extensive work with Gauss's law, Ampere's law (without the extra term), and Faraday's law. This is the only quantitative material you will face on the AP test. You should be familiar, however, with the interpretation of the extra term in Ampere's law and the lack of magnetic monopole interpretation of the third equation.

KEY FORMULAS

Rail System Induced Voltage $V_{\text{in}} = BLv$

Magnetic Flux $\Phi_B = BA\cos\theta$

$$\Phi_B = \oint_{\text{area}} \vec{B} \cdot d\vec{A}$$

Faraday's Law $V_{\text{in}} = -N\dfrac{d\Phi_B}{dt}$

$$\oint_{\substack{\text{closed} \\ \text{loop}}} \vec{E} \cdot d\vec{l} = -\frac{d}{dt}\oint_{\text{area}} \vec{B} \cdot d\vec{A}$$

Inductor Potential Drop $V_{\text{in}} = -L\dfrac{di}{dt}$

Inductive Time Constant $\tau = \dfrac{L}{R}$

RL Circuit $i(t) = \dfrac{V_B}{R}\left(1 - e^{-\frac{R}{L}t}\right)$ (growing)

$i(t) = i_0 e^{-\frac{R}{L}t}$ (decaying)

Inductor Energy $U_L = \dfrac{1}{2}Li^2$

Magnetic Energy Density $u_B = \dfrac{B^2}{2\mu_0}$

LC Oscillation Period $T = 2\pi\sqrt{LC}$

PRACTICE EXERCISES

SECTION I MULTIPLE CHOICE

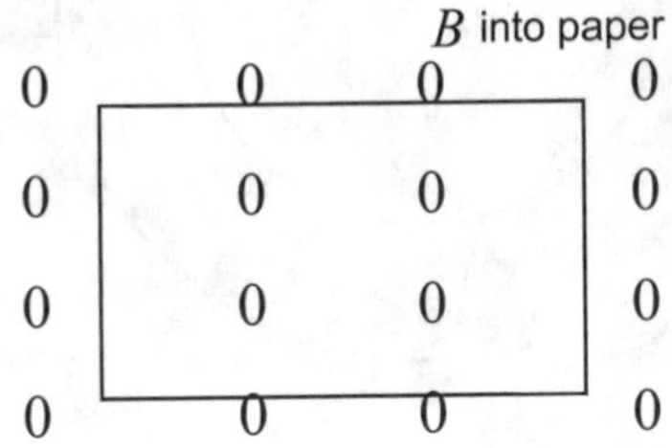

B into paper

```
0      0      0      0
  ┌─────────────────┐
0 │  0      0       │ 0
  │                 │
0 │  0      0       │ 0
  │                 │
0 └─────────────────┘ 0
     0      0      0
```

figure 14

1. A rectangular loop of dimensions 0.04 m by 0.06 m is at rest in a uniform magnetic field of magnitude 0.5 T. The field is perpendicular to the plane of the loop coming out of the page. The magnetic flux through the loop is

   (A) $12 \, T \cdot m^2$ (B) 0   (C) $0.12 \, T \cdot m^2$ (D) $12 \times 10^{-4} \, T \cdot m^2$ (E) $0.5 \, T \cdot m^2$

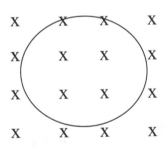

figure 15

2. A flexible conducting loop is placed in a magnetic field with the plane of the loop perpendicular to the field. Which of the following will NOT induce a current in the loop?

   (A) increasing the magnitude of the field
   (B) stretching the loop, making a larger circle
   (C) moving the loop parallel to the field
   (D) removing the loop from the field
   (E) rotating the loop about a diameter

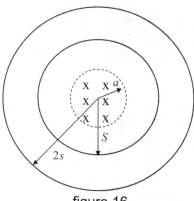

figure 16

3. Two concentric loops have radii s and $2s$. A spatially uniform magnetic field over the range $r < a$ with $a < s$ is changing at a constant rate. The voltage induced in the outer loop is V_{in}. The voltage induced in the inner loop is

(A) 0   (B) $\dfrac{V_{in}}{2}$ (C) $\dfrac{V_{in}}{4}$ (D) $2V_{in}$ (E) V_{in}

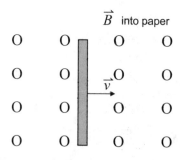

figure 17

4. A wire of constant length is moved through a **uniform** magnetic field at a constant velocity with the velocity vector perpendicular to the field. A graph of the induced voltage between the ends of the wire as a function of time would look like

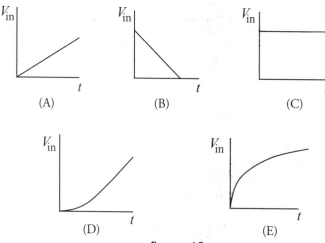

figure 18

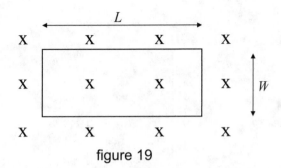

figure 19

5. A rectangular loop of dimensions L and W and resistance R is stationary in a changing magnetic field. To produce a current I in the loop, the field must change at a rate of

(A) $\dfrac{LW}{IR}$ (B) $\dfrac{IR}{LW}$ (C) $\dfrac{L}{IR}$ (D) $\dfrac{IRL}{W}$ (E) $\dfrac{IRW}{L}$

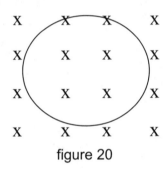

figure 20

6. A magnetic field perpendicular into the page to a circular loop is decreasing as time goes on. In which direction will the current induced in the loop flow?

(A) counterclockwise   (B) clockwise   (C) No current will flow.
     (D) out of the page   (E) into the page

Questions 7 and 8

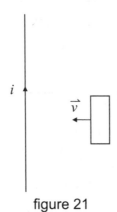

figure 21

7. A rectangular loop is moving toward a long wire carrying current up as shown in the figure. In which direction will the induced current in the loop flow?

   (A) counterclockwise   (B) clockwise   (C) No current will flow.
   (D) out of the page   (E) into the page

8. The force exerted on the loop by the long wire will be directed

   (A) into the page   (B) out of the page   (C) left
   (D) right   (E) down

Questions 9–11

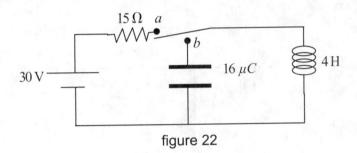

figure 22

9. In the circuit shown in the figure, the switch is thrown from the open position to *a*. Which of the following is true?

   (A) The current will immediately rise to 7.5 A and then decay more slowly to 0.
   (B) The current will immediately rise to 2 A and then decay more slowly to 0.
   (C) The current will grow to 7.5 A and then remain constant.
   (D) The current will grow to 2 A and then remain constant.
   (E) The current will reach a constant value immediately after the switch is thrown.

10. The maximum energy stored in the inductor is closest to

   (A) 0   (B) 16 J   (C) 8 J   (D) 110 J   (E) 60 J

11. After a long time, the switch is thrown to *b*. Which of the following is true?

   (A) The current will immediately drop to 0.
   (B) The current will decrease uniformly to 0 over a few seconds.
   (C) The current will decrease exponentially to 0.
   (D) The current will oscillate with a period of close to 0.05 s.
   (E) The current will oscillate with a period close to 0.5 s.

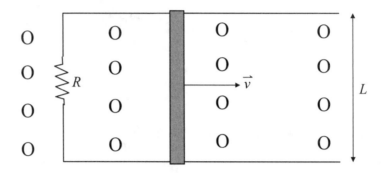

figure 23

1. A conducting rail, positioned to slide without friction over fixed conducting rails separated by a distance L, is pulled along at a constant speed v by some external force $\vec{F}$. A uniform magnetic field $\vec{B}$ points out of the paper, perpendicular to the plane of the loop. The fixed rails are connected by a resistance R.
   (a) On the diagram, indicate the direction of the induced current flow.
   (b) Determine the magnitude of the induced current.
   (c) Determine the magnitude of force F needed to keep the rail moving at a constant speed.
   (d) The force $\vec{F}$ is suddenly removed. How much energy will be dissipated in the resistor as the rail slows to a stop?

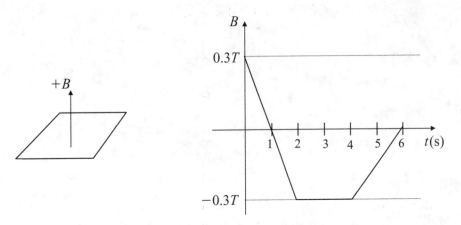

figure 24

2. A square loop of resistance 0.5 Ω and side 0.6 m is oriented so that the plane of the loop is perpendicular to a magnetic field that is uniform spatially but changing in time as depicted in the graph below. The positive direction of $\vec{B}$ is up.
   (a) Calculate the flux through the loop at $t = 4$ s.
   (b) Find the induced voltage at $t = 5$ s.
   (c) On the axes below, sketch the induced current as a function of time. Indicate numerical values on the current axis and assume counterclockwise current is positive.

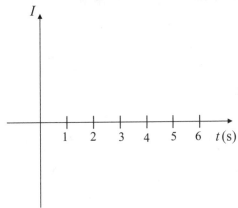

figure 25

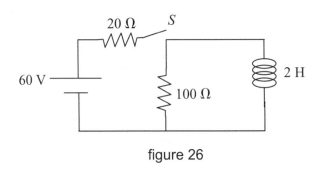

figure 26

3. In the circuit shown in the figure, the switch S is closed at $t = 0$.
   (a) Determine the following immediately after the switch is thrown:
      (i) current in the inductor
      (ii) current in the 100 Ω resistor
      (iii) the rate at which current is changing in the inductor
   (b) Determine the following a long time after the switch has been thrown:
      (i) current in the 100 Ω resistor
      (ii) energy stored in the inductor

After a long time, the switch is opened.
   (c) Determine the voltage drop across the 100 Ω resistor immediately after the switch is opened.
   (d) Determine the energy in the magnetic field of the inductor 0.06 s after the switch was thrown.

Answers and Explanations

MULTIPLE CHOICE

1. The answer is D. The area of the loop is 24×10^{-4} m^2. Since $\Phi = BA$, the result follows by multiplying by 0.5 T.

2. The answer is C. Moving the loop parallel to the field won't change how much of the field cuts through the loop. All other possibilities given will change the flux, either by changing the field in the loop (A and D), the area (B), or the orientation of the field with respect to the area (E). Changing the flux will induce a current.

3. The answer is E. The changing flux through either loop is $\frac{\Delta B}{\Delta t}(\pi a^2)$. Since $a < s$, whatever flux cuts through the smaller loop will also cut through the larger loop. While the two loops will have the same induced voltage, in general they will have different currents induced because in general they will have different resistances. Within each loop will be different electric fields induced as well, but only C-level students need to address this level of complexity.

4. The answer is C. As the wire cuts across the field, a voltage of $V_{in} = BLv$ is induced between the ends of the wire. All of these quantities are constant.

5. The answer is B. The induced voltage from the changing flux will produce a current $I = \frac{V_{in}}{R} = \frac{\frac{\Delta B}{\Delta t}(LW)}{R}$. Solving for $\frac{\Delta B}{\Delta t}$ gives the result.

6. The answer is B. Since the field is *decreasing* into the loop, by Lenz's law the induced current will flow to try to *increase* the field into the loop. The loop right-hand rule then gives a clockwise direction for the current flow.

7. The answer is A. As the loop moves closer to the wire, the field is getting stronger. This field points into the paper at the position of the loop, so the flux is increasing into the paper. Lenz's law then tells you that the induced current will create a field that points out of the paper, and the loop right-hand rule gives a counterclockwise direction.

8. The answer is D. This is the force direction that will oppose the change. You can analyze the segments of the loop to see how this happens. From question 7 you know the current flows counterclockwise. The two shorter-width sections will experience equal but opposite ilB forces. The length section closer to the long wire will feel an ilB force directed away from the long wire, using the force right-hand rule. While the other length section feels a force toward the long wire, the field is weaker at its position, so the net force is away.

9. The answer is D. The inductor resists the change from 0 current, and the value of the current will rise from 0 to the value determined by the battery and resistance $i = \frac{30}{15} = 2$ A. Notice that the inductive time constant $\frac{L}{R}$ is about 0.25 s.

10. The answer is C. Use $U_L = \frac{1}{2}Li^2 = \frac{1}{2}(4)(2)^2 = 8$ J

11. The answer is D. The LC circuit oscillates with a period
$$T = 2\pi\sqrt{LC} = 2\pi\sqrt{64 \times 10^{-6}} = 50.2 \times 10^{-3} \text{ s}$$

FREE RESPONSE

1. (a) The current will flow clockwise around the rectangular loop. The area of the loop is getting larger, causing the flux out of the loop to increase. By Lenz's law, the induced current will flow to oppose the increase in flux, and this can be accomplished by creating a field *into the page*. The right-hand rule then gives the clockwise direction.

   (b) The induced voltage is $V_{in} = BLv$.
   The induced current will then be $I = \frac{BLv}{R}$, since the voltage drop across the resistor is V_{in}.

   (c) The moving rail will feel a force to the left because the current I flowing in the rail is experiencing the magnetic field $\vec{B}$. This force is $F_{left} = ILB$. An equal force will have to be applied to the right to keep the rail moving at constant speed. Substituting for I, you have
   $$F = \frac{B^2L^2v}{R}$$

   (d) At the instant the force is removed, the rail is moving at speed v and has kinetic energy $\frac{1}{2}mv^2$. Conservation of energy then says that all of this energy will eventually appear as thermal energy in the resistor, so the answer is $\frac{1}{2}mv^2$.

2. (a) At $t = 4$ s, the field is 0.3 T. The area of the loop is $(0.6 \text{ m})^2 = 0.36 \text{ m}^2$, so
   $$\Phi_B = BA = 0.3(0.36) = 0.108 \text{ webers}$$

   (b) At $t = 5$ s, the field is changing at the rate of $\frac{0.3}{2} = 0.15\frac{T}{s}$. This is the slope of the last line segment in the graph. Since the area doesn't change, the flux will be changing at the rate
   $$\frac{\Delta\Phi_B}{\Delta t} = \frac{\Delta B}{\Delta t}A = 0.15(0.36) = 0.054 \text{ V}$$

This is the induced voltage by Faraday's law.

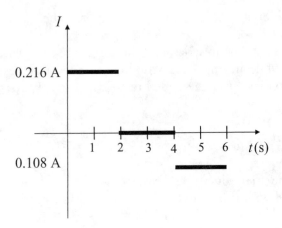

figure 27

(c) Over the first 2 s, the field changes at the rate of $\frac{0.6}{2} = 0.3\frac{T}{s}$ (slope), and the induced voltage will be

$$\frac{\Delta \Phi}{\Delta t} = \frac{\Delta B}{\Delta t}A = 0.3(0.36) = 0.108 \text{ V}$$

The induced current then will be $I = \frac{V_{in}}{R} = \frac{0.108}{0.5} = 0.216$ A. By Lenz's law, this current will flow in such a way as to oppose the change in flux created by the decreasing field. This means the current will create a field in the $+$ direction, and the right-hand rule then gives a counterclockwise direction for the flow. This is the $+$ current direction.

Over the interval from 2–4 s, there's no change in flux, so the current will be 0. Over the last 2 seconds, you can see that the slope is just half of the slope over the first 2 seconds, so the induced current will be just half as much. In this case, however, the field is increasing, causing the flux up through the loop to increase. The induced current will flow to oppose this change in flux; this means that the current must flow clockwise, creating its own field down through the loop. This is the negative current direction.

3. (a) (i) At $t = 0$, the inductor will resist its change for the 0 current state, so it will have 0 current.

   (ii) The two resistors are then in series, and the current in each will be $i = \frac{60}{120} = 0.5$ A.

   (iii) The inductor, while having 0 current instantaneously, does have a voltage drop across it equal to that across the 100 Ω resistor, since they are in parallel. That means you can write

$$L\frac{di_{in}}{dt} = V_{100\,\Omega} = 0.5(100) \qquad \Rightarrow \frac{di_{in}}{dt} = 25\frac{A}{s}$$

   (b) (i) After a long time, the inductor will behave like a piece of zero resistance wire. Since this is in parallel with the 100 Ω resistor, this resistor must have 0 current.

   (ii) The current after a long time will be $i = \frac{60}{20} = 3$ A, so the energy stored will be $U_L = \frac{1}{2}Li^2 = \frac{1}{2}(2)(3)^2 = 9$ J.

   (c) The inductor will instantaneously maintain the 3 A it had just before the switch was opened. This current will be forced to move through the 100 Ω resistor, and from Ohm's law you have
$$V = iR = 3(100) = 300 \text{ V}$$

   (d) The inductive time constant of the final circuit is $\tau = \frac{L}{R} = 0.02$ s. The 0.06 s is 3 time constants. The current will have decayed according to

$$i = i_0 e^{-\frac{R}{L}t} = i_0 e^{-3} = 0.05 i_0$$

The energy left will be

$$U = \frac{1}{2}Li^2 = (0.05)^2 \frac{1}{2}Li_0^2 = (0.05)^2(9) = 0.022 \text{ J}$$

AP Physics and the Laboratory

Lab Questions on the Exam

Since 1996, the AP Physics Exam has increased its focus on the lab aspect of the AP curriculum. The test now includes free-response questions that require you to be familiar with common lab apparatus and how it's used. The lab questions ask you to design a lab setup that will measure a certain property, perhaps with restrictions on the types of measuring instruments that can be used. Typically, the questions call for a written description, a diagram, and an analysis showing how the instrument readings lead to the final measurement result. There are many possible correct answers to these questions. In addition, some questions give you data, and you're required to graph it directly or manipulate it before graphing it. The graphs then must be interpreted. Let's look at some examples.

1. You're given a simple pendulum that consists of a small spherical mass m attached to a long piece of string. You're also supplied with a metal stand and rods to hang the string from. Using this apparatus along with other common lab apparatus, you're asked to determine g, the acceleration due to gravity.
   (a) List any other measuring devices and equipment you need.
   (b) Describe how you would perform the lab. If you wish, you can make a sketch to clarify your description.
   (c) Show how the data you have taken can be used to determine g.

Possible Response
   (a) meter stick, stopwatch
   (b) For small amplitudes, the period is independent of the amplitude. With the pendulum attached to its support, measure the length of the string. Pull it out a small angle and release, starting the stopwatch. Record the time T_5 for 5 complete oscillations. Repeat these procedures for several measured lengths of the pendulum.
   (c) The experimental value for the period will be

$$T = \frac{T_5}{5}$$

Theoretically, you would expect the period to be related to the length by the equation

$$T = 2\pi\sqrt{\frac{l}{g}}$$

You can reorganize this to get

$$l = \left(\frac{g}{4\pi^2}\right)T^2$$

If you plot the length on the vertical axis and T^2 on the horizontal, you get a straight line with slope $\frac{g}{4\pi^2}$. Graphically determine the slope, equate it to $\frac{g}{4\pi^2}$, and solve for g.

Comments

It's better to use several data points and a graph rather than a single point and the equation. Depending on your calculator and your proficiency with it, you could fit the T vs. length data directly with a power fit and then extract g from the coefficient in the equation. You would have more precision in the answer if the length in the period formula were replaced with $l + r$, where r is the radius of the spherical mass. This would be the distance from the pivot to the center of mass.

2. You're given a wooden block of mass 0.20 kg in the shape of a rectangular solid and a flat, wooden plank 1 m long, with a width 3 times the width of the block. You're asked to determine the coefficient of kinetic friction between the block and the plank.
   (a) List the measuring devices and equipment you will need.
   (b) Make a sketch of your setup, clearly labeling all the components.
   (c) Describe how you would perform the experiment.
   (d) Show how the coefficient of friction can be determined from the measurements made.

Possible Response

The appropriate techniques all involve determining the acceleration. You can do this in a number of ways, ranging from low-tech "dot timers" using paper strips and carbon paper, to high-tech sonic rangers and smart pulleys. The AP test writers have emphasized that students should be familiar with technology, so let's look at an approach using a smart pulley.
   (a) weights, string, smart pulley, graphing calculator software
   (b) (figure 1)

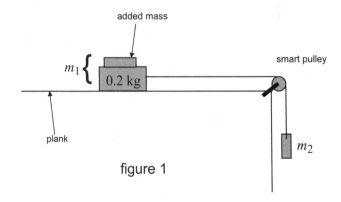

figure 1

(c) Set up the wood block and plank as shown in the figure. Attach a known mass m_2 with a string over a smart pulley. Set up the graphing calculator software to receive smart pulley input, and release the masses. Determine the acceleration from the slope of the v vs. t graph displayed by the calculator readout. Repeat this procedure several times, each time adding some mass to the wood block. The added mass and the original block are designated m_1.

(d) The normal force N between the block and the plank is

$$N = m_1 g$$

You can calculate the friction force between the block and plank from the masses and the measured acceleration, using Newton's third law applied to the system:

$$netF = ma$$

$$m_2 g - f = (m_1 + m_2)a$$

$$f = m_2 g - (m_1 + m_2)a$$

Each trial will give you a new value of f and N. If you plot the friction force on the vertical axis and the normal force on the horizontal, the slope will equal the coefficient of friction.

Comments

The same apparatus and analysis technique would need to be modified only slightly to accommodate some other method of measuring acceleration. While a single data point can be used to get a value of μ, the graph provides higher precision.

In preparing for these questions (there won't be more than one per year), be sure to look over your lab work and focus on the capabilities of the apparatus you used: how it works and what it measures.

Here are two more problems, with explanations at the end of the chapter. Try doing them yourself, even referring to notes or books, before looking at the method described here. There will be more than one correct procedure for most lab questions.

Practice Exercises

1. You are given several 20 cm × 30 cm sheets of conducting paper, and your task is to determine the resistivity of the paper. You're told that the paper is 0.12 mm thick, and you have the following equipment available:

     variable power supply
     voltmeter
     ammeter
     connecting wires and clips
     meter stick
     scissors and utility knife

   Describe a procedure that will allow you to determine the resistivity using these instruments only. Sketch a diagram showing your setup, and clearly label its components. Explain how to use your measurements to obtain the resistivity value.

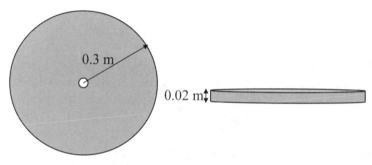

figure 2

2. You're given a circular-shaped solid of a uniform thickness 0.02 m, radius 0.3 m, mounted on an axle with a low friction bearing at its center as shown in figure 2. The solid has a mass distribution that's radially symmetric about the axis but isn't uniform throughout the disc. You need to determine its moment of inertia about the bearing axis.
   The following apparatuses have been provided for you:
     photogate timer
     weights
     string, paper, scissors, tape, tacks
     meter stick

   (a) Describe a procedure that would allow you to determine the moment of inertia using just the given apparatus.
   (b) Sketch your setup, clearly labeling the components and any variables that you will be measuring.
   (c) Show how your measurements can be used to determine the desired result.

Answers and Explanations

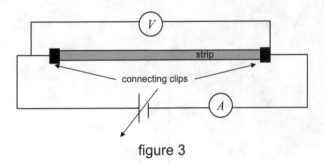

figure 3

1. Cut a strip of the material 1 cm wide by 20 cm long and connect it as shown in figure 3. The electric current will conduct down the length of this "wire" that has a cross-sectional area

    $$A = (\text{width})(\text{thickness}) = (0.01)(1.2 \times 10^{-4}) = 1.2 \times 10^{-6}\,\text{m}^2$$

    For the initial length of 0.2 m, determine the resistance of the strip by making several measurements of voltage and current, using the variable power supply to change the voltage. From a plot of V vs. I with V on the vertical axis, determine the slope, which will be the resistance.

    Repeat this procedure several times, cutting off a centimeter of length on the strip each time and recording the length value. This will produce a set of resistance vs. length data. Plot this data with R on the vertical axis and length on the horizontal, and determine the slope of the line. Since you know that $R = \rho\frac{l}{A}$, the slope will be equal to $\frac{\rho}{A}$, from which you can get the resistivity since you know A.

2. (a) Wrap a string around the rim of the disc a couple of times, securing one end with tape or a tack. Hang a known mass from the string. As the mass is allowed to fall from rest, gravitational potential energy is converted into translational KE of the falling mass and rotational KE of the disc. Conservation of energy will relate these. You can measure the speed of the falling mass with the photogate, attaching a paper "blocker" of length 0.05 m to the mass to pass through the gate, which will read out a time T. The linear speed of the mass can be related to the angular speed of the disc, since the rim points move at the same linear speed as the falling mass.

(b) (figure 4)

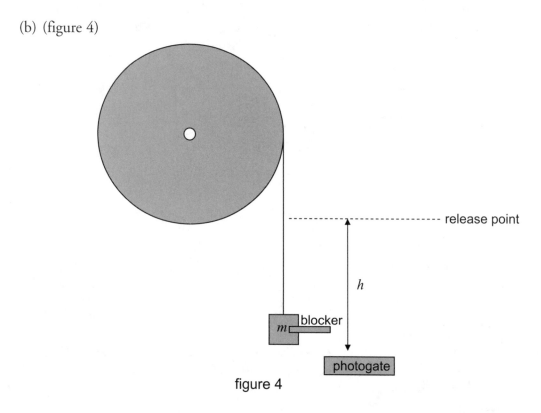

figure 4

(c) After the mass has fallen h, it passes through the photogate, which reads T. This means that $v = \frac{0.05}{T}$ is the speed of the mass, and $\omega = \frac{v}{R} = \frac{v}{0.3}$ is the angular speed of the disc. Conservation of energy implies:

$$mgh = \frac{1}{2}I\omega^2 + \frac{1}{2}mv^2 \quad \omega = \frac{v}{R}$$

This can be rearranged to give

$$h = \frac{1}{2g}\left(\frac{I}{mR^2} + 1\right)v^2$$

If you perform the experiment several times, placing the photogate at different h-values using a meter stick, but always releasing the mass from the same point, you generate a set of h vs. v data. Then plot h vs. v^2 and find the slope of the line. From the above relation, you can see that

$$slope = \frac{1}{2g}\left(\frac{I}{mR^2} + 1\right)$$

Solving for I, you have

$$I = (mR^2)(2g(slope) - 1)$$

15

Physics C and Calculus

Sometimes the C-level test includes questions that call for a more sophisticated use of calculus. These questions involve writing down a differential equation and solving it, or setting up an integration and performing it. This chapter will address these types of questions and bring together all the basic calculus techniques you'll need to know.

Differential Equations

A differential equation relates a function and its derivatives with respect to a certain variable. It's a vast subject, but what you need to know for the AP test is quite limited. These equations come up in a number of ways.

MECHANICS

Applying Newton's second law to a moving body will always involve the acceleration, which is the first derivative of the velocity and the second derivative of the position. If the force depends on the velocity or the position, the law becomes an equation relating position or velocity and its derivatives.

The harmonic oscillator equation is an example that involves the position and its second derivative. Since $F = -kx$, you have

$$F = ma = -kx$$

$$\frac{d^2x}{dt^2} + \frac{k}{m}x = 0$$

This equation involves the second derivative of the position, so it's called a second-order differential equation. This is the only second-order equation you need to be familiar with, and you've verified in the oscillations chapter that its most general solution is

$$x(t) = A\cos(\omega t + \phi) \qquad \omega^2 = \frac{k}{m}$$

with A, ϕ determined by initial conditions.

First order differential equations occur in mechanics when there's a force proportional to the velocity. The most common situation occurs when the force is a retarding force, such as air resistance or friction. Suppose an object is dropped from rest and experiences an air resistance force $F = -bv$, where b is a constant. Applying the second law, you have

$$netF = ma$$

$$mg - bv = m\frac{dv}{dt}$$

$$\frac{dv}{dt} + \frac{b}{m}v = g$$

This is called the "exponential approach" equation. As the object accelerates, the retarding force increases. Eventually the mass reaches a **terminal speed**, and it stops accelerating. You can determine the terminal speed without actually solving the differential equation.

At terminal speed, $\frac{dv}{dt} = 0$, so the equation gives you

$$v_T = \frac{mg}{b}$$

The object approaches this speed exponentially. To see this, let's outline the derivation, solving the differential equation. First, get all the quantities involving the velocity on one side of the equation.

$$\frac{dv}{v - \frac{mg}{b}} = -\frac{b}{m}dt$$

Now integrate both sides. Time varies from $0 \to t$ as v varies from $0 \to v$.

$$\int_0^v \frac{dv}{v - \frac{mg}{b}} = \int_0^t -\frac{b}{m}dt$$

$$\ln\left(\frac{v - \frac{mg}{b}}{-\frac{mg}{b}}\right) = -\frac{b}{m}t$$

Exponentiate both sides, remembering that $e^{\ln x} = x$. Reorganize to get

$$v(t) = \frac{mg}{b}\left(1 - e^{-\frac{b}{m}t}\right)$$

The graph of this is shown in figure 1a. The similarity of this solution to a charging capacitor or a building inductor is no accident, as you'll see.

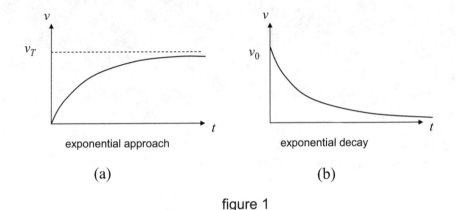

exponential approach

(a)

exponential decay

(b)

figure 1

It's possible to have a retarding force proportional to the velocity without the constant force of gravity present. For example, a bullet fired into a fixed wood block might experience a force $F = -bv$ acting horizontally. In this case, the second law gives

$$F = ma$$

$$-bv = m\frac{dv}{dt}$$

$$\frac{dv}{dt} + \frac{b}{m}v = 0$$

This is called the exponential decay equation. The object starts with a velocity v_0, and this will decrease as time develops. You can solve it in a similar manner to the preceding example.

$$\frac{dv}{v} = -\frac{b}{m}dt$$

$$\int_{v_0}^{v} \frac{dv}{v} = \int_{0}^{t} -\frac{b}{m}dt$$

$$\ln\left(\frac{v}{v_0}\right) = -\frac{b}{m}t$$

$$v(t) = v_0 e^{-\frac{b}{m}t}$$

The graph of this function is shown in figure 1b. Since the object eventually stops, you can determine the total displacement as it comes to rest. This involves expressing the velocity as the derivative of the displacement and performing a second integration.

$$v = \frac{dx}{dt} = v_0 e^{-\frac{b}{m}t}$$

$$\int dx = \int_0^\infty v_0 e^{-\frac{b}{m}t} dt$$

$$\Delta x = \frac{mv_0}{b}$$

This is the total area under the figure 1b curve.

ELECTRICITY AND MAGNETISM

Differential equations come up in circuit analysis when you apply the loop law. For the purposes of this chapter, there's nothing new here. A charging RC circuit produces the equation

$$\frac{dq}{dt} + \frac{1}{RC}q = \frac{V_B}{R}$$

This is just the exponential approach equation with q replacing v and different constants. The integration goes through in an identical manner to give

$$q(t) = CV_B\left(1 - e^{-\frac{t}{RC}}\right)$$

The building inductor circuit yields the equation

$$\frac{di}{dt} + \frac{R}{L}i = \frac{V_B}{L}$$

Once again, you have the exponential approach equation, this time with i replacing v and some different constants; the solution follows again:

$$i(t) = \frac{V_B}{R}\left(1 - e^{-\frac{R}{L}t}\right)$$

A discharging RC circuit and a decaying RL circuit will yield the differential equations

$$\frac{dq}{dt} + \frac{1}{RC}q = 0 \qquad\qquad \frac{di}{dt} + \frac{R}{L}i = 0$$

These are both exponential decay equations, and you can find the solutions as you did in the preceding examples.

$$q(t) = q_0 e^{-\frac{t}{RC}} \qquad\qquad i(t) = i_0 e^{-\frac{R}{L}t}$$

An interesting situation can develop with the rail system from electromagnetic induction. As the rail moves, the induced current feels a force consistent with Lenz's law:

$$F = -\frac{B^2 L^2}{R} v$$

This is a retarding force proportional to the velocity, so you can analyze it in the same way. If some agent supplies a constant external force to the rail, the rail will approach a terminal speed.

$$netF = F_{ext} - \frac{B^2 L^2}{R} v = ma = m\frac{dv}{dt}$$

exponential approach

$$\frac{dv}{dt} + \frac{B^2 L^2}{mR} v = \frac{F_{ext}}{m}$$

$$v(t) = \frac{RF_{ext}}{B^2 L^2}\left(1 - e^{-\frac{B^2 L^2}{mR} t}\right)$$

If the rail is given an initial velocity v_0 and no external force is applied, you have

$$netF = -\frac{B^2 L^2}{R} v = ma = m\frac{dv}{dt}$$

exponential decay

$$\frac{dv}{dt} + \frac{B^2 L^2}{mR} v = 0$$

$$v(t) = v_0 e^{-\frac{B^2 L^2}{mR} t}$$

Integrating once more, you can find the total displacement of the rail:

$$\Delta x = \frac{mv_0 R}{B^2 L^2}$$

Common Integration Schemes

In the previous section, you were integrating differential equations where time was always the integration variable. In this section, let's look at spatial integrations and the schemes you can apply in a given situation. They fall into three basic categories: linear, area, and volume integrations.

LINEAR

Imagine a stick with a given mass per unit length $\lambda(x)$; you're asked to determine the moment of inertia about some axis. Imagine a line of charge with a charge per unit length $\lambda(x)$; you're asked to determine the electric potential at some point. There is just one scheme in these linear problems. You can define a position variable x with respect to some point and introduce an integration element dx as shown in figure 2. You can then find the infinitesimal contribution from this element to the quantity you want to compute. Finally, you can decide on the limits and perform the integration.

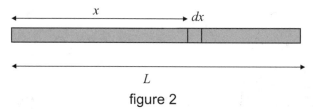

figure 2

Let's be concrete and assume you have a stick of length L and mass M with a uniform mass distribution. You want to find the moment of inertia about one end. For a uniform distribution, $\lambda(x) = \frac{M}{L}$. The contribution of the element is

$$dI = dmx^2 = (\lambda dx)x^2 = \frac{M}{L}x^2 dx$$

The integration is over the entire length, $0 \to L$, so you have

$$I = \int dI = \int_0^L \frac{M}{L}x^2 dx = \frac{1}{3}ML^2$$

AREA

Two schemes are possible here. You may have to integrate through a rectangular area where the quantity being integrated varies only along one dimension of the area. An example is shown in figure 3a. Here the element of area is a strip of thickness dr, and it's assumed that the quantity being integrated doesn't vary over the length L. The electromagnetic induction chapter gave an example of this scheme, where the integration involved finding the magnetic flux.

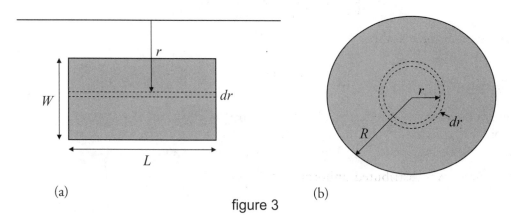

(a)   (b)

figure 3

The other scheme involves integrating a radially symmetric function through a circle or a disc of uniform thickness. The area element is a ring of thickness dr, as shown in figure 3b. The infinitesimal area in the ring is the differential increase in the circle of radius r:

$$dA = d(\pi r^2) = 2\pi r dr$$

As an example, figure 4 shows a disc of radius R with a total charge Q spread uniformly over the area.

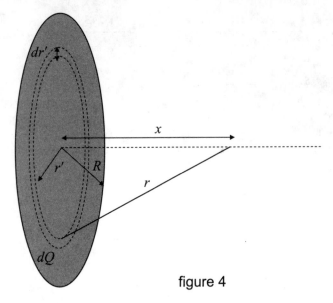

figure 4

To find the electric potential on the axis a distance x from the center, first find the contribution from your element and then integrate over the entire disc, letting r' vary as $0 \rightarrow R$. All the charge within the element is the same distance away from the axis point, so if you designate σ as the charge per unit area, you have

$$dV = \frac{dQ}{4\pi\varepsilon_0 r} = \frac{\sigma dA}{4\pi\varepsilon_0 r} = \frac{\sigma(2\pi r' dr')}{4\pi\varepsilon_0\sqrt{x^2 + r'^2}}$$

Changing integration variables:

$$u = x^2 + r'^2 \quad du = 2\pi r' dr' \quad u \text{ varies as } x^2 \rightarrow x^2 + R^2$$

you have

$$V = \int dV = \int_{x^2}^{x^2 + R^2} \frac{\sigma du}{4\varepsilon_0 u^{\frac{1}{2}}} = \frac{\sigma}{2\varepsilon_0}\left(\sqrt{x^2 + R^2} - x\right)$$

Since the charge was distributed uniformly, $\sigma = \frac{Q}{\pi R^2}$.

VOLUME

There are two schemes you need to learn for volume integrations. If the quantity being integrated is cylindrically symmetric, then you choose a volume element as shown in figure 5a.

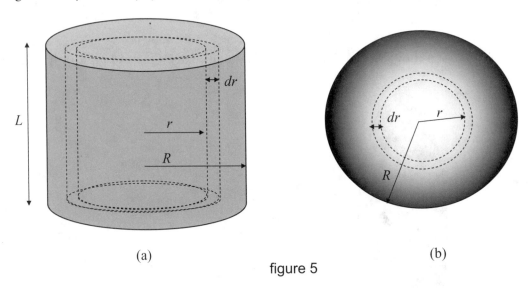

(a)

(b)

figure 5

The element has a length L and thickness dr. Its infinitesimal volume is the differential increase of a cylinder of radius r and length L, holding L fixed:

$$dV = d(\pi r^2 L) = 2\pi L r dr$$

The other scheme is used when the quantity being integrated is spherically symmetric. The volume element is a spherical shell with infinitesimal volume equal to the differential increase of a sphere of radius r:

$$dV = d\left(\frac{4}{3}\pi r^3\right) = 4\pi r^2 dr$$

These integrations can come up when you're applying Gauss's law to a symmetric but nonuniform charge distribution. For example, suppose a charge density is spherically symmetric but varies with r according to

$$\rho(r) = Cr^2 \qquad C \text{ is a constant.}$$

To find the charge contained inside a radius R_0, find the contribution of your volume element, then integrate.

$$dq = \rho dV = (Cr^2)(4\pi r^2 dr) = 4\pi Cr^4 dr$$

$$q(R_0) = \int dq = \int_0^{R_0} 4\pi Cr^4 dr = \frac{4}{5}\pi CR_0^5$$

CHAPTER 15

PRACTICE EXERCISES

SECTION I FREE RESPONSE

1. A 3 kg mass moves in one dimension with a velocity that has the equation

$$v(t) = \frac{4}{3 + 6t}$$

   (a) Determine the net force acting on the mass at $t = 2$ s.
   (b) Obtain an expression for the displacement of the mass as a function of time.

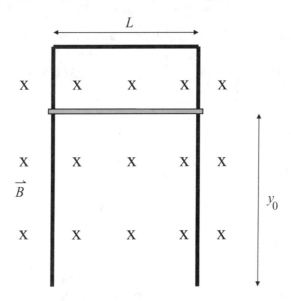

figure 6

2. A rail system consisting of a sliding rail of length L, resistance R, and mass m is attached to 2 vertical rails connected at their top by another fixed rail as shown in the figure. The vertical and connecting rail have 0 resistance. A constant magnetic field $\vec{B}$ is directed perpendicular to the loop made by the sliding rail and the other rails. The sliding rail is released from rest at a height y_0.
   (a) Assuming the rail reaches a terminal speed before it hits the ground, find the terminal speed.
   (b) Write the differential equation that can be used to determine the velocity of the rail as a function of time.
   (c) Solve for the velocity as a function of time.
   (d) How much energy is consumed in the rail resistance as the rail falls from rest through the height y_0?

3. A nonconducting sphere of radius R has charge distributed throughout its volume, with a charge density given by

$$\rho(r) = Cr^2$$

(a) Determine the total charge of the sphere.
(b) Find the electric field for points outside the sphere.
(c) Find the electric field for points inside the sphere.
(d) Find the potential difference between the surface and center of the sphere.

Answers and Explanations

1. (a) Take the derivative to find the acceleration, and then use Newton's second law.

$$a(t) = \frac{dv}{dt} = -\frac{24}{(3 + 6t)^2} \qquad \Rightarrow a(2) = 0.11\frac{m}{s^2}$$

$$netF(2) = ma(2) = 3(0.11) = 0.33 \text{ N}$$

(b) Use $v = \frac{dx}{dt}$ and integrate.

$$dx = vdt = \frac{4}{3 + 6t}dt$$

$$\Delta x = \int dx = \int_0^t \frac{4}{3 + 6t'}dt' = 4\ln\left(\frac{3 + 6t}{3}\right) = 4\ln(1 + 2t)$$

2. (a) At terminal speed, the force of gravity down will just equal the force exerted by the field on the induced current.

$$mg = iLB = \frac{B^2L^2}{R}v_T \quad \Rightarrow v_T = \frac{mgR}{B^2L^2}$$

(b) Using Newton's second law, you have

$$netF = ma = m\frac{dv}{dt}$$

$$mg - \frac{B^2L^2}{R}v = m\frac{dv}{dt}$$

$$\frac{dv}{dt} + \frac{B^2L^2}{mR}v = g$$

(c) This is the exponential approach, so you can write down the solution immediately or reiterate the steps shown in the chapter.

$$v(t) = \frac{mgR}{B^2L^2}\left(1 - e^{-\frac{B^2L^2}{mR}t}\right)$$

(d) The difference in the final KE and the initial PE will be the energy appearing as thermal energy in the rail resistance.

$$E_{thermal} = -\left(\frac{1}{2}mv_T^2 - mgy_0\right)$$

$$E_{thermal} = mgy_0 - \frac{1}{2}m\left(\frac{mgR}{B^2L^2}\right)^2$$

3. (a) The charge density is the same as in the example given in the text. The steps outlined there to find the charge within a given radius are the same here, with R replacing R_0.

$$dq = \rho dV = (Cr^2)(4\pi r^2 dr) = 4\pi Cr^4 dr$$

$$q = \int dq = \int_0^R 4\pi Cr^4 dr = \frac{4}{5}\pi CR^5$$

(b) Outside the sphere, the distribution acts like a point charge.

$$E = \frac{q}{4\pi\varepsilon_0 r^2} \qquad r > R$$

(c) Inside, it's only the charge within a radius r that contributes when you apply Gauss's law. This charge is calculated just as you did above, but replacing R with r.

$$\oint \vec{E} \cdot d\vec{A} = \frac{q_{in}}{\varepsilon_0}$$

$$E(4\pi r^2) = \frac{\frac{4}{5}\pi Cr^5}{\varepsilon_0}$$

$$E = \frac{Cr^3}{5\varepsilon_0}$$

(d) From the definition of potential difference, you have

$$\Delta V = -\oint \vec{E} \cdot d\vec{l} = -\int_R^0 \frac{Cr^3}{5\varepsilon_0} dr = \frac{CR^4}{20\varepsilon_0}$$

TABLE OF INFORMATION

CONSTANTS AND CONVERSION FACTORS		UNITS		PREFIXES		

CONSTANTS AND CONVERSION FACTORS

1 unified atomic mass unit	$1u = 1.66 \times 10^{-27}$ kg $= 931$ MeV/c^2
proton mass	$m_p = 1.67 \times 10^{-27}$ kg
neutron mass	$m_n = 1.67 \times 10^{-27}$ kg
electron mass	$m_e = 9.11 \times 10^{-31}$ kg
magnitude of electron charge	$e = 1.60 \times 10^{-19}$ C
Avogadro's number	$N_0 = 6.02 \times 10^{23}$ mol^{-1}
universal gas constant	$R = 8.31$ J/(mol.K)
Boltzmann's constant	$k_B = 1.38 \times 10^{-23}$ J/K
speed of light	$c = 3 \times 10^8$ m/s
Planck's constant	$h = 6.63 \times 10^{-34}$ J.s $= 4.14 \times 10^{-15}$ eV.s $hc = 1.99 \times 10^{-25}$ J.m $= 1.24 \times 10^3$ eV.nm
vaccum permittivity	$\varepsilon_0 = 8.85 \times 10^{-12}$ C^2/N.m^2
Coulomb's law constant	$k = \dfrac{1}{4\pi\varepsilon_0}$ $= 9.0 \times 10^9$ N.m^2/C^2
vacuum permeability	$\mu_0 = 4\pi \times 10^{-7}$ (T.m)/A
magnetic constant	$k' = \dfrac{\mu_0}{4\pi}$ $= 10^{-7}$ (T.m)/A
universal gravitational constant	$G = 6.67 \times 10^{-11}$ m^3/kg.s^2
acceleration due to gravity at Earth's surface	$g = 9.8$ m/s^2
1 atmosphere pressure	1 atm $= 1.0 \times 10^5$ N/m^2 $= 1.0 \times 10^5$ Pa
1 electron volt	1 eV $= 1.60 \times 10^{-19}$ J

UNITS

Name	Symbol
meter	m
kilogram	kg
second	s
ampere	A
kelvin	K
mole	mol
hertz	Hz
Newton	N
pascal	Pa
joule	J
watt	W
coulomb	C
volt	V
ohm	Ω
henry	H
farad	F
degree Celsius	°C
electron-volt	eV

PREFIXES

Factor	Prefix	Symbol
10^9	giga	G
10^6	mega	M
10^3	kilo	k
10^{-2}	centi	c
10^{-3}	milli	m
10^{-6}	micro	μ
10^{-9}	nano	n
10^{-12}	pico	p

VALUES OF TRIGONOMETRIC FUNCTIONS FOR COMMON ANGLES

θ	$\sin\theta$	$\cos\theta$	$\tan\theta$
0°	0	1	0
30°	$\frac{1}{2}$	$\frac{\sqrt{3}}{2}$	$\frac{\sqrt{3}}{2}$
37°	$\frac{3}{5}$	$\frac{4}{5}$	$\frac{3}{4}$
45°	$\frac{\sqrt{2}}{2}$	$\frac{\sqrt{2}}{2}$	1
53°	$\frac{4}{5}$	$\frac{3}{5}$	$\frac{4}{3}$
60°	$\frac{\sqrt{3}}{2}$	$\frac{1}{2}$	$\sqrt{3}$
90°	1	0	∞

The following conventions are used in this examination.

I. Unless otherwise stated, the frame of reference of any problem is assumed to be inertial.

II. The direction of any electric current is the direction of flow of positive charge (conventional current).

III. For any isolated electric charge, the electric potential is defined as zero at an infinite distance from the charge.

ADVANCED PLACEMENT PHYSICS C EQUATIONS

Mechanics

$v = v_0 + at$ a = acceleration

$x = x_0 + v_0 t + \frac{1}{2}at^2$ F = force

$v^2 = v_0^2 + 2a(x - x_0)$ f = frequency

$\sum \vec{F} = \vec{F}_{net} = m\vec{a}$ h = height

$\vec{F} = \dfrac{d\vec{p}}{dt}$ I = rotational inertia

$\vec{J} = \int \vec{F} dt = \Delta \vec{p}$ J = Impulse

$\vec{p} = m\vec{v}$ K = kinetic energy

$F_{fric} \leq \mu N$ k = spring constant

$W = \int \vec{F} \cdot d\vec{r}$ l = length

$K = \frac{1}{2}mv^2$ L = angular momentum

$P = \dfrac{dW}{dt}$ m = mass

$P = \vec{F} \cdot \vec{v}$ N = normal force

$\Delta U_g = mgh$ P = power

$a_c = \dfrac{v^2}{r} = \omega^2 r$ r = radius or distance

$\vec{\tau} = \vec{r} \times \vec{F}$ T = period

$I = \int r^2 dm = \sum mr^2$ t = time

$\vec{r}_{CM} = \dfrac{\sum m\vec{r}}{\sum m}$ U = potential energy

$v = r\omega$ v = velocity or speed

$\vec{L} = \vec{r} \times \vec{p} = I\vec{\omega}$ W = work done on system

$K = \frac{1}{2}I\omega^2$

$\omega = \omega_0 + \alpha t$ x = position

$\theta = \theta_0 + \omega_0 t + \frac{1}{2}\alpha t^2$ μ = coefficient of friction

$\vec{F}_s = -k\vec{x}$ θ = angle

$U_s = \frac{1}{2}kx^2$ τ = torque

$T = \dfrac{2\pi}{\omega} = \dfrac{1}{f}$ ω = angular speed

$T_s = 2\pi \sqrt{\dfrac{m}{k}}$ α = angular acceleration

$T_p = 2\pi \sqrt{\dfrac{l}{g}}$

$\vec{F}_G = -\dfrac{Gm_1 m_2}{r^2}\hat{r}$

$U_G = -\dfrac{Gm_1 m_2}{r}$

Electricity and Magnetism

$\vec{F} = \dfrac{1}{4\pi\varepsilon_0}\dfrac{q_1 q_2}{r^2}$ A = area

$\vec{E} = \dfrac{\vec{F}}{q}$ B = magnetic field

$\oint \vec{E} \cdot d\vec{A} = \dfrac{Q}{\varepsilon_0}$ C = capacitance

$E = \dfrac{-dV}{dr}$ d = distance

$V = \dfrac{1}{4\pi\varepsilon_0}\sum_i \dfrac{q_i}{r_i}$ E = electric field

$U_E = qV = \dfrac{1}{4\pi\varepsilon_0}\dfrac{q_1 q_2}{r}$ ε = emf

$C = \dfrac{Q}{V}$ F = force

$C = \dfrac{\kappa \varepsilon_0 A}{d}$ I = current

$C_p = \sum_i C_i$ L = inductance

$\dfrac{1}{C_S} = \sum_i \dfrac{1}{C_i}$ l = length

$I = \dfrac{dQ}{dt}$ n = number of loops of wire per unit length

$U_C = \frac{1}{2}QV = \frac{1}{2}CV^2$

$R = \dfrac{\rho l}{A}$ P = power

$V = IR$ Q = charge

$R_S = \sum_i R_i$ q = point charge

$\dfrac{1}{R_p} = \sum_i \dfrac{1}{R_i}$ R = resistance

$P = IV$ r = distance

$\vec{F}_M = q\vec{v} \times \vec{B}$ t = time

$\oint \vec{B} \cdot d\vec{l} = \mu_0 I$ U = potential or stored energy stored energy

$\vec{F} = \int I d\vec{l} \times \vec{B}$

$B_S = \mu_0 n I$ V = electric potential

$\phi_m = \int \vec{B} \cdot d\vec{A}$ v = velocity or speed

$\varepsilon = -\dfrac{d\phi_m}{dt}$ ρ = resistivity

$\varepsilon = -L\dfrac{di}{dt}$ φ_m = magnetic flux

$U_L = \frac{1}{2}LI^2$ κ = dielectic constant

Geometry and Trigonometry

Rectangle

$A = bh$

Triangle

$A = \frac{1}{2}bh$

Circle

$A = \pi r^2$

$C = 2\pi r$

Parallelepiped

$V = lwh$

Cylinder

$V = \pi r^2 l$

$S = 2\pi rl + 2\pi r^2$

Sphere

$V = \frac{4}{3}\pi r^3$

$S = 4\pi r^2$

Right Triangle

$a^2 + b^2 = c^2$

$\sin\theta = \dfrac{a}{c}$

$\cos\theta = \dfrac{b}{c}$

$\tan\theta = \dfrac{a}{b}$

$A =$ area

$C =$ circumference

$V =$ volume

$S =$ surface area

$b =$ base

$h =$ height

$l =$ length

$w =$ width

$r =$ radius

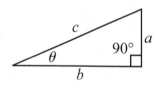

Calculus

$$\frac{df}{dx} = \frac{df}{du}\frac{du}{dx}$$

$$\frac{d}{dx}(x^n) = nx^{n-1}$$

$$\frac{d}{dx}(e^x) = e^x$$

$$\frac{d}{dx}(\ln x) = \frac{1}{x}$$

$$\frac{d}{dx}(\sin x) = \cos x$$

$$\frac{d}{dx}(\cos x) = -\sin x$$

$$\int x^n dx = \frac{1}{n+1}x^{n+1}, \; n \neq -1$$

$$\int e^x dx = e^x$$

$$\int \frac{dx}{x} = \ln|x|$$

$$\int \cos x dx = \sin x$$

$$\int \sin x dx = -\cos x$$

Physics C
Practice Exam

AP PHYSICS C TEST

SECTION I—Mechanics
Time: 45 minutes
35 Questions

Directions: Each of the questions or incomplete statements below is followed by 5 suggested answers or completions. Select the one that is best in each case.

Note: To simplify calculations, you may use $g = 10$ m/s^2 in all calculations

1. A 20-kg mass moving at 10 m/s decelerates uniformly to rest in 5 s. During this time, the mass has traveled a distance of

    (A) 2 m   (B) 50 m   (C) 25 m   (D) 125 m   (E) 12.5 m

2. A 2-kg mass is projected straight up with an initial speed of 20 m/s. In describing the velocity and acceleration of the object, a student chooses the starting point as the origin and the positive direction as up. At the highest point of the projectile, how will the student describe the velocity and acceleration of the mass?

	Velocity	Acceleration
(A)	negative	positive
(B)	positive	negative
(C)	0	0
(D)	0	positive
(E)	0	negative

Questions 3 and 4

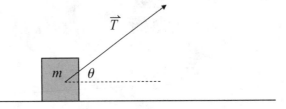

A mass m is pulled along a rough surface at a constant speed by a force maintained at an angle θ with the horizontal.

3. The work done by $\vec{T}$ as the mass moves a distance D is

    (A) 0   (B) $TD \cos \theta$ (C) $\dfrac{T}{m} \cos \theta$ (D) $TD \sin \theta$ (E) $\dfrac{T}{m} \sin \theta$

4. The coefficient of friction is

    (A) $\tan \theta$ (B) $\dfrac{T \cos \theta}{mg - T \sin \theta}$ (C) $\dfrac{T \cos \theta}{T \sin \theta + mg}$ (D) $\dfrac{T \sin \theta}{mg - T \cos \theta}$ (E) $\dfrac{T \sin \theta}{T \cos \theta + mg}$

GO ON TO THE NEXT PAGE

5. A satellite of mass M moves with speed v in a circular orbit of radius R around Earth. Which of the following is true?
    I. To place a larger mass in the same orbit would require a larger orbit speed.
    II. The centripetal acceleration is independent of the mass of Earth.
    III. The angular momentum of the satellite is constant.

    (A) I only   (B) I and III only   (C) I and II only   (D) III only   (E) II and III only

6. A mass m falls from rest and experiences an air resistance force of the form $F_{air} = -bv^2$. The terminal speed of the mass is

    (A) $\dfrac{mg}{b}$ (B) $\sqrt{\dfrac{mg}{b}}$ (C) $\sqrt{\dfrac{b}{mg}}$ (D) $\sqrt{\dfrac{g}{b}}$ (E) $\dfrac{g}{b}$

Questions 7 and 8

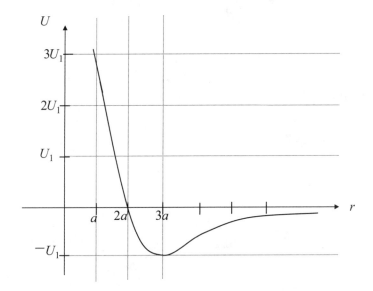

A mass m moves under the influence of a potential energy function given by the graph above.

7. At the point $r = 2a$, the force exerted on the mass is closest to

    (A) 0   (B) $\dfrac{U_1}{a}$ (C) $\dfrac{4U_1}{a}$ (D) $\dfrac{3U_1}{a}$ (E) $\dfrac{3U_1}{2a}$

8. The maximum speed of a mass released from rest at the point $r = a$ is

    (A) $\sqrt{\dfrac{U_1}{m}}$ (B) $\sqrt{\dfrac{2U_1}{m}}$ (C) $\sqrt{\dfrac{4U_1}{m}}$ (D) $\sqrt{\dfrac{6U_1}{m}}$ (E) $\sqrt{\dfrac{8U_1}{m}}$

GO ON TO THE NEXT PAGE

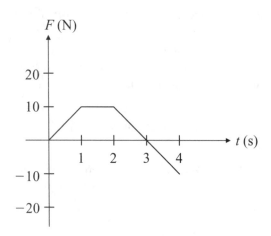

9. An object experiences the nonconstant net force shown in the figure. The change in momentum of the object over the 4 seconds that the force acts is closest to

(A) $10 \dfrac{\text{kg} \cdot \text{m}}{\text{s}}$ (B) $15 \dfrac{\text{kg} \cdot \text{m}}{\text{s}}$ (C) $20 \dfrac{\text{kg} \cdot \text{m}}{\text{s}}$ (D) $25 \dfrac{\text{kg} \cdot \text{m}}{\text{s}}$ (E) $30 \dfrac{\text{kg} \cdot \text{m}}{\text{s}}$

10. A mass $6m$ moving with speed $+v$ across a smooth horizontal surface explodes into three pieces of masses m, $2m$, and $3m$, respectively. After the explosion, the mass m is stationary, and the mass $2m$ is moving with velocity $+2v$. What is the velocity of the other mass?

(A) $\dfrac{1}{2}v$ (B) $\dfrac{1}{3}v$ (C) 0   (D) $\dfrac{2}{3}v$ (E) $\dfrac{3}{2}v$

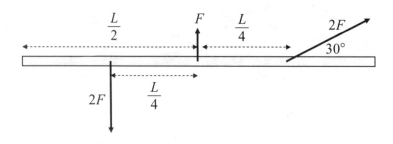

11. Three forces act on a light stick as indicated in the figure. The net torque about the center of the stick is

(A) 0   (B) $\dfrac{1}{2}FL$ (C) $\dfrac{3}{4}FL$ (D) FL (E) $2FL$

GO ON TO THE NEXT PAGE

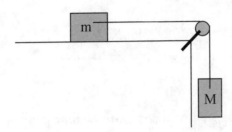

12. A mass m is pulled across a frictionless horizontal surface by a string attached to a descending mass M over a light, frictionless pulley. The tension in the string is

(A) Mg (B) $\dfrac{mM}{m+M}g$ (C) $\dfrac{m}{M}g$ (D) $\dfrac{M}{m}g$ (E) $\dfrac{mM}{M-m}g$

13. A satellite of mass m moves in a circular orbit of radius R about the Earth. The angular momentum of the satellite about the center of the Earth has a magnitude

(A) $m\sqrt{\dfrac{M_e R}{G}}$ (B) $m\sqrt{\dfrac{GR}{M_e}}$ (C) $m\sqrt{\dfrac{GM_e}{R}}$ (D) $m\sqrt{GM_e R}$ (E) $m\sqrt{\dfrac{R}{GM_e}}$

14. A physical pendulum oscillates through small angles about the vertical with the angle, measured in radians, obeying the differential equation $\dfrac{d^2\theta}{dt^2} = -4\pi\theta$. The period of the oscillations in seconds is

(A) $\dfrac{1}{8\pi}$ (B) 8π (C) $\dfrac{1}{4}$ (D) $\sqrt{\pi}$ (E) 4π

GO ON TO THE NEXT PAGE

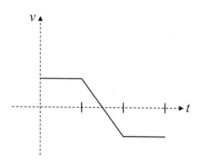

15. An object moves in one dimension with a velocity vs. time graph as shown above. The graph that best represents the displacement of the object over the same time interval is which of the following?

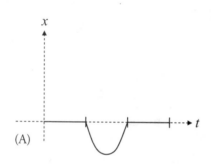

(A)

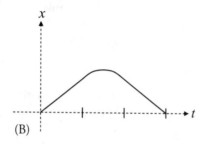

(B)

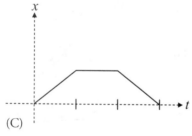

(C)

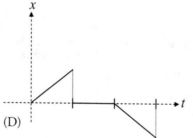

(D)

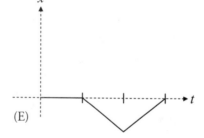

(E)

GO ON TO THE NEXT PAGE

16. A mass m is projected with a velocity of magnitude 50 m/s, making an angle of 37° with the horizontal, the x-axis. At the highest point, which of the following could be values for the magnitude of the velocity components and the vertical acceleration component?

	v_x	v_y	a_y
(A)	30 m/s	40 m/s	10 m/s^2
(B)	40 m/s	0	10 m/s^2
(C)	30 m/s	0	10 m/s^2
(D)	40 m/s	0	0
(E)	40 m/s	30 m/s	10 m/s^2

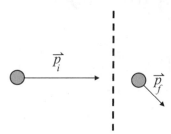

17. A mass with momentum $\vec{p_i}$ is acted upon by a force, causing the momentum to change to $\vec{p_f}$. The vector that best represents the impulse delivered by the force during the change is

(A) ↖ (B) ↗ (C) ↙ (D) ↘ (E) ←

Questions 18 and 19
A 4 kg mass oscillates on a smooth surface at the end of a horizontal spring according to the equation $x(t) = 0.5 \cos\left(6\pi t + \frac{\pi}{8}\right)$, with x measured in meters.

18. The value of the spring constant is

(A) 24π (B) $\frac{\pi^2}{4}$ (C) $\frac{\pi}{2}$ (D) $144\pi^2$ (E) $36\pi^2$

19. The maximum acceleration of the mass is

(A) 3π (B) $18\pi^2$ (C) $\frac{\pi}{16}$ (D) $\frac{\pi^2}{128}$ (E) $\frac{9}{2}\pi^2$

GO ON TO THE NEXT PAGE

Questions 20–22

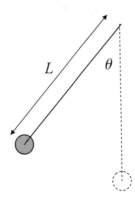

A simple pendulum initially making an angle θ with the vertical is released from rest.

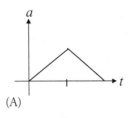

(A)

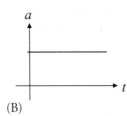

(B)

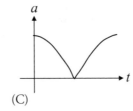

(C)

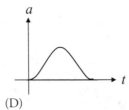

(D)

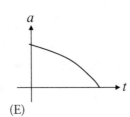

(E)

20. During the first half-period of the motion, the graph that best represents the centripetal acceleration of the mass as a function of time is

    (A) A   (B) B   (C) C   (D) D   (E) E

21. During the first half-period of the motion, the graph that best represents the magnitude of the tangential acceleration of the mass as a function of time is

    (A) A   (B) B   (C) C   (D) D   (E) E

GO ON TO THE NEXT PAGE

22. The work done by the tension force as the object moves to its lowest point is

    (A) $mgL(1 - \cos \theta)$ (B) $mgL(1 - \sin \theta)$ (C) $mgL \cos \theta$ (D) $mgL \sin \theta$ (E) 0

23. A 2 kg mass moves in one dimension under the influence of a position-dependent force given by $F(x) = 2x - 8x^3$. The work done by this force as the object moves from $x = 2$ m to $x = 1$ m is closest to

    (A) -6 J   (B) -27 J   (C) 6 J   (D) 27 J   (E) 8 J

24. A mass m falls from a height H onto a previously compressed spring. The mass rebounds with twice its incoming speed. If the spring and mass are in contact for a time T, the average power delivered to the mass by the spring is

    (A) $\dfrac{mgh}{T}$ (B) $\dfrac{2mgH}{T}$ (C) $\dfrac{\sqrt{2}mgH}{T}$ (D) $\dfrac{4mgH}{T}$ (E) $\dfrac{3mgH}{T}$

25. A mass m moving with speed v in the $+x$ direction collides head-on with a mass $4m$ moving with speed $\frac{1}{2} v$ in the $-x$ direction. If the two masses stick together, the velocity after collision is

    (A) 0   (B) $\frac{1}{5}v$, $+x$ direction   (C) $\frac{3}{5}v$, $+x$ direction

    (D) $\frac{1}{5}v$, $-x$ direction   (E) $\frac{3}{5}v$, $-x$ direction

26. A wheel with rotational inertia I is rotating with a constant angular velocity ω_0 when a torque is applied, slowing the wheel to $\frac{1}{2}\omega_0$ in a time T. The magnitude of the torque applied is

    (A) $\dfrac{I\omega_0}{2T}$ (B) $\dfrac{I\omega_0}{T}$ (C) $\dfrac{3I\omega_0}{2T}$ (D) $\dfrac{2I\omega_0}{T}$ (E) $\dfrac{5I\omega_0}{2T}$

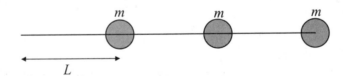

27. Three equal masses are connected at equal distances along a rod of length $3L$ and negligible mass. The moment of inertia about the left end of the rod is

    (A) $3mL^2$ (B) $9mL^2$ (C) $14mL^2$ (D) $17mL^2$ (E) $27mL^2$

GO ON TO THE NEXT PAGE

28. Planet X has an acceleration due to gravity at its surface that is 3 times that at Earth's surface. If the mass of X is twice the mass of the Earth, the radius of X in terms of R_e, the radius of Earth, is

(A) $\frac{2}{3}R_e$ (B) $\frac{3}{2}R_e$ (C) $\sqrt{\frac{2}{3}}R_e$ (D) $\sqrt{\frac{3}{2}}R_e$ (E) $\frac{2}{\sqrt{3}}R_e$

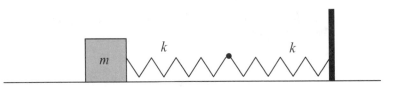

29. Two identical springs with spring constant k are connected as shown in the figure, and a mass m is attached. When the mass is displaced from equilibrium, the period of oscillation is

(A) $2\pi\sqrt{\frac{m}{k}}$ (B) $2\pi\sqrt{\frac{m}{2k}}$ (C) $2\pi\sqrt{\frac{2m}{k}}$ (D) $4\pi\sqrt{\frac{m}{k}}$ (E) $2\sqrt{2}\pi\sqrt{\frac{m}{k}}$

30. The position of a 3-kg mass moving in one dimension is given in meters as a function of time by the following equation: $x(t) = t^3 - 4t^2 + 7$. At $t = 1$ s, the force on the object is

(A) 12 N   (B) 15 N   (C) 36 N   (D) -6 N   (E) -2 N

31. A toy air gun can fire a dart to a height H when fired straight up. What is the maximum height that the projectile will reach if it's fired at an angle of 60° with the vertical?

(A) $\frac{\sqrt{3}}{2}H$ (B) $\frac{3}{4}H$ (C) $\frac{1}{2}H$ (D) $\frac{1}{4}H$ (E) $\frac{1}{3}H$

32. A 40-kg child and an 80-kg man are ice skating in tandem, with the child in front of the man. When they're moving at 10 m/s, the man pushes the child so that she moves at 15 m/s relative to the ice. After she separates, what will be the velocity of their center of mass?

(A) 7.5 m/s   (B) 9 m/s   (C) 10 m/s   (D) 12.5 m/s   (E) 15 m/s

33. A circular hoop of mass M and radius R rolls down an incline without slipping, from an initial height H. The translational kinetic energy at the bottom of the incline is

(A) mgH (B) $\frac{1}{2}mgH$ (C) $\frac{1}{3}mgH$ (D) $\frac{2}{3}mgH$ (E) $\frac{1}{4}mgH$

GO ON TO THE NEXT PAGE

34. A block slides down a rough incline, experiencing a constant force of friction. At the bottom of the incline, it encounters an uncompressed, massless spring and eventually rebounds back up the incline. After the mass has reached its highest point on the rebound, which of the following is true for the work done by gravity and the work done by the spring force?

	Gravity	Spring
(A)	positive	0
(B)	negative	0
(C)	0	positive
(D)	negative	positive
(E)	0	0

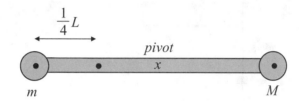

35. A stick of mass m and length L has its mass distributed nonuniformly so that its center of mass is $\frac{1}{4} L$ from the left. A mass m is attached to the left end of the stick. What mass M must be attached to the right end of the stick so that the system won't rotate when it's pivoted about the geometrical center of the stick?

(A) $\frac{1}{2}m$ (B) m (C) $\frac{3}{2}m$ (D) $2m$ (E) $\frac{5}{2}m$

STOP
END OF SECTION I, MECHANICS

IF YOU FINISH BEFORE TIME IS CALLED, YOU MAY CHECK YOUR WORK ON
SECTION I, MECHANICS ONLY.

DO NOT TURN TO ANY OTHER TEST MATERIALS.

STOP

AP PHYSICS C TEST

SECTION I—Electricity and Magnetism
Time: 45 minutes
35 Questions

Directions: Each of the questions or incomplete statements below is followed by 5 suggested answers or completions. Select the one that is best in each case.

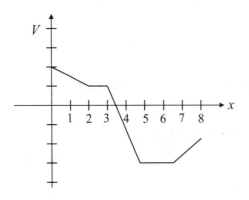

1. The graph shows the electric potential as a function of position along the *x*-axis. At which position would a charged particle experience the greatest magnitude of force?

   (A) *x* = 1 m   (B) *x* = 2.5 m   (C) *x* = 3.5 m   (D) *x* = 5 m   (E) *x* = 7 m

Questions 2 and 3

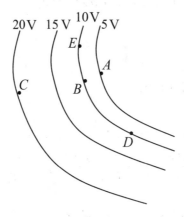

The figure shows some equipotential surfaces in a region of space.

2. An electron placed at *B* would be most likely to approach which point after being released from rest?

   (A) *A*   (B) *B* (stay there)   (C) *C*   (D) *D*   (E) *E*

GO ON TO THE NEXT PAGE

3. A +2C charge is placed at B and then moved slowly to C, and then slowly to D. The total work that this takes is closest to

    (A) 20 J   (B) −20 J   (C) 0   (D) 40 J   (E) −40 J

4. If you know the value of the electric field $\vec{E}$ at every point in a region of space, which of the following Gaussian surfaces could be used to determine the charge contained within the surface?
    I.   sphere
    II. cylinder
    III. cube

    (A) I and II only   (B) I and III only   (C) II and III only   (D) I only   (E) I, II, and III

Questions 5 and 6 refer to the two charges shown in the figure below.

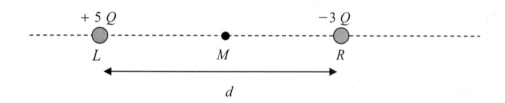

5. The electric field along the line is 0 at a point in which region?
    (A) to the left of L
    (B) between L and M
    (C) between M and R
    (D) to the right of R
    (E) The field is 0 only at infinity.

6. The value of the electric potential at M is equal to

    (A) $\dfrac{1}{4\pi\varepsilon_0}\dfrac{2Q}{d}$ (B) $\dfrac{1}{4\pi\varepsilon_0}\dfrac{4Q}{d}$ (C) $\dfrac{1}{4\pi\varepsilon_0}\dfrac{8Q}{d}$ (D) $\dfrac{1}{4\pi\varepsilon_0}\dfrac{16Q}{d}$ (E) $\dfrac{1}{4\pi\varepsilon_0}\dfrac{5Q}{3d}$

7. A spherical conductor of radius R carries a charge $+Q$. A neutral conductor of radius $\frac{1}{3}R$ is brought into contact with the first sphere and then separated from it. The charge on the smaller sphere after separation is closest to

    (A) Q (B) $\frac{1}{3}Q$ (C) $\frac{1}{4}Q$ (D) $\frac{1}{9}Q$ (E) $3Q$

GO ON TO THE NEXT PAGE

Questions 8–10

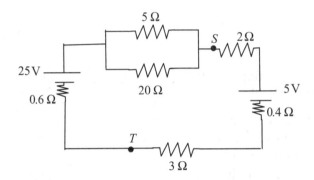

In the circuit above, the battery voltages and resistances are as indicated, with the internal resistances of each battery 0.6 Ω and 0.4 Ω, respectively.

8. The energy consumed by the 2 Ω resistor in 1 minute is
   (A) 18 J   (B) 8 J   (C) 1,080 J   (D) 480 J   (E) 240 J

9. The terminal voltage of the 5 V battery is
   (A) 5.4 V   (B) 5.8 V   (C) 5 V   (D) 4.6 V   (E) 4.2 V

10. A voltmeter connected between *T* and *S* would have what magnitude reading?
    (A) 15.8 V   (B) 5.8 V   (C) 11.2 V   (D) 21.2 V   (E) 12.8 V

Questions 11 and 12 refer to the combination of capacitors shown below.

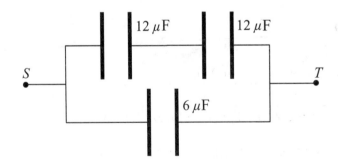

11. What is the equivalent capacitance of this combination of capacitors?
    (A) 30 μF   (B) 18 μF   (C) 12 μF   (D) 6 μF   (E) 9 μF

GO ON TO THE NEXT PAGE

12. What voltage would have to be applied to produce equal magnitude charges on the plates of all three capacitors?

 I. 20 V
 II. 30 V
 III. 40 V

(A) I only   (B) II only   (C) I and II only   (D) II and III only   (E) I, II, and III

13. A resistor R, a capacitor C, and an inductor L are connected in series to a battery of terminal voltage V_B. If i is the current in the circuit and Q is the charge on the capacitor, which of the following equations best describes this circuit?

(A) $iR + \frac{Q}{C} + L\frac{di}{dt} = 0$

(B) $V_B - iR - \frac{Q}{C} + L\frac{di}{dt} = 0$

(C) $V_B - i^2 R - \frac{Q}{C} - L\frac{di}{dt} = 0$

(D) $V_B - iR - \frac{Q}{C} - L\frac{di}{dt} = 0$

(E) $-i^2 R + \frac{1}{2}\frac{Q^2}{C} + \frac{1}{2}Li^2 = 0$

Questions 14 and 15 refer to the circuit below containing a combination of a battery, switch, inductor, and 3 resistors.

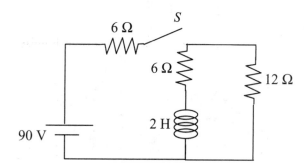

14. What is the current in the 12 Ω resistor immediately after the switch S is thrown?

(A) 0   (B) 3 A   (C) 5 A   (D) 6 A   (E) 9 A

15. After S has been closed for a long time, it is opened again. How much energy will be consumed in the circuit resistors after S is opened?

(A) 0   (B) 9 J   (C) 25 J   (D) 36 J   (E) 81 J

GO ON TO THE NEXT PAGE

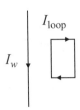

16. A long wire carries a current I_w as shown in the figure. Next to the wire lies a rectangular loop that carries a current I_{loop}. The net force on the loop is

   (A) to the left   (B) to the right   (C) toward the top of page
   (D) toward the bottom of page   (E) 0

17. A long wire of radius a carries a current I. Which graph best describes the magnitude of the magnetic field created by the wire as a function of r, the distance from the center of the wire?

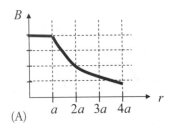

(A)

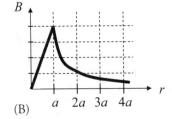

(B)

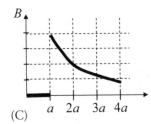

(C)

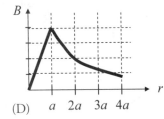

(D)

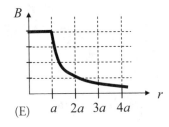

(E)

GO ON TO THE NEXT PAGE

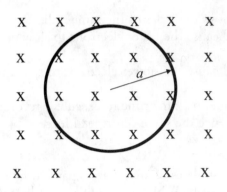

18. A circular loop of radius a and resistance R is stationary in a spatially uniform magnetic field. From the time $t = 0$ to $t = T$, the field increases into the paper according to $B = bt^2$. At $t = \frac{1}{2}T$, the current in the loop is

(A) $\pi a^2 \dfrac{bT^2}{R}$ (B) $\pi a^2 \dfrac{bT^2}{4R}$ (C) $\pi a^2 \dfrac{bT}{R}$ (D) $\pi a^2 \dfrac{bT}{2R}$ (E) $\pi a^2 \dfrac{bT}{4R}$

Questions 19 and 20

In a region of space the electric potential is cylindrically symmetric and described by the formula $V(r) = -Cr^{\frac{3}{2}}$, where r is the distance to the symmetry axis and C is a constant.

19. What is the magnitude of the electric field at a distance R from the axis?

(A) $CR^{\frac{1}{2}}$ (B) $\dfrac{3}{2}CR^{\frac{1}{2}}$ (C) 0 (D) $CR^{\frac{3}{2}}$ (E) $\dfrac{2}{5}CR^{\frac{5}{2}}$

20. An electron is placed at a point a distance R from the axis. Which of the following is true?

(A) The electron will remain stationary.
(B) The electron will move away from the axis with a constant acceleration.
(C) The electron will move away from the axis with an acceleration that decreases.
(D) The electron will move toward the axis with a constant acceleration.
(E) The electron will oscillate about the axis.

GO ON TO THE NEXT PAGE

21. Electrons with a range of speeds move in a region of uniform magnetic field, perpendicular to the field. Which of the following is true?

(A) All the electrons will move in circles of the same radius.
(B) The magnetic field will cause the faster electrons to slow down more quickly than the slower electrons.
(C) The magnetic field will cause the slower electrons to speed up more quickly than the faster electrons.
(D) All the electrons will take the same time to execute 1 revolution.
(E) All the electrons experience the same centripetal force.

22. Two large isolated conducting plates of area A are separated by a distance d. The two plates carry charges $+Q$ and $-Q$, respectively. Which of the following best describes the behavior of the electric field in the region between the plates and the potential difference between the two plates when d is increased to $2d$, keeping the charge on each plate fixed?

	Electric Field	Potential Difference
(A)	decreases by $\frac{1}{2}$	stays the same
(B)	decreases by $\frac{1}{2}$	doubles
(C)	stays the same	doubles
(D)	decreases by $\frac{1}{4}$	stays the same
(E)	decreases by $\frac{1}{4}$	doubles

23. An electron with mass m_e and charge $-e$ is released from rest a distance d from a stationary proton with mass m_p and charge $+e$. When the electron is a distance $\frac{1}{2}d$ from the proton, its speed is closest to

(A) $\sqrt{\dfrac{e^2}{4\pi\varepsilon_0 m_e d}}$ (B) $\sqrt{\dfrac{e^2}{2\pi\varepsilon_0 m_e d}}$ (C) $\sqrt{\dfrac{e^2}{4\pi\varepsilon_0 m_p d}}$ (D) $\sqrt{\dfrac{e^2}{2\pi\varepsilon_0 m_p d}}$ (E) $\sqrt{\dfrac{e^2}{8\pi\varepsilon_0 m_e d}}$

24. A neutral conductor has a spherical cavity within it. A point charge Q is placed at the center of the cavity. Which of the following is true when equilibrium is established?
   I. The flux through any closed surface surrounding the charge will equal $\frac{Q}{\varepsilon_0}$.
   II. The electric field will be 0 within the conductor, but non-zero outside of the cavity.
   III. Within the cavity, the electric potential is constant.

(A) I only   (B) II only   (C) III only   (D) I and II only   (E) I and III only

GO ON TO THE NEXT PAGE

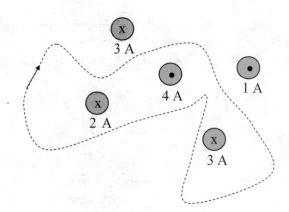

25. Five current segments carry the indicated currents shown in the figure, with x and • indicating the current going into or out of the paper, respectively. The value of $\oint_{path} \vec{B} \cdot \vec{dl}$ around the dotted path is

(A) μ_0 (B) $-\mu_0$ (C) $2\mu_0$ (D) $-2\mu_0$ (E) $9\mu_0$

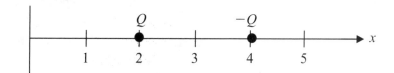

26. Two equal and opposite charges lie along the x-axis as shown in the figure. The graph of the electric potential as a function of x is closest to which of the following?

(A)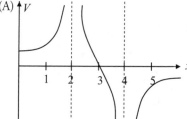

(B)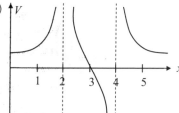

(C)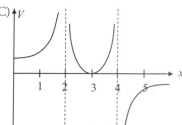

(D)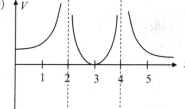

(E)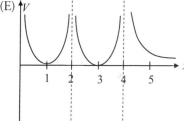

GO ON TO THE NEXT PAGE

27. A parallel plate capacitor with plate area A and plate separation d has a dielectric of thickness $\frac{1}{2}d$, area A, and dielectric constant κ inserted between the plates. If the capacitance before the dielectric was inserted was C, the capacitance after insertion is

    (A) κC (B) $\frac{\kappa}{2}C$ (C) $2\kappa C$ (D) $\frac{2\kappa}{\kappa + 1}C$ (E) $\frac{\kappa}{\kappa + 1}C$

28. If you know the value of the electric potential at a point, which of the following can you determine from this value? Assume the zero of electric potential is at infinity.
    I.   the electric field at the point
    II. the work it would take to slowly move a given charge from the point to infinity
    III. the work it would take to slowly move a given charge from the point to another point not at infinity

    (A) I only   (B) II only   (C) III only   (E) I and II only   (C) II and III only

29. A long, nonconducting cylinder of radius R carries a uniform charge density ρ. To determine the electric field within the cylinder, you use a cylindrical Gaussian surface of radius $r < R$ and length L. Properly applying Gauss's law to this surface would yield which of the following equations?

    (A) $E(\pi R^2 L) = \dfrac{\rho(\pi R^2 L)}{\varepsilon_0}$ (B) $E(4\pi R^2) = \dfrac{\rho\left(\frac{4}{3}\pi R^2\right)}{\varepsilon_0}$ (C) $E(2\pi RL) = \dfrac{\rho(\pi R^2 L)}{\varepsilon_0}$

    (D) $E(2\pi rL) = \dfrac{\rho(\pi r^2 L)}{\varepsilon_0}$ (E) $E(2\pi RL) = \dfrac{\rho(\pi r^2 L)}{\varepsilon_0}$

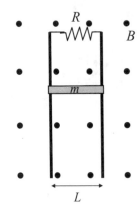

30. A conducting rail of length L and mass m is connected to slide without friction on two vertical rails connected by a resistance R. A uniform magnetic field is directed out of the page. The terminal speed of the rail is

    (A) $\dfrac{BL}{mgR}$ (B) $\dfrac{B^2 L^2}{mgR}$ (C) $\dfrac{mg}{BLR}$ (D) $\dfrac{mgR}{B^2 L^2}$ (E) $\dfrac{mgR}{BL}$

GO ON TO THE NEXT PAGE

31. A wire of length L, uniform cross-sectional area A, and resistivity ρ is connected across a battery and found to consume energy at the rate P. The wire is then stretched to twice its original length. When connected across the same battery, it will consume energy at the rate

(A) P (B) $\frac{1}{2}P$ (C) $\frac{1}{4}P$ (D) $\frac{1}{8}P$ (E) $\frac{1}{16}P$

32. An isolated parallel plate capacitor has a potential difference V between the plates. Which of the following best describes what happens when a nonconducting material is introduced to fill the region between the plates?

(A) Since the material is a nonconductor, nothing happens.
(B) The nonconducting material will develop a uniform charge density throughout its volume, causing the potential drop across the capacitor to decrease.
(C) The nonconducting material will develop a uniform charge density throughout its volume, causing the potential drop across the capacitor to increase.
(D) The nonconducting material will polarize, inducing a surface charge density near the conducting plates, causing the potential drop to decrease.
(E) The nonconducting material will polarize, inducing a surface charge density near the conducting plates, causing the potential drop to increase.

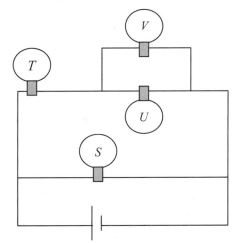

33. Bulbs S, T, U, and V all behave as identical ideal resistors in the circuit shown above. If bulb V is unscrewed, which of the following is true?

	Bulb S	Bulb T	Bulb U
(A)	stays the same	gets brighter	gets brighter
(B)	stays the same	gets brighter	gets dimmer
(C)	stays the same	gets dimmer	gets brighter
(D)	stays the same	gets dimmer	gets dimmer
(E)	gets brighter	gets dimmer	gets dimmer

GO ON TO THE NEXT PAGE

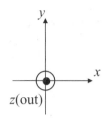

34. An electron is moving along the x-axis in the positive x direction. An electric field is directed in the +y direction. Which direction must the minimum strength magnetic field be pointed to allow the electron to move undeflected?

(A) $+y$ (B) $-y$ (C) $+z$ (D) $-z$ (E) $-x$

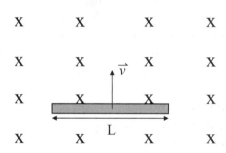

35. A conducting rail of length L is pulled at constant velocity $\vec{v}$ through a uniform magnetic field $\vec{B}$ directed into the page. The magnitude and direction of the electric field induced in the rail is

	Magnitude	Direction
(A)	BLv	points to the left
(B)	BLv	points to the right
(C)	Bv	points to the left
(D)	Bv	points to the right
(E)	Bv	points out of page

STOP
END OF SECTION I, ELECTRICITY AND MAGNETISM
IF YOU FINISH BEFORE TIME IS CALLED, YOU MAY CHECK YOUR WORK ON
SECTION 1, ELECTRICITY AND MAGNETISM ONLY.
DO NOT TURN TO ANY OTHER TEST MATERIALS.

STOP

AP PHYSICS C TEST
SECTION II—MECHANICS
Time: 45 minutes

3 Questions

Directions: Answer all 3 questions. The suggested time is about 15 minutes for answering each of the questions, which are worth 15 points each. The parts within a question may not have equal weight.

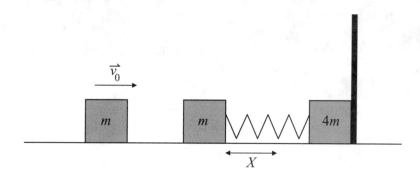

1. Two masses m and $4m$ are connected by a spring on a smooth horizontal surface. The larger mass is currently in contact with a barrier that will not move, and a third mass m moving with speed v_0 slides across the surface and strikes the smaller mass as shown in the figure. Upon impact, the two equal masses stick together, and the spring compresses a maximum X. Answer the following in terms of m, v_0, and X.

   (a) Determine the speed of the smaller masses immediately after impact.
   (b) Determine the force constant of the spring.
   (c) How much mechanical energy is lost as a result of the collision?

   The barrier is now removed so that the larger mass is free to move on the surface, and the collision is repeated. The same initial conditions are reproduced so that one of the smaller masses moving with speed v_0 collides with the other, sticking to it.

   (d) When the spring is at maximum compression, what will be the speed of each mass?
   (e) Determine the new maximum compression of the spring.

GO ON TO THE NEXT PAGE

2. A tall glass cylinder contains a clear liquid. When a small spherical mass m is gently placed into the liquid, it experiences a resistive force $\vec{F} = -bm\vec{v}$ proportional to the velocity of the mass as it falls. b is a constant that depends on properties of the liquid.
   (a) What is the initial acceleration of the mass just as it is released?
   (b) Determine the terminal speed of the mass under the conditions described.
   (c) Write the differential equation that could be used to find the velocity of the mass at any time $t > 0$.
   (d) Determine the time it takes for the mass to reach $\frac{1}{2}$ its terminal speed.
   (e) You are given a supply of several different clear liquids. Describe an experimental procedure for determining the b-values for these liquids. You may use the apparatus described earlier and any of the following.

meter stick	stopwatch	set of known masses
roll of string	spring	

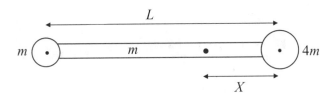

3. Two masses m and 4m are connected by light pins to the ends of a stick of mass m and length L. The stick is pivoted to rotate vertically about a horizontal axis at the center of mass of the system, located a distance X from the larger mass.
   (a) Determine the value of X in terms of m and L.
   (b) What is the moment of inertia of the system about its center of mass? The moment of inertia of a uniform stick of mass m and length L about is center is $\frac{1}{12}mL^2$.

   With the system initially at rest and the stick horizontal, another mass m is dropped onto the smaller mass. Just before it strikes the mass, it is moving *down* with speed v, and just after the collision, it is moving *up* with speed $\frac{v}{3}$.
   (c) Describe the motion of the pivoted system after the collision.
   (d) Find the angular speed of the stick after the collision.
   (e) Find the force exerted on the larger mass by its connecting pin when this mass is at its lowest position.

STOP
END OF SECTION II, MECHANICS

IF YOU FINISH BEFORE TIME IS CALLED, YOU MAY CHECK YOUR WORK ON SECTION II, MECHANICS ONLY.

DO NOT TURN TO ANY OTHER TEST MATERIALS.

STOP

AP PHYSICS C TEST
SECTION II—ELECTRICITY AND MAGNETISM
Time: 45 minutes
3 Questions

Directions: Answer all 3 questions. The suggested time is about 15 minutes for answering each of the questions, which are worth 15 points each. The parts within a question may not have equal weight.

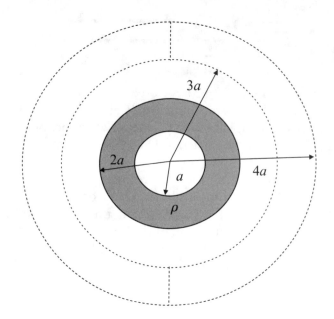

1. A nonconducting shell of radii a and $2a$ has a uniform charge density ρ.
    (a) Determine the electric field in the following regions:
        (i) $r > 2a$
        (ii) $2a > r > a$
        (iii) $r < a$

    (b) Determine the electric potential in the regions:
        (i) $r > 2a$
        (ii) $2a > r > a$
        (iii) $r < a$

    (c) Two neutral conducting hemispheres of radii $3a$ and $4a$ are assembled concentric to the nonconductor, making a single conducting sphere enclosing the nonconductor. Qualitatively describe how the potential at the center of the nonconductor changes.

GO ON TO THE NEXT PAGE

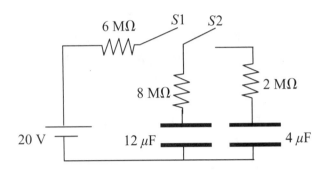

2. In the circuit shown in the figure, switch S1 is closed at $t = 0$.
   (a) Find the current in the 8 MΩ resistor immediately after the switch is closed.
   (b) Find the maximum charge that will reside on the 12 μF capacitor.
   (c) How much energy is stored in the capacitor when it's fully charged?

   After a long time, S1 is first opened and then S2 is closed.
   (d) Find the current in the 2 MΩ resistor just after S2 is closed.
   (e) Letting q be the charge on the 4 μF capacitor at any time, write a differential equation that could be used to determine q as a function of time.
   (f) Find the current in the 2 MΩ resistor 1 minute after S2 is closed.
   (g) Determine the final energy stored in the capacitors.

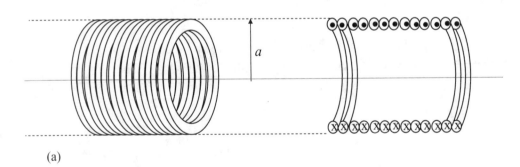

   (a)

3. A long solenoid with radius a and n turns per meter carries a steady current i.
   (a) By applying Ampere's law to an appropriate path, determine the magnetic field within the solenoid. Be sure to clearly show your path on the figure.

GO ON TO THE NEXT PAGE

The current in the solenoid is now allowed to oscillate according to $i(t) = i_0 \cos \omega t$. Two loops are inserted concentric to the solenoid as shown in the following figure. One loop, with radius $b < a$, has resistance R_b. The other loop, with radius $c > a$, has resistance R_c.

(b)

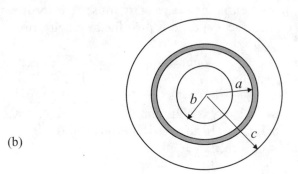

(b) Find the magnitude of the induced current in the smaller loop as a function of time.
(c) Find the magnitude of the induced electric field at a point in the smaller loop as a function of time.
(d) Find the magnitude of the induced electric field at a point in the larger loop as a function of time.

STOP
END OF SECTION II, ELECTRICITY AND MAGNETISM

IF YOU FINISH BEFORE TIME IS CALLED, YOU MAY CHECK YOUR WORK ON SECTION II, ELECTRICITY AND MAGNETISM ONLY.

DO NOT TURN TO ANY OTHER TEST MATERIALS.

MC Mechanics Answers and Explanations

1. The answer is C. Use $\Delta x = \frac{1}{2}(v_0 + v)t = \frac{1}{2}(0 + 10)(5) = 25$ m

2. The answer is E. At the highest point the velocity must be 0 (or it would go higher), but the velocity is still changing. The acceleration is just due to gravity, directed down.

3. The answer is B. Work is the component of the force in the direction of the displacement, $T\cos\theta$ multiplied by the displacement, D.

4. The answer is B. Since the velocity is constant, $T\cos\theta - F_{fric} = ma = 0$. To get the friction force, you need the normal force. In the vertical direction, the forces add to 0 as well because there's no movement in this direction at all, so
   $$N + T\sin\theta - mg = ma_y = 0$$
   $$N = mg - T\sin\theta$$
   Then the friction force is $F_{fric} = \mu N = \mu(mg - T\sin\theta)$.
   Plugging into the first equation gives B.

5. The answer is D. Since the orbital speed is $v = \sqrt{\frac{GM_e}{R}}$, independent of the satellite's mass, I isn't true. Since the centripetal acceleration is proportional to v^2, which depends on the Earth's mass, II isn't true. The gravitational force exerts no torque about the Earth's center, so III is true.

6. The answer is B. At terminal speed there is 0 acceleration, so the net force is 0. Then you have
   $mg - bv^2 = 0 \Rightarrow v = \sqrt{\frac{mg}{b}}$.

7. The answer is D. The force is the negative slope of the graph. At $r = 2a$, the curve is well approximated by a straight line. At the $a \to 2a$ interval, the graph decreases from $3U_1 \to 0$, so the slope is $-\frac{3U_1}{a}$.

8. The answer is E. Use conservation of energy, recognizing that the mass loses $4U_1$ of potential energy as it moves to the lowest PE at $r = 3a$, so
   $$-\Delta U = \Delta K$$
   $$4U_1 = \frac{1}{2}mv^2 \Rightarrow v = \sqrt{\frac{8U_1}{m}}$$

9. The answer is B. The area under the F vs. t graph is the impulse delivered by the force, which will equal the change in momentum of the object if it's the net force. The area from $3 \to 4$ s is negative, so this contribution cancels out the $0 \to 1$ s contribution. You're left with a rectangle from $1 \to 2$ s and a triangle from $2 \to 3$ s, so $10 + 5 = 15 \frac{kg \cdot m}{s}$.

10. The answer is D. Using momentum conservation, you have
    $$P_i = P_f$$
    $$6mv = m(0) + 2m(2v) + 3mv' \qquad \Rightarrow v' = \frac{2}{3}v$$

11. The answer is C. The force at the center exerts 0 torque, and the other two both exert torques directed out of the page, so they have the same sign.

$$net\tau = 2F\left(\frac{L}{4}\right) + 0 + 2F\sin 30\left(\frac{L}{4}\right) = \frac{3}{4}FL$$

12. The answer is B. Looking at the system as a whole and applying the second law gives

$$netF = Mg = (m + M)a \Rightarrow a = \frac{M}{m + M}g$$

Only the tension accelerates m, so applying the second law to it, you have

$$netF = T = ma = \frac{mM}{m + M}g$$

13. The answer is D. For circular orbit, combine the fact that $l = mvR$ and $v = \sqrt{\frac{GM_e}{R}}$.

$$l = m\sqrt{\frac{GM_e}{R}}R = m\sqrt{GM_eR}$$

14. The answer is D. From the form of the equation, $\omega^2 = 4\pi$. Since $T = \frac{2\pi}{\omega}$, D follows.

15. The answer is B. Because v is positive and constant over the first interval, x must be linearly increasing over this interval. Over the third interval, v is negative and constant, so x must be linearly decreasing. Over the second interval, the acceleration is constant and negative, which implies a parabolic shape, and the three segments must be continuous. Only B fits these categories.

16. The answer is B. The initial horizontal velocity, $v_{x0} = 50\cos 37 = 40$ m/s, remains the same throughout the motion. At the highest point, the y-component of the velocity will be 0, because otherwise it would go higher. The acceleration is provided by gravity, which acts downward with a magnitude of 10 m/s^2 throughout the motion.

17. The answer is C. Since $net\vec{F}\Delta t = \Delta\vec{p}$, you can determine the direction of the net force from the direction of $\vec{p_f} - \vec{p_i} = \vec{p_f} + (-\vec{p_i})$. C follows from the rules for vector addition.

18. The answer is D. From the form of the equation, $\omega^2 = 6\pi$. From knowledge of the harmonic oscillator equation for a spring-mass system, you have $\omega^2 = \frac{k}{m}$. Combining the two gives you D.

19. The answer is B. The second derivative of x is $a(t) = -(0.5)(6\pi)^2\cos\left(6\pi t + \frac{\pi}{8}\right)$. The maximum value of this is $18\pi^2$ since the cosine has a maximum value of 1.

20. The answer is D. The centripetal acceleration is proportional to v^2, which begins at 0, hits a maximum after $\frac{1}{4}$ period, and returns to 0 again after $\frac{1}{2}$ period, so A and D are possible. The derivative of v^2 is obviously continuous, so A is ruled out. The cusp implies nonphysical behavior at the low point of the motion.

21. The answer is C. The tangential acceleration is just $g \sin \theta$, which has a maximum magnitude at the beginning and after $\frac{1}{2}$ period; it is 0 at the low point after $\frac{1}{4}$ period. Only C fits these categories.

22. The answer is E. The tension always acts perpendicular to the displacement, so it does no work.

23. The answer is D. $W = \int_{x_i}^{x_f} F(x)\,dx = \int_2^1 (2x - 8x^3)\,dx = (x^2 - 2x^4)_2^1 = 1 - 2 - 4 + 32 = 27$ J

24. The answer is E. The average power is the change in KE divided by the time during which the change occurred.

$$\Delta K = \frac{1}{2}m(2v)^2 - \frac{1}{2}mv^2 = 3\frac{1}{2}mv^2$$

Conservation of energy tells you that $\frac{1}{2}mv^2 = mgH$. Substitution gives

$$P = \frac{\Delta K}{T} = 3\frac{mgH}{T}$$

25. The answer is D. Use momentum conservation.

$$mv + 4m\left(-\frac{1}{2}v\right) = 5mv' \Rightarrow v' = -\frac{1}{5}v$$

26. The answer is A. Use a motion equation to find the angular acceleration, then the fixed axis dynamic equation to find the torque.

$$\frac{1}{2}\omega_0 = \omega_0 + \alpha T \Rightarrow \alpha = \frac{\omega_0}{2T}$$

$$net\ \tau = I\alpha = -\frac{I\omega_0}{2T}$$

27. The answer is C. $I = \sum mR^2 = mL^2 + m(2L)^2 + m(3L)^2 = 14mL^2$

28. The answer is C. The value of g at the surface of a planet is proportional to $\frac{M_p}{R_p^2}$. Taking ratios of planet-X values to those of Earth, you have

$$3 = \frac{g_X}{g_E} = \frac{\left(\dfrac{2M_E}{R_X^2}\right)}{\left(\dfrac{M_E}{R_E^2}\right)} = \frac{2R_E^2}{R_X^2}$$

29. The answer is C. If the mass is displaced an amount x from equilibrium, each spring will be stretched only $\frac{1}{2}x$. Since only one spring acts directly on the mass, it experiences a restoring force $F = -\frac{1}{2}kx$ for a displacement x, as if there were just a single spring with spring constant $\frac{1}{2}k$. The period will then be $T = 2\pi\frac{m}{\frac{1}{2}k}$.

30. The answer is D. Take two derivatives to find acceleration, and then use the second law.

$$v = \frac{dx}{dt} = 3t^2 - 8t \qquad a = \frac{dv}{dt} = 6t - 8 \qquad a(1) = -2\,\frac{m}{s^2}$$

$$netF = ma = 3(-2) = -6 \text{ N}$$

31. The answer is D. In the vertical direction, the maximum height reached is proportional to the square of the initial vertical component of velocity, as you can see from the motion equation

$$v_y^2 = v_{y0}^2 - 2g\Delta y \;\Rightarrow\; \Delta y = \frac{v_{y0}^2}{2g}$$

when $v_y = 0$ at the highest point. If you call H' the maximum height when the dart is fired at $60°$, you can set up the ratio

$$\frac{H'}{H} = \frac{(v_0 \sin 60)^2}{v_0^2} = \frac{3}{4}$$

32. The answer is C. As they move in tandem at 10 m/s, the CM is also moving at 10 m/s. Since the forces exerted are internal to the child-man system, the CM will continue to move at the same velocity.

33. The answer is B. Use conservation of energy and the fact that the moment of inertia about the CM of a hoop is simply MR^2 because all the mass is the same distance from the CM.

$$MgH = \frac{1}{2}Mv^2 + \frac{1}{2}I\omega^2 = \frac{1}{2}Mv^2 + \frac{1}{2}(MR^2)\left(\frac{v}{R}\right)^2 = Mv^2$$

Thus,

$$KE_{trans} = \frac{1}{2}Mv^2 = \frac{1}{2}MgH$$

34. The answer is A. The force of gravity and the spring force are both conservative, so the work they do is independent of path. Because friction was acting, the mass will rebound to a lower height than its initial height. The work done by gravity in descending to a lower height is positive. The spring ends up as it started, uncompressed, so it did 0 work.

35. The answer is C. The net torque about the geometrical center will be 0.

$$\tau_m + \tau_{stick} + \tau_M = 0$$

$$mg\left(\frac{L}{2}\right) + mg\left(\frac{L}{4}\right) - Mg\left(\frac{L}{2}\right) = 0 \;\Rightarrow\; M = \frac{3}{2}m$$

MC E & M Answers and Explanations

1. The answer is C. Since $E = -\dfrac{dV}{dx}$ is the negative slope of the graph, the magnitude of E is greatest where the graph is steepest.

2. The answer is C. The electric field points from higher potential to lower, perpendicular to the equipotential surfaces. Electrons accelerate opposite the field direction.

3. The answer is C. The electrostatic force is conservative, so the work is independent of path. Moving from $B \rightarrow D$ takes no work because there's no potential difference.

4. The answer is E. If you know the value of $\vec{E}$ at all points, then $\oint_{\text{closed surface}} \vec{E} \cdot d\vec{A}$ can be calculated for any surface. Since this integral equals $\dfrac{q_{\text{in}}}{\varepsilon_0}$, you can determine the charge inside the surface.

5. The answer is D. Between the two charges, the contributions to the field from each charge reinforce each other, so they cannot cancel out. To the left of L, the two contributions oppose each other, but being closer to the larger charge ensures they will never cancel out completely. To the right of R there will be one position where the two contributions exactly cancel out.

6. The answer is B. By superposition, you can add the two individual potential contributions:

$$V = \frac{1}{4\pi\varepsilon_0}\left(\frac{5Q}{\frac{d}{2}} + \frac{-3Q}{\frac{d}{2}}\right)$$

7. The answer is C. When the spheres are touched, charge will redistribute until both spheres are at the same potential. Since $V \propto \frac{1}{r}$, the charge on the smaller sphere after touching will be $\frac{1}{3}$ of what will end up on the larger sphere; the charge redistributes in a 3-to-1 ratio. Since you start with Q, this means $\frac{3}{4}Q$ on the larger sphere and $\frac{1}{4}Q$ on the smaller sphere.

8. The answer is D. The two batteries oppose each other, so the equivalent battery voltage is 20 V. The parallel pair of resistors yields $\frac{1}{R} = \frac{1}{20} + \frac{1}{5} = \frac{1}{4} \Rightarrow R = 4\,\Omega$. Since all the other resistors are in series with the 4 Ω, the equivalent resistance of the circuit is 10 Ω. Then, the current is $i = \frac{20}{10} = 2A$ in the batteries and the 2 Ω resistor. Using the power relation, you have

$$E_{2\Omega} = Pt = (i^2 R_{2\Omega})t = (2^2 2)60 = 480 \text{ W}$$

9. The answer is B. This battery is recharging, so $V_T = V_B + ir = 5 + 2(0.4) = 5.8$ V.

10. The answer is A. Starting at S, you can add the voltage drops, proceeding clockwise to T. Each resistor produces a drop equal to iR, and the battery produces a drop equal to its terminal voltage. $V_{ST} = -2(2) - 5.8 - 2(3) = -15.8$ V

11. The answer is C. First, find the equivalent capacitance of the two 12 μF capacitors in series, and then combine with the 6 μF using the parallel formula.

$$\frac{1}{C_s} = \frac{1}{12} + \frac{1}{12} = \frac{1}{6} \Rightarrow 6 \mu F$$
$$C_p = 6 + 6 = 12 \mu F$$

12. The answer is E. The two 12 μF caps will always have equal charge on their plates because they are in series. Since the equivalent capacitance of these two is 6 μF, symmetry tells you that the top and bottom branch will also have equal charge, independent of the voltage applied.

13. The answer is D. Applying the loop law to the series circuit, you have $+V_B$ through the battery, $-iR$ across the resistor, $-\frac{Q}{C}$ across the capacitor, and $-L\frac{di}{dt}$ across the inductor. These must all add to 0.

14. The answer is C. Since the inductor keeps current from flowing through it at $t = 0$, the current in the 6 Ω and 12 Ω resistors is the same, and applying the loop law around the outer loop yields $90 - 18i = 0$.

15. The answer is D. A long time after S is closed, the inductor is behaving as a piece of zero resistance wire. At this time, the overall resistance in the circuit is 10 Ω, since the 6 Ω and the 12 Ω in parallel yield 4 Ω. This means that the battery has established 9 A in the circuit, which breaks up into a 2-to-1 ratio at the junction. The 6 Ω resistor and the inductor will have 6 A established in them. The inductor has stored energy given by

$$E = \frac{1}{2}Li^2 = \frac{1}{2}(2)(6)^2 = 36 \text{ J}$$

This is the total energy consumed as the current decays to 0 when S is opened.

16. The answer is B. The field created by I_w in the region of the loop is directed out of the page using the long wire right-hand rule. Each element of the top segment will feel a force down ($d\vec{l} \times \vec{B}$), but there will always be a corresponding element on the bottom segment that will feel a force up, so these contributions cancel out. The far right segment of the loop feels a force to the left, but the left side of the loop feels a force to the right, and since it is closer to the wire, it experiences a stronger field and a stronger force, so this dominates.

17. The answer is D. Inside a wire, the field rises linearly from 0. It is continuous at the surface of the wire and then drops off as $\frac{1}{r}$ outside the wire. Notice that B drops off as $\frac{1}{r^2}$.

18. The answer is C. Using Faraday's law, you get the induced voltage. Then, use Ohm's law for the current.

$$V_{in} = \frac{d\Phi}{dt} = \frac{d}{dt}(bt^2(\pi a^2)) = 2\pi a^2 bt \Rightarrow V_{in}\left(\frac{1}{2}T\right) = \pi a^2 bt$$
$$i_{in} = \frac{V_{in}}{R} = \frac{\pi a^2 bt}{R}$$

19. The answer is B. $E(r) = -\frac{dV}{dr} = -\frac{d}{dr}\left(-Cr^{\frac{3}{2}}\right) = \frac{3}{2}Cr^{\frac{1}{2}}$

20. The answer is E. The field points radially away from the symmetry axis, so the electron will experience a force toward the axis. It will first gain speed as it moves to the axis, reaching a maximum speed at $r = 0$, and then it will slow down, stop, and move back toward the axis, eventually ending at its starting position, an oscillation.

21. The answer is D. Charges with the same $\frac{q}{m}$ ratio moving perpendicular to a magnetic field will move in circles that depend on their speeds, but the period of revolution, $T = \frac{2\pi m}{qB}$, is the same for each, independent of speed.

22. The answer is C. The field between the plates of a parallel plate capacitor is given by $E = \frac{Q}{\varepsilon_0 A}$, as you can see by applying Gauss's law to a little cylinder embedded in one of the plates. This is independent of the separation. Since $V = Ed$, as d doubles, so does V.

23. The answer is B. Use conservation of energy.

$$\Delta K = -\Delta U$$

$$\frac{1}{2}m_e v^2 = -\left(\frac{-e^2}{4\pi\varepsilon_0}\right)\left(\frac{1}{\frac{d}{2}} - \frac{1}{d}\right) = \frac{e^2}{4\pi\varepsilon_0 d} \Rightarrow v^2 = \frac{e^2}{2\pi\varepsilon_0 m_e d}$$

24. The answer is B. Since the Q in the cavity causes charge to separate in the conductor, a closed surface surrounding Q can enclose some of the separated charge. In fact, if the surface lies inside the conductor but outside the cavity, it encloses 0 total charge. This means that I isn't true. Within the cavity, there is certainly a field, as you can see by enclosing Q in a small spherical surface. It takes work to move a test charge toward Q, implying that the potential isn't constant. Choice III is not true. Choice II is true as long as equilibrium is established, because conductors contain charges free to move.

25. The answer is A. The integration direction tells you that currents moving into the page are positive. The path then yields $\oint\limits_{path} \vec{B} \cdot \vec{dl} = \mu_0(2 + 3 - 4) = \mu_0$.

26. The answer is A. The potential must approach $+\infty$ as you get close to $+Q$ and $-\infty$ as you get close to $-Q$. This is the only graph that does this whether you approach the charges from the left or the right.

27. The answer is D. If you imagine the capacitor as charged to Q and isolated before the dielectric is inserted, introducing the dielectric will reduce the voltage drop across the dielectric by $\frac{1}{\kappa}$, but it won't affect the other space between the plates. The total voltage drop across the plates will be $V' = \frac{V}{2} + \frac{V}{2\kappa}$, where V is the original voltage drop $\frac{Q}{C}$. From the definition of capacitance, you have

$$C' = \frac{Q}{V'} = \frac{Q}{\frac{V}{2}\left(1 + \frac{1}{\kappa}\right)} = \frac{Q}{V}\frac{2\kappa}{1 + \kappa}$$

28. The answer is B. To find the field, you need to know the potential in a region around the point, because $E = -\frac{dV}{dx}$. Just knowing a single value gives you no information about how it's changing, so I isn't possible. Choice II follows from the definition of potential difference. The work it takes to move a charge from the point to infinity is just Q times the potential difference, and since you know V at infinity is 0, the potential difference is just the negative of the potential value. A similar argument tells you that III cannot be determined because you don't know the potential at the other point.

29. The answer is D. When you apply Gauss's law to the surface, you're integrating over a cylindrical surface of radius r, so $\oint_{\text{surface}} \vec{E} \cdot d\vec{A} = E(2\pi rL)$. On the right-hand side of the equation, you must have the charge inside this surface, which is $\rho V = \rho(\pi r^2 L)$. Dividing by ε_0 gives the result.

30. The answer is D. At terminal speed, the force of gravity will equal the force on the induced current.

$$mg = i_{\text{in}}LB = \frac{BLv_T}{R}LB \Rightarrow v_T = \frac{mgR}{B^2L^2}$$

31. The answer is C. Since the voltage is fixed, you should use the power equation $P = \frac{V^2}{R}$. When the wire is made twice as long, its cross-sectional area becomes $\frac{1}{2}$ its original area, to keep the volume constant. Then,

$$R' = \rho\frac{L'}{A'} = \rho\frac{2L}{\frac{A}{2}} = 4\rho\frac{L}{A} = 4R,$$

where R is the original resistance. Thus,

$$P' = \frac{V^2}{4R} = \frac{P}{4}.$$

32. The answer is D. The electric field in the capacitor will polarize the dielectric material. This induces a surface charge density on the dielectric that is opposite in sign to the plate that surface is closest to. As a result, points within the dielectric are shielded from the original charge on the plates, reducing the field and the potential difference.

33. The answer is C. The brightness of a bulb is determined by the power i^2R it consumes from the circuit. Since all bulbs have the same resistance, more current will mean brighter when comparing bulbs. S stays the same because it is in parallel with the battery and is unaffected by the other bulbs. When V is unscrewed, the resistance in the top branch increases, so T will have less current and will get dimmer. Since U no longer shares the current established in T with V, it will get brighter.

34. The answer is C. The electric force on the electron will be in the $-y$ direction, opposite to the field, so you need the magnetic force to be in the $+y$ direction to oppose this. Since the velocity is in the $+x$ direction, to get $-\vec{v} \times \vec{B}$ in the $+y$ direction, $\vec{B}$ must be in the $+z$ direction. Notice that you can use $-\vec{v} \times \vec{B}$ because you have an electron.

35. The answer is D. As the rail moves, the charge separation induced by the magnetic field creates an electric field, and at equilibrium the electric force and magnetic force on charges in the rail will be equal: $qE = qvB \Rightarrow E = Bv$. From the magnetic force on a moving charge, you can see that negative charges initially tend to be forced to the right, so the left side becomes positively charged. This creates an electric field pointing to the right.

FR Mechanics Answers and Explanations

1. (a) Use momentum conservation before and after impact.

$$mv_0 = 2mv \qquad\qquad \Rightarrow v = \frac{v_0}{2}$$

(b) Energy is conserved after the collision, with the KE just after the collision equal to the final spring PE.

$$\frac{1}{2}(2m)v^2 = \frac{1}{2}(2m)\left(\frac{v_0}{2}\right)^2 = \frac{1}{2}kX^2$$

$$k = \frac{mv_0^2}{2X^2}$$

(c) Find the difference in kinetic energy before and after the collision.

$$\Delta E = \frac{1}{2}(2m)\left(\frac{v_0}{2}\right)^2 - \frac{1}{2}mv_0^2 = -\frac{1}{4}mv_0^2$$

(d) With the barrier removed, there are no external horizontal forces, so the center of mass will move at a constant velocity throughout the entire process. Before the collision, the velocity of the CM is determined by

$$v_{CM} = \frac{mv_0 + 0 + 0}{6m} = \frac{1}{6}v_0$$

At maximum compression, the two masses at the ends of the spring will have 0 velocity with respect to each other; otherwise, they would continue to get closer. Since they're moving at the same velocity, this must also be the velocity of the center of mass $\frac{1}{6}v_0$.

(e) Energy is still conserved after the collision. The speed of the $2m$ mass is still $\frac{1}{2}v_0$ just after collision, and at maximum compression you now know the speed:

$$E_i = E_f$$

$$\frac{1}{2}(2m)\left(\frac{v_0}{2}\right)^2 = \frac{1}{2}(6m)\left(\frac{v_0}{6}\right)^2 + \frac{1}{2}kX_{max}^2 = \frac{1}{2}(6m)\left(\frac{v_0}{6}\right)^2 + \frac{1}{2}\left(\frac{mv_0^2}{2X^2}\right)X_{max}^2$$

$$X_{max} = \sqrt{\frac{2}{3}}X$$

2. (a) At release, the resistive force is 0 because the velocity is 0, so the second law gives

$$netF = ma = mg \quad \Rightarrow \quad a = g$$

(b) At terminal speed, the acceleration is 0 since the velocity is no longer changing. Once again, you use the second law:

$$netF = mg - bmv_T = 0 \quad \Rightarrow v_T = \frac{g}{b}$$

(c) Now apply the second law for intermediate times.

$$netF = ma = m\frac{dv}{dt} = mg - bmv \quad \Rightarrow \frac{dv}{dt} + bv = g$$

(d) The solution to the equation is $v = \frac{g}{b}(1 - e^{-bt})$

Substitute $v = \frac{g}{2b}$ and solve for t.

$$\frac{g}{2b} = \frac{g}{b}(1 - e^{-bt}) \quad \Rightarrow t = \frac{\ln 2}{b}$$

(e) To determine the value of b, you need to measure the terminal speed of the sphere. Assuming that terminal speed is reached fairly quickly, choose a point far enough below the surface where you can be sure that terminal speed has been reached. Measure the distance H from this point to the bottom of the tube. Release the sphere at the surface, and start the stopwatch as the sphere reaches the beginning of the H distance interval. When the sphere reaches the bottom, stop the watch and record the time T. Assuming it moved at the terminal speed over this interval, the terminal speed formula will give you b:

$$v_T = \frac{g}{b} = \frac{H}{T} \quad \Rightarrow b = \frac{gT}{H}$$

3) (a) Use the CM formula, with the large mass as the origin.

$$X = \frac{(4m)(0) + m\left(\frac{L}{2}\right) + mL}{6m} = \frac{1}{4}L$$

(b) The moment of inertia about the CM of the system will have 3 contributions, two from the masses at each end and one from the stick. Treating the masses at the end as point masses, you have

$$I = 4m\left(\frac{L}{4}\right)^2 + m\left(\frac{3L}{4}\right)^2 + I_{stick}$$

The moment of inertia of the stick about the system CM can be found from the parallel axis theorem, remembering that the moment of inertia of a uniform stick about its center is

$$I_{stick}^{center} = \frac{1}{12}mL^2$$

Thus the parallel axis theorem gives you

$$I_{stick} = \frac{1}{12}mL^2 + m\left(\frac{L}{4}\right)^2 = \frac{7}{48}mL^2$$

Putting all of this together you have

$$I = 4m\left(\frac{L}{4}\right)^2 + m\left(\frac{3L}{4}\right)^2 + \frac{7}{48}mL^2 = \frac{23}{24}mL^2$$

(c) Because it is pivoted about the CM, gravity will exert no torque on it after the collision, and the angular speed acquired from the collision will remain constant. This means that the pivoted system will rotate at a constant angular velocity after the collision.

(d) There is no torque exerted about the CM, so you can use angular momentum conservation about this point. The initial angular momentum comes from the single moving mass, while the final angular momentum will have a contribution from the rebounding mass and the pivoted system as it starts to rotate.

$$L_0 = L_f$$

$$mv\left(\frac{3L}{4}\right) = m\left(\frac{-v}{3}\right)\left(\frac{3L}{4}\right) + I\omega = m\left(\frac{-v}{3}\right)\left(\frac{3L}{4}\right) + \left(\frac{23}{24}mL^2\right)\omega$$

$$\omega = \frac{24v}{23L}$$

(e) Use Newton's second law with the centripetal acceleration of the larger mass. The pin exerts a force toward the center, while the weight acts away from the center.

$$netF = 4ma = 4m\omega^2 R = 4m\left(\frac{24v}{23L}\right)^2\left(\frac{L}{4}\right)$$

$$F_{pin} - 4mg = \frac{576}{529}\frac{mv^2}{L} \qquad\qquad F_{pin} = 4mg + \frac{576}{529}\frac{mv^2}{L}$$

E & M Free-Response Explanations

1. (a) Use Gauss's law with spherical symmetry to find $\vec{E}$ in the three regions. In each case, choose a sphere concentric with the nonconducting shell as the Gaussian surface.

$$\oint_{area} \vec{E} \cdot d\vec{A} = \frac{q_{in}}{\varepsilon_0}$$

$$E(4\pi r^2) = \frac{q_{in}}{\varepsilon_0}$$

(i) $r > 2a$, $q_{in} = q_{total} = \rho \frac{4}{3}\pi((2a)^3 - a^3) = \rho \frac{4}{3}\pi(7a^3)$

$$E_i = \frac{q_{total}}{4\pi\varepsilon_0 r^2} = \frac{\rho(7a^3)}{3\varepsilon_0 r^2}$$

(ii) $2a > r > a$, $q_{in} = \rho \frac{4}{3}\pi(r^3 - a^3)$

$$E_{ii} = \frac{\rho \frac{4}{3}\pi(r^3 - a^3)}{4\pi\varepsilon_0 r^2} = \frac{\rho}{3\varepsilon_0}\left(r - \frac{a^3}{r^2}\right)$$

(iii) $r < a$, $q_{in} = 0$

$$E_{iii} = 0$$

(b) Use the definition of electric potential, integrating the field from infinity to the point in question.

$$V(r) = -\int_{\infty}^{r} \vec{E} \cdot d\vec{l}$$

(i) For $r > 2a$, the distribution behaves as if the total charge were at the center of symmetry.

$$V_i(r) = -\int_{\infty}^{r} \frac{q_{total}}{4\pi\varepsilon_0 r^2} dr = \frac{q_{total}}{4\pi\varepsilon_0 r} = \frac{\rho(7a^3)}{3\varepsilon_0 r}$$

(ii) $V_{ii}(r) = -\int_{\infty}^{r} \vec{E} \cdot d\vec{l} = -\int_{\infty}^{2a} \vec{E} \cdot d\vec{l} - \int_{2a}^{r} \vec{E}_{ii} \cdot d\vec{l} = V_i(2a) - \int_{2a}^{r} \frac{\rho}{3\varepsilon_0}\left(r - \frac{a^3}{r^2}\right)dr$

$$V_{ii}(r) = \frac{\rho(7a^3)}{3\varepsilon_0(2a)} - \frac{\rho}{3\varepsilon_0}\left(\frac{r^2}{2} - \frac{(2a)^2}{2} + \frac{a^3}{r} - \frac{a^3}{2a}\right) = \frac{\rho}{3\varepsilon_0}\left(6a^2 - \frac{r^2}{2} - \frac{a^3}{r}\right)$$

(iii) Since the field is 0 inside, the potential will be constant, equal to the value at the inner surface of the nonconductor.

$$V_{iii}(r) = V_{ii}(2a) = \frac{3\rho a^2}{2\varepsilon_0}$$

(c) When the conducting sphere is put in place, the electric field will be the same everywhere except for the region within the conductor itself, where the field will be 0. This follows from Gauss's law and the fact that the conductor carries no excess charge. Integrating the field in from infinity in this case, you get a different contribution in the region only from $d \to c$, which now gives a 0 contribution. The potential difference at the center will now be *less* by an amount equal to the old potential difference from $d \to c$.

2. (a) At $t = 0$, the 12 μF capacitor behaves as a short circuit. The left loop has a resistance of 14 $M\Omega$, and

$$i = \frac{20}{14 \times 10^6} = 1.43 \ \mu A$$

(b) When fully charged, the 12 μF capacitor has a 20 V potential difference.

$$Q_{max} = CV = 12(20) = 240 \ \mu C$$

(c) Use the capacitor energy formula.

$$U = \frac{1}{2}CV^2 = \frac{1}{2}(12)(20)^2 = 2{,}400 \ \mu J$$

(d) Just after $S2$ is closed, the 4 μF capacitor will have 0 potential drop, while the 12μF will have 20 V. Applying the loop law to the right loop gives you

$$20 - 10 \times 10^6 i = 0 \quad \Rightarrow \quad i = 2 \ \mu A$$

(e) More generally, if q resides on the 4 μF, then $Q_{max} - q$ resides on the 12 μF, and $i = \dfrac{dq}{dt}$. The loop law then gives you

$$\frac{Q_{max} - q}{12 \times 10^{-6}} - 10 \times 10^6 i - \frac{q}{4 \times 10^{-6}} = 0 \quad \Rightarrow \quad \frac{Q_{max} - q}{12} - 10i - \frac{q}{4} = 0$$

$$\frac{dq}{dt} + \frac{q}{30} = 2 \qquad q \text{ in } \mu C \text{ units}$$

(f) This is a charging capacitor equation with $q_{max} = 60\ \mu C$, so the solution is

$$q(t) = 60\left(1 - e^{-\frac{t}{30}}\right)$$

$$i(t) = \frac{dq}{dt} = 2e^{-\frac{t}{30}} \quad \Rightarrow \quad i(t = 60) = 2e^{-2} = 0.271\ \mu A$$

(g) Since the $4\ \mu F$ ends with $q_{max} = 60\ \mu C$, the $12\ \mu F$ must end with $180\ \mu C$ to conserve charge. Each capacitor will have a potential drop of $15\ V$, so the final energy stored is

$$U = \frac{1}{2}(12)(15)^2 + \frac{1}{2}(4)(15)^2 = 1{,}800\ \mu J$$

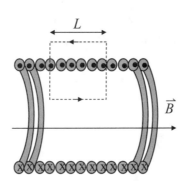

3. (a) Applying Ampere's law to the path shown in dotted lines and recognizing that the field is 0 outside the solenoid, you have

$$\oint_{path} \vec{B} \cdot d\vec{L} = \mu_0 i_{en}$$

$$BL = \mu_0 nLi \quad \Rightarrow \quad B = \mu_0 ni$$

(b) The flux through the smaller loop will be

$$\Phi = B\pi b^2 = \mu_0 ni\pi b^2 = \mu_0 n\pi b^2 i_0 \cos \omega t$$

Then from Faraday's law, you have

$$V_{in} = -\frac{d\Phi}{dt} = \mu_0 n\pi b^2 \omega i_0 \sin \omega t$$

Then, the induced current is

$$i_b = \frac{V_{in}}{R_b} = \frac{\mu_0 n\pi b^2 \omega i_0}{R_b} \sin \omega t$$

(c) To find the induced electric field, use Faraday's law for the fields.

$$\oint \vec{E} \cdot \vec{dl} = -\frac{d}{dt}\oint \vec{B} \cdot \vec{dA}$$

$$E(2\pi b) = \mu_0 n\pi b^2 \omega i_0 \sin \omega t$$

$$E = \frac{1}{2}\mu_0 nb\omega i_0 \sin \omega t$$

(d) For the loop outside the solenoid, the flux is contained within a radius a. From Faraday's law, you have

$$\oint \vec{E} \cdot \vec{dl} = -\frac{d}{dt}\oint \vec{B} \cdot \vec{dA}$$

$$E(2\pi c) = \mu_0 n\pi a^2 \omega i_0 \sin \omega t$$

$$E = \frac{1}{2c}\mu_0 na\omega i_0 \sin \omega t$$

Glossary

acceleration The time rate of change of velocity. There are two types of acceleration: **average acceleration**, given by the change in velocity over an interval, divided by the size of the time interval, and **instantaneous acceleration**, the limit of the average acceleration over an infinitesimally small interval.

Amperean path A closed loop introduced for the purpose of applying Ampere's law.

ampere The SI unit of electric current. 1 ampere corresponds to 1 coulomb/second.

Ampere's law A law that relates the line integral of the magnetic field around a closed loop to the current contained within the loop.

amplitude The magnitude of the largest displacement of an oscillating system.

angular acceleration The rate at which angular velocity changes.

angular displacement The angle through which an object rotates in a given time interval.

angular frequency The coefficient of the time in the phase of an oscillator.

angular momentum a measure of the motion of an object about an axis. Its time rate of change is determined by the net torque acting on the system. It is conserved if no external torques act on the system.

angular momentum conservation law A law stating that the total angular momentum of a system won't change if no external torques are acting on the system.

angular velocity The rate at which the angular measure of position changes.

apparent weight The reading of a bathroom scale that's in the same state of motion as the object resting on it.

Biot-Savart A law that describes the magnetic field produced by an element of current at an arbitrary point outside the current distribution.

capacitance The ratio of the charge separated per potential drop for a capacitor. Capacitance measures the ability to store charge; it increases when the conductors get larger or closer together.

capacitor A circuit device that consists of two separated conductors.

center of mass The average coordinate of a system of particles, with the average weighted by the mass at each coordinate. The CM obeys the dynamic equation of a point particle moving under the influence of only the external forces acting on the system.

centripetal acceleration For a circularly moving object, the component of the acceleration directed toward the center.

centripetal force For a circularly moving object, the component of the net force directed toward the center.

conductor A material that contains many mobile charges within it that can partake in an electric current if a local electric field is established.

conservation laws Principles that state that under certain conditions, some physical quantities don't change; they are "conserved." Examples include the conservation laws for energy, momentum, angular momentum, and electric charge.

conservation of mechanical energy A principle that states that if only conservative forces act on a system, the total mechanical energy won't change.

conservation of momentum principle A statement that when no external forces act on a system, its total linear momentum won't change.

conservative force A force with the property that the work done by the force is independent of path. Only for conservative forces can a potential energy be meaningfully defined.

contact force A force exerted between two systems as a result of their actually touching each other.

conventional current The electric current produced by imagining positive charges are moving instead of electrons. It flows in the opposite direction to the electron flow.

coulomb The SI unit of electric charge.

Coulomb's law The inverse square law that describes the force exerted between two point charges.

cross product A type of vector multiplication that results in a third vector perpendicular to each of the two vectors in the product. The direction is determined by the right-hand rule. Parallel vectors produce a cross product of 0.

current density A vector quantity whose flux through an area gives the electric current through the area.

dielectric A nonconducting material often placed between the conductors of a capacitor to increase the capacitance.

displacement The change in position of an object.

dot product A type of vector multiplication that results in a scalar. It's maximized when the two vectors in the product are parallel, and it's 0 when they are perpendicular.

drift speed The slow speed acquired by conduction electrons as a result of an impressed electric field within the conductor.

elastic collision A collision where the total kinetic energy doesn't change.

electric charge A fundamental property possessed by many of the basic constituents of matter. The basic unit of charge is 1.6×10^{-19} C. Electrons carry 1 negative unit, and protons carry 1 positive unit.

electric current The rate at which charge flows across a given cross-sectional area.

electric field A vector quantity defined at every point in space as the electric force per unit charge. The direction of the electric field is determined by its effect on a positive charge. Electric fields are created by charges and changing magnetic fields.

electric field lines A representation of the electric field. The electric field is tangential to the field lines, and the strength of the field is directly proportional to the density of the lines in space. For electrostatic fields, field lines begin on positive charges and end on negative charges. For induced fields, the field lines close on themselves.

electric flux A measure of how much electric field lines cut through an area.

electric potential difference The work per unit charge needed to move a charge between two points.

electric potential energy (difference) The negative of the work done by the electric field as a charge is slowly repositioned.

electrical resistance The property of a conductor or other electrical device that determines how much current will be established in the material or device for a given potential drop.

electrostatic equilibrium The condition achieved when all mobile charges have ceased moving in response to an imposed electric field.

electrostatic field An electric field created by stationary charges.

electrostatics The study of the properties of charges at rest.

energy of assembly The work needed to construct a charge distribution from scratch with all elements initially at infinity.

equilibrium position For an oscillating system, the position where the restoring force is 0.

equipotential surface A connected surface that has zero potential difference between any two points on the surface. The electric field will be perpendicular to the equipotential surfaces. It takes zero work to move a charge along such a surface.

escape velocity The initial velocity a projectile must be given to completely escape the influence of some force.

farad The SI unit of capacitance corresponding to 1 coulomb per volt.

Faraday's law A law that relates the voltage induced in a loop to the change in the flux through the loop. More generally, it relates an induced electric field to a changing magnetic field.

freebody diagram An abstract representation of an interacting system. The system is usually depicted in a simplified form, and forces acting on it are shown as arrows with an organized labeling scheme.

frequency The number of repetitions per second for an oscillating system.

friction force The component of the force between two surfaces that is parallel to the surfaces. It is called kinetic friction when the two surfaces slide past each other, and static friction when the two surfaces don't move with respect to each other.

Gaussian surface A closed surface over which Gauss's law is applied. Such surfaces are often abstract, introduced just for the application of the law.

Gauss's law A fundamental law of electromagnetism that relates the electric flux through a closed surface to the total charge inside the surface.

geosynchronous Having a period of 1 day. A satellite in geosynchronous orbit over the equator always remains over the same point on the Earth's surface.

harmonic oscillator equation The second-order differential equation that describes the motion of simple oscillating systems.

henry SI unit of inductance equal to $1 \, \frac{V \cdot s}{A}$.

impulse A vector quantity that, for constant forces, is equal to the product of a force and the time over which it acts. The impulse delivered by the net force will equal the change in momentum of the system.

induced surface charge The charge density that appears on the surface of a dielectric placed between the conductors of a charged capacitor. It arises from the polarization induced in the dielectric molecules by the electric field in the capacitor.

induced voltage An electric potential difference created in a circuit by changing magnetic flux through the circuit.

inductive time constant The time it takes for a building RL circuit to reach 63 percent of the steady state current value. It's also the time it takes for a decaying RL circuit to reach 37 percent of its initial value.

inelastic collision A collision where kinetic energy is transformed into some other form of energy. In a totally inelastic collision, the colliding objects move as one after the collision.

inertia The property of all matter manifested by its persistence in its current state of motion, either at rest or with constant speed in a straight line, unless an unbalanced force is present.

internal resistance The effective resistance added to a circuit by a battery.

inverse square law A force law between two objects where the force varies inversely as the square of the separation between the objects. Newton's law of gravity and Coulomb's law of electrostatics are both inverse square laws.

junction law The first of Kirchhoff's laws, stating that current entering a junction equals current leaving a junction. The junction law is a manifestation of the conservation of charge principle.

kinetic energy The energy associated with the motion of an object. For an object moving so that all parts have the same velocity vector, it's referred to as **translational** kinetic energy. For an object that can be considered to be rotating about some axis, it's referred to as **rotational** KE.

Kirchhoff's laws Rules that determine what currents will be established in a given connection of circuit elements.

LC circuit A circuit that consists of an inductor and capacitor in series. With the capacitor initially charged, the circuit will oscillate.

Lenz's law A law stating that an induced current will always flow in such a way as to oppose the change that caused it.

linear momentum A vector quantity equal to the product of an object's mass and velocity. The linear momentum of a system of particles is equal to the product of the total mass and the system center of mass velocity. Linear momentum of a system will be conserved if no external forces act on the system.

long wire rule A right hand rule used to determine the magnetic field direction in a region surrounding a long wire.

loop law The second of Kirchhoff's laws, stating that the sum of the potential drops around a closed circuit loop must add to 0. It's a result of the conservative nature of the electric force.

loop right-hand rule A mnemonic device used to determine the direction of the magnetic field within a current carrying planar loop. Curl the fingers of the right hand around the loop in the direction of the current flow. The thumb will point in the direction of the magnetic field within the loop created by this current.

magnetic field A vector quantity defined at every point in space. The field exerts forces on moving charges and is created by moving charges and changing electric fields.

magnetic field lines A representation of the magnetic field. The field is tangential everywhere to the field lines, and the strength of the field is proportional to the density of field lines.

magnetic flux A measure of how much of a magnetic field cuts through a given area.

mechanics The branch of physics that deals with the description and causes of motion.

moment of inertia A measure of an object's resistance to angular acceleration about a particular axis. For a point mass, it's the product of the mass and the square of the distance to the axis.

net force The vector sum of all forces acting on a system.

Newton's first law The law that describes the property of inertia.

Newton's law of gravity The quantitative statement that relates the properties of two masses to their mutual gravitational attraction. For point masses, this force is proportional to the product of the masses, inversely proportional to the square of their separation, and directed along the line connecting the two masses.

Newton's second law The law that quantitatively defines force in terms of mass and acceleration.

Newton's third law The law that recognizes the equal but opposite nature of all forces exerted between interacting systems.

noncontact force A force exerted between two systems when they aren't actually touching each other.

normal force The component of the force exerted between two surfaces that is perpendicular to the surfaces.

ohm The SI unit of electrical resistance corresponding to 1 volt per ampere.

Ohm's law A statement of the linear relation between voltage and current for a conductor.

parallel A connection condition in a circuit. Two devices in parallel always have the same potential drop across them.

parallel axis theorem A theorem that expresses the relation between the moment of inertia about an axis through the CM and any other axis parallel to this axis.

period The time it takes for a repetitive motion to repeat itself once.

phase The current state of an oscillation. The phase is determined by the current value of the displacement and by how it is changing. Mathematically, the phase is the argument of the trigonometric function used in describing the motion of the oscillator.

position The specific place where an object resides. It is given quantitatively by the coordinates of the point in some coordinate system.

position vector A vector with its tail at the origin and its head at the position of an object.

potential energy The energy an object has as a result of its position. PE is measured with respect to a zero point that can be arbitrarily chosen.

power The rate at which work is done. Its SI units are watts.

projectile An object moving near the Earth's surface solely under the influence of gravity.

quantized A property is said to be quantized if there is a basic unit of the quantity that cannot be subdivided. Electric charge and photon energy are quantized properties.

RC circuit A circuit that has a resistor and capacitor in series.

RC time constant In a charging RC circuit, the time it takes to reach 63 percent of the limiting charge on the capacitor. For a discharging circuit, it's the time it takes for the charge to decay to 37 percent of the initial value.

resistor A circuit element obeying Ohm's law.

restoring force The generic name given to the force that tends to bring an oscillating system back to its equilibrium position.

resultant The sum of two or more vectors.

right-hand rule A rule that determines the direction of the cross product of two vectors. You curl the fingers of your right hand from the first vector in the product into the second, with the thumb then pointing in the appropriate direction.

RL circuit A circuit configuration consisting of a resistor and inductor in series.

rolling Describes the motion of an object across a surface when the contact point between the two surfaces is always instantaneously at rest. Rolling can be considered a pure rotation about this contact point.

rotational equilibrium That state of a system with 0 net torque acting upon it.

rotational kinetic energy The energy associated with the rotational motion of an object.

scalar A physical quantity that can be quantified by a single number.

self induction The process whereby a potential difference is created across an electric component due to the changing current within the component.

self-inductance A measure of a circuit's ability to create an induced voltage within itself as the current in the circuit changes.

series A connection condition in a circuit that requires that the two devices in series always have the same current established within them.

simple circuit A circuit consisting of batteries and resistors, with the batteries in series and the resistors connected in such a way that the equivalent resistance of the entire circuit can be determined using the series and parallel rules for resistor combinations.

simple harmonic motion A repetitive motion caused by a restoring force that's directly proportional to the displacement. The description given to any variable that obeys the harmonic oscillator equation.

solenoid A length of wire formed to make many consecutive coils with a common cylindrical axis.

spring constant A parameter that indicates the stiffness of a spring. It's the proportionality constant in the equation that relates the force exerted by a spring and the amount of extension or compression the spring has acquired.

steady state A nonequilibrium state of a system that doesn't change. A battery connected across a conductor will create a steady state in which a constant current flows in the conductor.

superposition principle A principle stating that a complex interaction of several systems can be analyzed in terms of individual components of the interaction as if the others weren't present. The complete analysis of the complex interaction is then obtained by putting together the individual contributions in an additive manner, taking their scalar or vector natures into account.

tension The force exerted by a rope or rod.

terminal speed The limiting speed approached by an object experiencing a resistive force that increases as the speed increases.

terminal voltage The potential difference across a battery when current is established within it. Terminal voltage can be less than or greater than the battery's ideal voltage, depending on how the battery is connected.

tesla The SI unit for magnetic field, equal to $1 \frac{N \cdot s}{C \cdot m}$.

test charge A small positive charge.

torque The measure of a force that indicates how effective it is in causing angular velocity to change.

total mechanical energy The sum of the kinetic and potential energy associated with all objects in a system.

transient A short-lived state that a system passes through as it approaches a steady state or equilibrium.

translational equilibrium That state of a system with 0 net force acting upon it.

unit vector Any vector whose magnitude is 1 unit.

universal gravitational constant "Big G," the constant that appears in Newton's law of gravity. Its small value, $6.67 \times 10^{-11} \frac{N \cdot m^2}{kg^2}$, indicates that the gravitational force is weak.

vector A physical quantity that requires both a magnitude and a direction to completely specify it.

velocity The time rate of change of position. You can distinguish between two types of velocity: **average velocity**, given by the total displacement during an interval divided by the size of the time interval, and **instantaneous velocity**, which is the limit of the average velocity over an infinitesimally small interval.

volt The unit of electric potential difference. One volt equals 1 joule per coulomb.

weber An SI unit of magnetic flux, equal to $1 \text{ T} \cdot m^2$.

weight The force exerted by Earth (or some other large celestial body) on masses near its surface.

work A scalar quantity equal to the product of the component of a force in a given direction and the magnitude of the displacement in that direction. The work done by the net force on an object will equal the change in the kinetic energy of the object.

work-energy theorem A principle stating that the work done by the net force acting on a point mass will equal the change in the KE of the mass.